BBC

Bitesize

Bitesize
Pearson Edexcel
GCSE (9–1)
COMBINED SCIENCE
REVISION WORKBOOK
HIGHER

Series Consultant:
Harry Smith

Authors:
Nora Henry
Pauline Anning
Sue Kearsey

Published by BBC Active, an imprint of Educational Publishers LLP, part of the Pearson Education Group, 80 Strand, London, WC2R 0RL.

www.pearsonschools.co.uk/BBCBitesize

© Educational Publishers LLP 2020
BBC logo © BBC 1996. BBC and BBC Active are trademarks of the British Broadcasting Corporation.

Typeset by Newgen KnowledgeWorks Pvt. Ltd., Chennai, India
Produced and illustrated by Newgen Publishing UK
Cover design by Andrew Magee & Pearson Education Limited 2020
Cover illustration by Darren Lingard / Oxford Designers & Illustrators

The rights of Nora Henry, Pauline Anning and Sue Kearsey to be identified as authors of this work have been asserted by them in accordance with the Copyright, Designs and Patents Act 1988.

First published 2020

23 22 21 20
10 9 8 7 6 5 4 3 2 1

British Library Cataloguing in Publication Data
A catalogue record for this book is available from the British Library

ISBN 978 1 406 68574 9

Acknowledgements
Content written by Karen Bailey and Jen Randall is included.

Text
P 1-232: © BBC; **P 31:** Trinh P, Jung TH, Keene D, et al. Temporal and spatial associations between influenza and asthma hospitalisations in New York City from 2002 to 2012: longitudinal ecological study, © BMJ Open 2018. doi:10.1136/ bmjopen-2017-020362. Used with permission; **P 31:** Health matters: harmful drinking and alcohol dependence, 21 January 2016, © Crown copyright; **P 33:** Impact of HIV co-infection on the evolution and transmission of multidrug resistant tuberculosis by Vegard Eldholm, 09 August 2016, © Eldholm et al. T. Attribution 4.0 International (CC BY 4.0); **P 39:** Achievements in Public Health, 1900–1999: Control of Infectious Diseases, July 30, 1999 / 48(29);621–629, CDC; **P 41:** Waist-hip ratio is the dominant risk factor predicting cardiovascular death in Australia by Timothy A Welborn, © 2003, Medical Journal of Australia; **P 42:** Prescott, Eva, Hippe, Merete, Schnohr, Peter, Hein, Hans Ole, Vestbo, Jørgen, Smoking and risk of myocardial infarction in women and men: longitudinal population study, © British Medical Journal 1998 Apr 4; 316(7137): 1043-1047. 10.1136/bmj.316.7137.1043; **P 43:** Data from Long-Term Safety and Effectiveness of Mechanical Versus Biologic Aortic Valve Prostheses in Older Patients Results From the Society of Thoracic Surgeons Adult Cardiac Surgery National Database by J. Matthew Brennan, September 15, © 2019, American Heart Association, Inc; **P 43:** Chung J, Shum-Tim D. The Current Indications and Options for Aortic Valve Surgery. J Surgery. 2014;2(1): 6. Attribution 4.0 International (CC BY 4.0); **P 55:** Jakob Suckale, Michele Solimena – Solimena Lab and Review Suckale Solimena 2008 Frontiers in Bioscience, original data: Daly et al. 1998. CC-BY 3.0; **P 66:** Global average temperature 1850–2011, © Crown copyright 2014. Contains public sector information licensed under the Open Government Licence v1.0; **P 69:** Data from Fig 3.31B Water quality and pollution by oxygen consuming substances, © European Environment Agency, 07 Nov 2018; **P 70:** Data from Hope Farm: Farming for food, profit and wildlife, © 2012, Royal Society for the Protection of Birds; **P 69:** The German Water Sector, Policies and Experiences, Umweltbundesamt (DE) – EEA data service. Federal Ministry for the Environment, Nature Conservation and Nuclear Safety. Used with permission; **P 236:** National Diabetes Audit Executive Summary 2009–2010, The NHS Information Centre, National Diabetes Audit Executive Summary, Copyright © 2011. Contains public sector information licensed under the Open Government Licence v3.0; **P 236:** Adult obesity and type 2 diabetes, Public Health England, © Crown copyright 2014. Contains public sector information licensed under the Open Government Licence v3.0.

Photographs
Key: T-top; B-bottom; C-centre; L-left; R-right
123RF: Jarun Ontakrai 1, Pchweat 172, **Alamy Stock Photo:** Nigel Cattlin 36c, Nigel Cattlin 47, David Paterson/Picade LLC 184br, Kevin Britland 227, Photo Researchers/Science History Images 233, **Getty Images:** Ed Reschke/Photolibrary 5, De Agostini Picture Library 6, BSIP/Universal Images Group 15, **Science photo library:** CNRI 6, Gary Carlson 14, Edelmann 16; **Shutterstock:** Jeerawut Thiratrak 36r, Tyler Olsen 36l, Angelika Smile 90, Michael Stokes 172, Lzf 173, Stephen Meese 184t, Francois Boizot 184bl, IndustryAndTravel 185, Rido 189t, Suttha Burawonk 189b, Medwether 192, Bixstock 205, Ruslan Ivantsov 182, 218, Brent Hofacker 228, Sathienpong Prempetch 230.

All other images © Pearson Education

Contents

Grades have been assigned to most questions in this workbook. These are intended to show you the level of challenge of those questions, and to help you track your progress. In your exam, your grade will be based on your overall mark, and not on your responses to individual questions.

✓ Tick off each topic as you go.

🕑 Each bite-sized chunk has a **timer** to indicate how long it will take. Use them to plan your revision sessions.

Scan the **QR codes** to visit the BBC Bitesize website. It will link straight through to revision resources on that subject. You can also access these by visiting www.pearsonschools.co.uk/BBCBitesizeLinks.

Levels of organisation

② Quick quiz

Draw **one** line from each key word to its definition.

Key word	Definition
tissue	the smallest structural and functional unit of an organism
organ system	a group of organs working together
cell	a group of similar cells working together

⑤ Organisation of the human body — Grade 5

1. The human body has four main levels of organisation.

Use words from the box to complete the order of the levels of organisation in the circulatory system, from least complex to most complex. **[3 marks]**

| blood | circulatory system | red blood cell | heart |

A red blood cell → **B** blood → **C** heart → **D** circulatory system

⑩ Tissues and organs — Grades 5–6

2. (a) The human stomach is an organ. Define the term 'organ'. **[1 mark]**

A group g tissues in a living organism that are adapted to perform a specific junction

(b) Name the organ system that the stomach belongs to. Digestive system **[1 mark]**

(c) Explain the importance of organising the body into systems. **[2 marks]**

To categorise the organs that do similar things

⑩ Drawing from observation — Grades 5–6

3. Figure 1 shows a white blood cell and some red blood cells seen under a light micrograph.

(a) Draw and label the white blood cell. **[2 marks]**

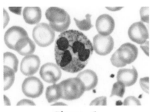

Figure 1

> **Exam focus** 📌
> Remember to follow the rules for drawing scientific drawings.

(b) The white blood cell has a diameter of 18 μm. Estimate the diameter of one of the red blood cells. **[2 marks]**

9. μm

Eukaryotic and prokaryotic cells

② Quick quiz

The following pairs of statements compare prokaryotic and eukaryotic cells.

For each pair, write a P in the box if the statement applies to prokaryotic cells and E if the statement applies to eukaryotic cells.

cells contain a nucleus	E	cells have no nucleus	P
cells are usually smaller	P	cells are usually larger	E
bacterial cells	P	plant, animal and yeast cells	E

⑩ Comparing prokaryotic and eukaryotic cells · Grade 4

1. (a) Identify each sub-cellular structure in **Figure 1** by writing the correct name from the box in the spaces below. The diagrams are not to scale. **[6 marks]**

cell membrane	cell wall	cytoplasm
mitochondrion	nucleus	ribosomes

A *cytoplasm*   B *Cell membrane*

C *nucleus*   D *Mitochondrion*

E *ribosomes*   F *cell wall*

cell 2

cell 1

A
B
C
E
D
F

Figure 1

(b) Name **one** structure in part **(a)** that is not visible under a light microscope. Give a reason for your answer. **[2 marks]**

Ribosomes because *they are too small to be seen under a light microscop*

(c) State and explain what types of cell are shown in **Figure 1**. **[4 marks]**

Cell 1 is *eukaryotic cell* because ~~prokaryotic~~ *it has a nucleus*

Cell 2 is *prokaryotic cell* because *it has plasmid DNA*

(d) Describe the function of sub-cellular structure F in **Figure 1**. **[1 mark]**

protects the cell.

⑩ Cell size units · Grade 6

2. A scientist observed a kidney cell using an electron microscope. He calculated that the kidney cell was 16 µm wide.

(a) What does µm stand for? Tick **one** box. **[1 mark]**

centimetre ☐   millimetre ☐   micrometre ☑   nanometre ☐

(b) Give the width of the kidney cell in the following units.

(i) millimetres, mm .... **[1 mark]**

(ii) nanometres, nm .... **[1 mark]**

(iii) centimetres, cm .... **[1 mark]**

Maths skills
You need to understand the scale and size of cells and use the correct prefixes: centi, milli, micro or nano.

 Made a start   Feeling confident   Exam ready

Animal and plant cells

The diagram shows a plant cell.

Label the parts of the cell.
Use the boxes provided.

You must be able to interpret images of plant and animal cells by their identifying structures. You also need to be able to draw and label cell diagrams from photographic images.

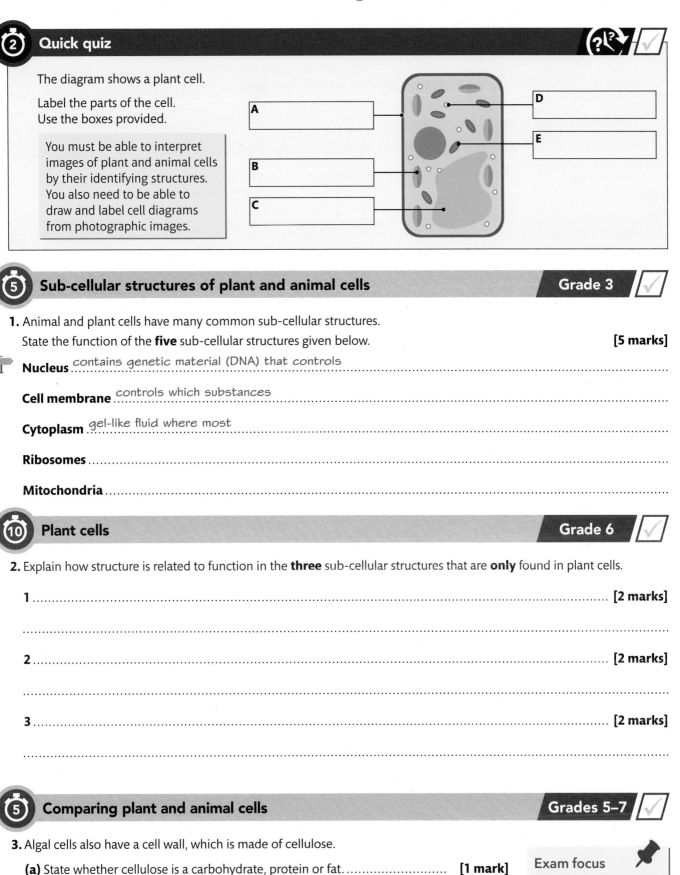

A

B

C

D

E

Sub-cellular structures of plant and animal cells   Grade 3

1. Animal and plant cells have many common sub-cellular structures.
State the function of the **five** sub-cellular structures given below.   **[5 marks]**

Nucleus *contains genetic material (DNA) that controls* ....

Cell membrane *controls which substances* ....

Cytoplasm *gel-like fluid where most* ....

Ribosomes ....

Mitochondria ....

⑩ Plant cells   Grade 6

2. Explain how structure is related to function in the **three** sub-cellular structures that are **only** found in plant cells.

1 .... **[2 marks]**

....

2 .... **[2 marks]**

....

3 .... **[2 marks]**

....

⑤ Comparing plant and animal cells   Grades 5–7

3. Algal cells also have a cell wall, which is made of cellulose.

(a) State whether cellulose is a carbohydrate, protein or fat. .... **[1 mark]**

(b) Suggest how algae make this substance. .... **[2 marks]**

....

....

Exam focus
The command word 'suggest' means you need to apply your knowledge about plants to a new situation.

Specialised animal cells

BBC

---

② Quick quiz

Use a word from the box to answer each question.

| bone | epithelial | muscle | neurone | sperm |

Name the specialised animal cells that can shorten to move parts of the skeleton. ....

Name the specialised animal cells that carry impulses throughout the body. ....

Name a type of animal cell that lines tubes and other surfaces. ....

---

⑤ Sperm cells   Grade 4

1. Figure 1 shows a sperm cell. Describe how the following parts of the cell help the cell to carry out its role in reproduction.

(a) Haploid nucleus   **[1 mark]**

....

> A haploid nucleus contains only one set of chromosomes. Think about where these cells come from.

acrosome

mitochondria

haploid nucleus

tail

10 μm

Figure 1

(b) Acrosome   **[1 mark]**

....

....

> The acrosome contains substances that digest cell membranes.

(c) Mitochondria   **[1 mark]**

release energy from ....

so that the ....

> Remember the function of mitochondria in respiration.

---

⑤ Egg cells   Grade 4

2. Describe the function of each of the following adaptations of egg cells.

(a) Nutrients in cytoplasm   **[1 mark]**

....

(b) Changes in cell membrane after fertilisation   **[1 mark]**

....

---

⑩ Ciliated cells   Grade 7

3. Ciliated epithelial cells line the tubes of the trachea and bronchi in the lungs.

(a) Describe how ciliated cells are specialised.   **[1 mark]**

....

(b) Mucus in the trachea and bronchi trap pathogens and dust. Explain how the ciliated cells in these tubes help to protect against infection of the lungs.   **[2 marks]**

....

....

 Made a start   **Feeling confident**   ✓ **Exam ready**

Microscopy

 Quick quiz

Microscopes have developed over time. The following statements are about different kinds of microscopes. Circle the correct word in **bold** to make each sentence correct.

Early microscopes were **light / electron** microscopes.

Improvements to early microscopes made it possible to see **cells / sub-cellular structures**.

Light microscopes have a **greater / lower** magnification than electron microscopes.

Electron microscopes allow us to see mitochondria in **less / more** detail than using light microscopes.

 Calculating magnification | Grade 5

1. **Figure 1** shows cheek cells as viewed with a light microscope.

   Suggest why the mitochondria are not clearly visible in the cells in **Figure 1**.   **[1 mark]**

   ☞ The mitochondria are too
   ....

Figure 1

2. Calculate the magnification of the cells in **Figure 1** when the eyepiece lens magnifies by ×4 and the objective lens magnifies by:

   ☞ **(a)** ×40 (high power) magnification = 4 (eyepiece lens) × 40 (objective lens) =   **[1 mark]**

   magnification = ×.................................

   (b) ×10 (medium power)   **[1 mark]**

   magnification = ×.................................

   | magnification = eyepiece lens magnification × objective lens magnification |

 Magnification, resolution and cell size | Grades 4–7

3. Give a reason why you can study ribosomes with an electron microscope but not with a light microscope.   **[2 marks]**

   ....

   ....

4. A scientist used an electron microscope to look at the sub-cellular structures in an animal cell.

   The size of the image of the structure was 36 mm. The magnification was ×10 000.

   $$\text{real size} = \frac{\text{size of image}}{\text{magnification}}$$

   (a) Calculate the real size of the sub-cellular structure.   **[2 marks]**

   real size = ...mm

   (b) Give your answer to **(a)** in: **[2 marks]**

   (i) standard form .... mm

   (ii) micrometres .... μm

   Maths skills

   In standard form, a number is always written as: $A \times 10^n$. A is always between 1 and 10 and n tells us how many places to move the decimal point.

 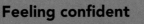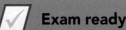

Practical: Using microscopes

② Quick quiz

The diagram shows a light microscope.
Use words from the box to label the diagram.

objective lens
mirror
eyepiece
stage
adjustment knob

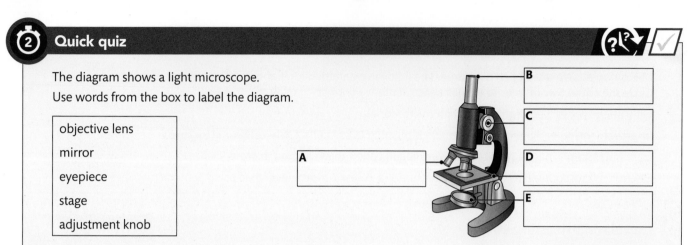

A
B
C
D
E

⑩ Magnification calculations

Grade 7

1. Figure 1 is a part of a kidney viewed with a light microscope.

The image of the kidney structure is 3 cm in diameter. The image has been magnified ×1000.

Calculate the actual size of the structure.

Give your answer in micrometres. **[3 marks]**

 Image size = 3 cm = 3 × 10 000 μm

= 30 000 μm

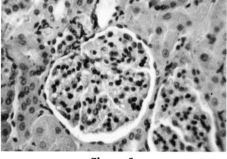

Figure 1

actual size of structure = ... μm

Maths skills
Convert units
1 cm = 10 000 μm
Use the formula

$$\text{magnification} = \frac{\text{size of image}}{\text{size of real object}}$$

Rearrange

$$\text{size of real object} = \frac{\text{size of image}}{\text{magnification}}$$

⑩ Estimating with scale bars

Grades 6–7

2. Figure 2 shows a mitochondrion viewed with an electron microscope.

(a) Use the scale bar on **Figure 2** to estimate the size of the mitochondrion.

[1 mark]

....

(b) Write your answer to part **(a)** in standard form. **[1 mark]**

....

1 μm

Figure 2

(c) Give a reason why estimations of the size of sub-cellular structures are useful. **[1 mark]**

....

 Made a start **Feeling confident** **Exam ready**

Enzyme action

---

② Quick quiz

The diagram shows the breakdown of a molecule by an enzyme to form two new molecules. Use the words in the box to label the diagram.

| active site | enzyme | products | substrate |

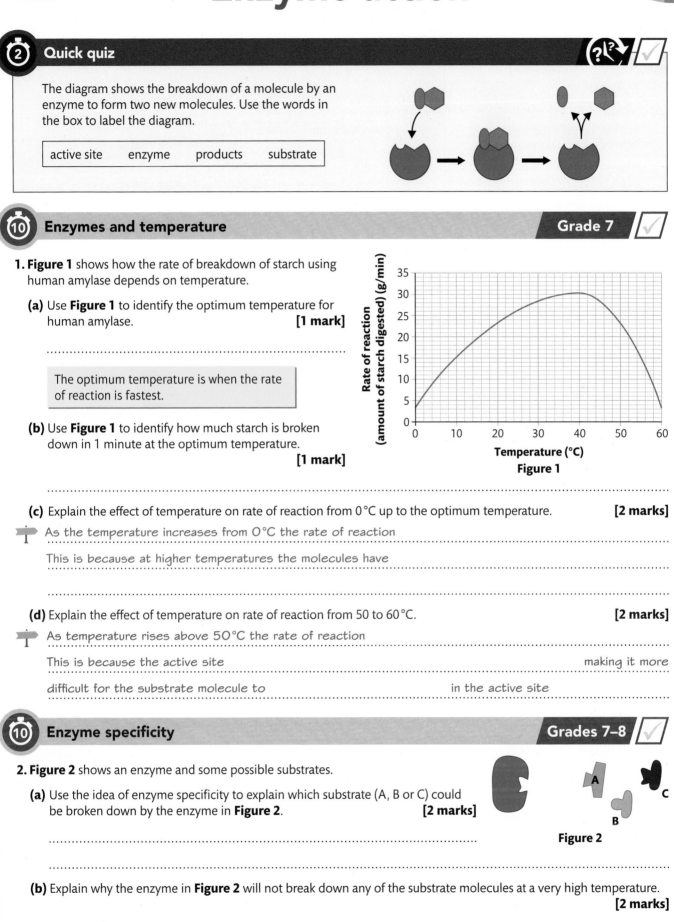

---

⑩ Enzymes and temperature   Grade 7

1. Figure 1 shows how the rate of breakdown of starch using human amylase depends on temperature.

(a) Use **Figure 1** to identify the optimum temperature for human amylase.   **[1 mark]**

....

> The optimum temperature is when the rate of reaction is fastest.

(b) Use **Figure 1** to identify how much starch is broken down in 1 minute at the optimum temperature.

[1 mark]

....

Figure 1 graph: Rate of reaction (amount of starch digested) (g/min) vs Temperature (°C)

Figure 1

(c) Explain the effect of temperature on rate of reaction from 0 °C up to the optimum temperature.   **[2 marks]**

As the temperature increases from 0°C the rate of reaction ....

This is because at higher temperatures the molecules have ....

....

(d) Explain the effect of temperature on rate of reaction from 50 to 60 °C.   **[2 marks]**

As temperature rises above 50°C the rate of reaction ....

This is because the active site .... making it more

difficult for the substrate molecule to .... in the active site ....

---

⑩ Enzyme specificity   Grades 7–8

2. Figure 2 shows an enzyme and some possible substrates.

(a) Use the idea of enzyme specificity to explain which substrate (A, B or C) could be broken down by the enzyme in **Figure 2**.   **[2 marks]**

....

....

Figure 2

(b) Explain why the enzyme in **Figure 2** will not break down any of the substrate molecules at a very high temperature.

[2 marks]

....

....

Practical: Enzymes

True or false?

Changing the pH has no effect on a lipase enzyme.	**True / False**
Increasing the temperature from 10 to 20 °C increases the rate of a reaction controlled by a human enzyme.	**True / False**
Above the optimum temperature, increasing temperature increases the rate of an enzyme-controlled reaction.	**True / False**
Above or below the optimum pH, an enzyme does not work as quickly because its active site changes shape.	**True / False**

⑩ **Investigating enzyme action** Grade 7

1. Students used a continuous sampling technique to investigate the effect of pH on amylase digestion of starch. **Figure 1** shows the results from a test at pH 6. A drop of starch/amylase mixture was added to the top left spot on the tile at time 0.

(a) Suggest a suitable time delay before adding a drop of starch/amylase mixture to the next spot on the tile. **[1 mark]**

....

Use your knowledge of your practical work to answer this question.

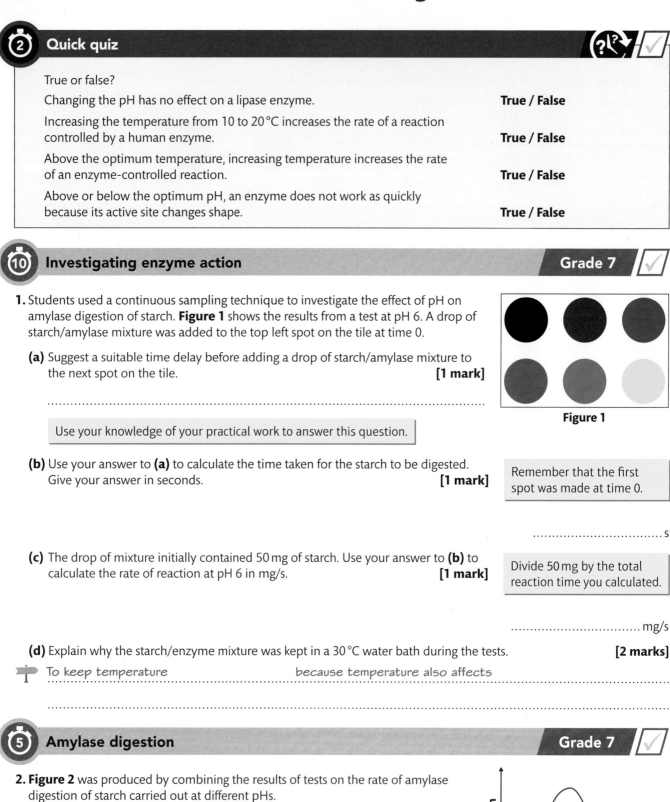

Figure 1

(b) Use your answer to **(a)** to calculate the time taken for the starch to be digested. Give your answer in seconds. **[1 mark]**

Remember that the first spot was made at time 0.

.... s

(c) The drop of mixture initially contained 50 mg of starch. Use your answer to **(b)** to calculate the rate of reaction at pH 6 in mg/s. **[1 mark]**

Divide 50 mg by the total reaction time you calculated.

.... mg/s

(d) Explain why the starch/enzyme mixture was kept in a 30 °C water bath during the tests. **[2 marks]**

To keep temperature   because temperature also affects

....

....

⑤ **Amylase digestion** Grade 7

2. **Figure 2** was produced by combining the results of tests on the rate of amylase digestion of starch carried out at different pHs.

(a) Describe the relationship shown in the graph. **[2 marks]**

....

....

(b) Explain the shape of the graph. **[2 marks]**

....

....

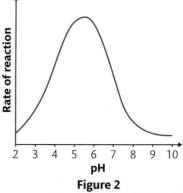

Figure 2

Digestion and enzymes

② Quick quiz

Draw **one** line from each enzyme to its substrate, then **one** line from each substrate to the products it forms.

Enzyme	Substrate	Products
lipase	protein	amino acids
carbohydrase (e.g. amylase)	fat	glucose
protease	carbohydrates (e.g. starch)	fatty acids and glycerol

⑩ Enzymes in digestion and synthesis   Grade 6

1. (a) Describe the role of enzymes in the digestion of food.   **[1 mark]**

....

(b) Explain the role of enzymes in digestion.   **[3 marks]**

⌐ Food molecules are too large to be ....

Digestive enzymes ....

....

(c) State what is synthesised in cells from amino acids.   **[1 mark]**

....

(d) Explain why enzymes are described as biological catalysts.   **[2 marks]**

⌐ Enzymes are biological because ....

Enzymes are catalysts because ....

(e) Explain why enzymes are important for life processes.   **[2 marks]**

....

....

⑩ Substrate concentration   Grades 7–8

2. Figure 1 shows how the concentration of an enzyme's substrate affects the rate of reaction.

(a) Use the idea of the availability of active sites in enzyme molecules to explain why an increase in substrate concentration increases the rate of reaction.   **[2 marks]**

....

....

....

(b) Explain why increasing substrate concentration at point **B** does not change the rate of reaction.   **[2 marks]**

....

....

Rate of reaction (y-axis)

Substrate concentration (x-axis)

Figure 1

Diffusion

② Quick quiz

The diagram shows diffusion across a cell membrane.

Complete the diagram using words from the box.

| high |
| low |
| net movement |
| concentration gradient |

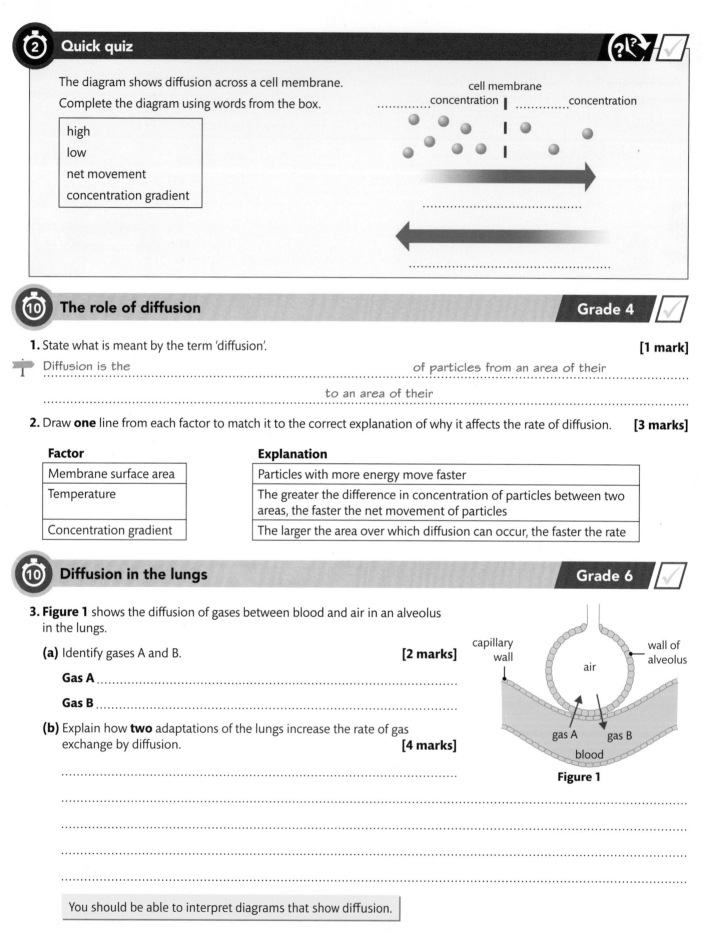

cell membrane

.... concentration ┃ .... concentration

⑩ The role of diffusion   Grade 4

1. State what is meant by the term 'diffusion'.   **[1 mark]**

Diffusion is the .... of particles from an area of their

.... to an area of their ....

2. Draw **one** line from each factor to match it to the correct explanation of why it affects the rate of diffusion.   **[3 marks]**

Factor	Explanation
Membrane surface area	Particles with more energy move faster
Temperature	The greater the difference in concentration of particles between two areas, the faster the net movement of particles
Concentration gradient	The larger the area over which diffusion can occur, the faster the rate

⑩ Diffusion in the lungs   Grade 6

3. Figure 1 shows the diffusion of gases between blood and air in an alveolus in the lungs.

(a) Identify gases A and B.   **[2 marks]**

Gas A ....

Gas B ....

(b) Explain how **two** adaptations of the lungs increase the rate of gas exchange by diffusion.   **[4 marks]**

....

....

....

....

....

capillary wall

wall of alveolus

air

gas A   gas B

blood

Figure 1

You should be able to interpret diagrams that show diffusion.

✓ **Made a start**   ✓ **Feeling confident**   ✓ **Exam ready**

Osmosis

② Quick quiz

Complete the sentences below. Use words from the box.

| permeable | osmosis | concentrated | dilute | diffusion |

Water molecules cross cell membranes by .... This is the .... of water from a ....

solution to a .... solution. This process occurs through a partially .... membrane.

⑩ Movement of water   Grades 5–6

1. The cytoplasm of a plant cell can be affected by the solute concentration of solution outside the cell.

(a) Explain how the cytoplasm changes when the cell is placed in distilled water.   **[2 marks]**

The water .... the cell by osmosis causing the cytoplasm to ....

This is because ....

> Osmosis is the net movement of water from a dilute to a concentrated solution.

(b) Explain how the cytoplasm changes when the cell is placed in a concentrated sugar solution.   **[2 marks]**

....

....

⑩ Investigating osmosis   Grades 6–7

2. Students investigated osmosis by filling some Visking tubing with a 30% sugar solution and leaving the tubing in a beaker of distilled water (**Figure 1**).

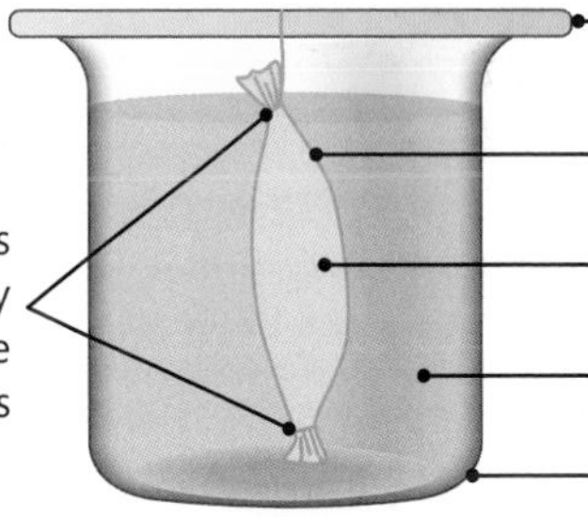

(a) Visking tubing is a partially permeable membrane. State the meaning of the term 'partially permeable membrane'.   **[1 mark]**

....

....

glass rod
Visking tubing
30% sugar solution
distilled water
beaker
threads tightly tied at the two ends

Figure 1

Every 15 minutes the students measured the mass of the filled Visking tubing. **Table 1** shows their results.

(b) Use the results to calculate the rate of osmosis over the 60 minutes in g/min.   **[3 marks]**

Exam focus
You should be able to recognise and interpret diagrams that model osmosis.

.... g/min

> Always show your working in a calculation question. In this question, you should start by calculating the change in mass.

(c) Predict how the change in mass of the tubing would differ if it was placed in a 15% solution. Explain your answer.   **[2 marks]**

....

....

Table 1

Time (minutes)	Mass of Visking tubing and contents (g)
0	10.00
15	11.50
30	13.25
45	14.75
60	16.00

Biology / Key concepts / Practical skills

Practical: Osmosis

② Quick quiz

The diagram shows a model of osmosis.

Complete the diagram by drawing an arrow to show the direction of osmosis.

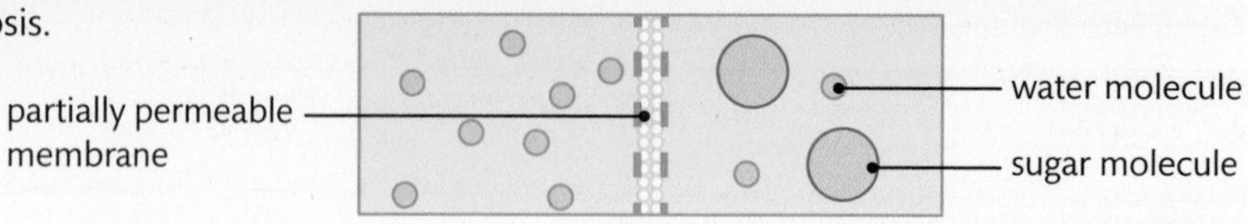

partially permeable membrane

water molecule

sugar molecule

---

⑤ Observing osmosis　　　　　　　　　　　　　　　　　　　　　**Grade 7**

1. A student investigates the effect of osmosis on the mass of potato cylinders. She places potato cylinders in beakers containing different concentrations of sugar solution. **Figure 1** shows the set-up of one beaker.

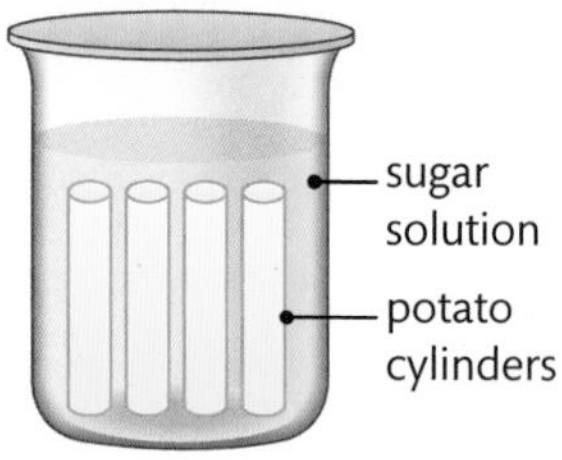

   (a) State the independent and dependent variables in this investigation.　　**[2 marks]**

   Independent variable: sugar solution concentration

   Dependent variable: change in mass of

sugar solution

potato cylinders

Figure 1

Exam focus

The independent variable is the variable you change. The dependent variable is the one that you measure.

Exam focus

Control variables are those that are kept constant, so they do not affect the results.

   (b) Suggest **two** variables that should be controlled in this investigation.　　**[2 marks]**

This is a required practical, so think back to how you carried out the experiment.

---

⑮ Observing osmosis　　　　　　　　　　　　　　　　　　　　　**Grade 7**

2. (a) Five potato cylinders have a mean mass of 1.13 g. The cylinders were placed in a beaker of distilled water for 30 minutes before being dried and reweighed. At the end of the experiment the mean mass of the cylinders was 1.25 g.

   Calculate the percentage change in the mean mass of the potato cylinders.　　**[2 marks]**

Maths skills

$$\text{percentage change} = \frac{\text{change in mass}}{\text{initial mass}} \times 100\%$$

Remember to calculate change in mass first.

   (b) Explain why percentage change in mass is calculated for comparison between solutions rather than just change in mass.　　**[2 marks]**

   (c) Use your knowledge of osmosis to explain the change in mass in distilled water.　　**[2 marks]**

   (d) Predict whether the mass of potato cylinders would increase or decrease when placed in a 20% sugar solution. Explain your answer.　　**[2 marks]**

12　　　　✓ **Made a start**　　　✓ **Feeling confident**　　　✓ **Exam ready**

Active transport

② **Quick quiz**

The following statements are about methods of transport in cells. Identify which method of transport is being described in each case. Write each of the letters **A–E** in the correct column of the table.

A movement of substances against a concentration gradient

B movement of water across a partially permeable membrane

C requires energy to take place

D can describe the movement of gases

E net movement of dissolved solute molecules down their concentration gradient

Diffusion	Osmosis	Active transport

⑩ **Active transport in root hair cells**   **Grades 6–8**

1. **Figure 1** shows a root hair cell from a plant.

   (a) Explain why plant roots are covered in millions of tiny root hairs.   **[2 marks]**

   ....

   ....

   (b) State how water is absorbed by root hair cells.   **[1 mark]**

   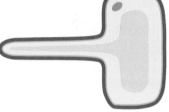

   Figure 1

   ....

   (c) Explain why some mineral ions are absorbed into root hair cells by active transport.   **[2 marks]**

    The concentration of mineral ions is usually higher in the
   ....

          Therefore, the mineral ions need to be moved against
   ....

   ....

⑩ **Transport in the small intestine**   **Grades 5–7**

2. The small intestine is lined with cells like those shown in **Figure 2**.

   (a) Describe the function of the small intestine.   **[1 mark]**

   highly folded surface

   ....

   (b) Name the sub-cellular structures labelled **Z**.   **[1 mark]**

   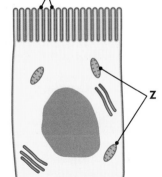

   ....

   (c) Explain why these cells contain many of the sub-cellular structures labelled **Z**.   **[2 marks]**

   ....

   ....

   (d) State and explain how **one** other adaptation of the cell in **Figure 2** helps it carry out its function well.   **[2 marks]**

   Figure 2

   ....

   ....

Mitosis and the cell cycle

② **Quick quiz**

Match each stage of mitosis with what happens in the cell.

prophase	chromosomes line up across equator of cell
metaphase	the cell surface membranes of the new cells form
anaphase	membrane forms around chromosomes at each side of cell to make nuclei of new cells
telophase	nucleus breaks down and spindle fibres form
cytokinesis	chromosome pairs pulled apart to opposite sides of cell

⑩ **Process and use of mitosis** | **Grades 5–6**

1. Explain the function of mitosis in multicellular organisms. **[2 marks]**

....

2. (a) Interphase is the stage of the cell cycle that takes place before mitosis.

Describe what happens during interphase. **[3 marks]**

➤ The cell increases in size. The number of sub-cellular structures, such as
....
The chromosomes
....

(b) Mitosis begins with a diploid body cell. Describe what is formed as a result of mitosis. **[2 marks]**

....

....

A diploid cell has two sets of chromosomes.

⑤ **Mitosis and the cell cycle** | **Grade 6**

3. Figure 1 shows cells at different stages of the cell cycle.

(a) State whether A or B shows a cell during mitosis. .... **[1 mark]**

(b) Give a reason for your choice. **[1 mark]**

....

....

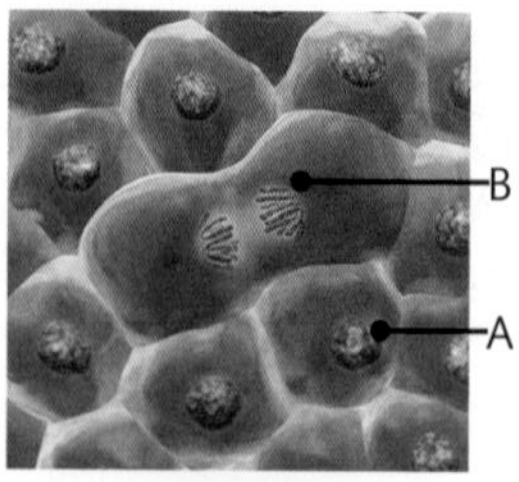

Figure 1

⑤ **Cell division by mitosis** | **Grade 7**

4. Complete **Figure 2** to show the chromosomes in the daughter cells produced when the cell divides by mitosis. **[1 mark]**

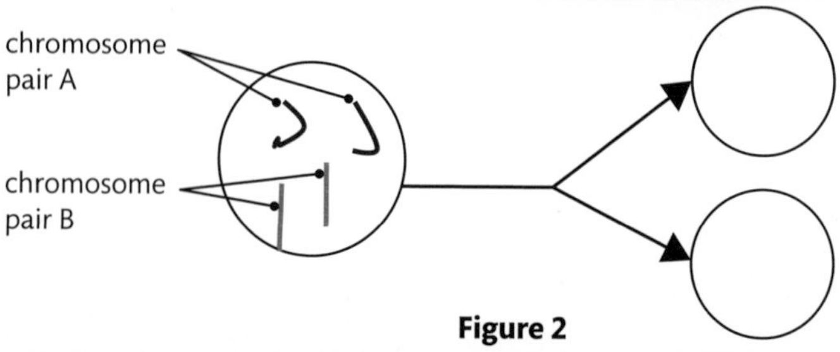

chromosome pair A

chromosome pair B

Figure 2

✓ **Made a start** ✓ **Feeling confident** ✓ **Exam ready**

Importance of mitosis

② Quick quiz

True or false?

Mitosis is the stage in the cell cycle when chromosomes and sub-cellular structures are copied. **True / False**

The type of cell division found in body cells is mitosis. **True / False**

Mitosis is the type of cell division that occurs to replace damaged cells. **True / False**

Mitosis produces cells that are genetically different from the parent cell. **True / False**

⑩ Reproduction and cell division — Grade 6

1. **Figure 1** shows a daffodil bulb in spring and in autumn. During the summer, daughter bulbs develop from the parent bulb. If the daughter bulbs are planted the next year, they will produce new daffodil plants.

   (a) Name the type of reproduction shown in **Figure 1**. **[1 mark]**

   ....

   > Remember how many parents are needed for asexual and sexual reproduction.

   (b) Name the type of cell division that produced the daughter bulbs from the parent bulb. **[1 mark]**

   ....

   > Remember the functions of mitosis and meiosis.

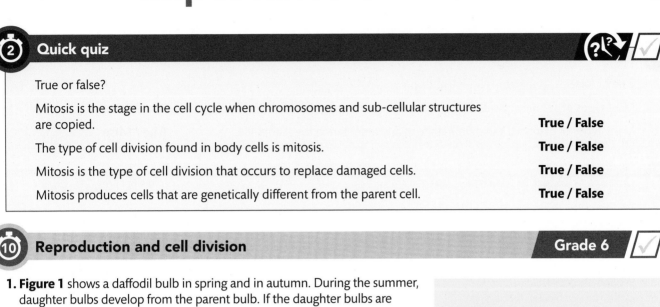

daughter bulbs

bulb in spring   **bulb in autumn**

Figure 1

   (c) The flowers produced by the parent bulb are white. State and explain whether flowers produced by the daughter bulbs will be like those of the parent or different. Give a reason for your answer. **[2 marks]**

   Like those of the parent, because ....

   ....

⑤ Cancer — Grade 7

2. **Figure 2** shows a cancer tumour growing on a person's skin.

   (a) State the type of cell division that produces a tumour. **[1 mark]**

   ....

   (b) Explain how cell division in a tumour differs from the cell division of normal body cells. **[2 marks]**

   ....

   ....

   ....

   ....

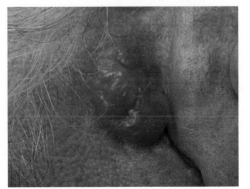

Figure 2

Cell differentiation and growth

---

② **Quick quiz**

True or false?

Most types of animal cell can differentiate at any time in the animal's life.	**True / False**
Many types of plant cell can differentiate at any time during the plant's life.	**True / False**

---

⑩ **Differentiation in animal growth** **Grades 5–6**

1. **Figure 1** shows a human embryo at the 8-cell stage. Over the next few weeks, there will be more cell division.

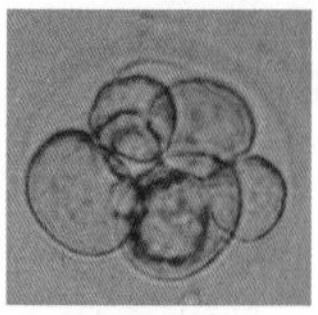

(a) Describe **one** other stage in growth and development that will take place to produce a baby. **[1 mark]**

☛ Cell .... also takes place to produce ....

cells for particular functions.

(b) Explain why differentiation is important in the early stages of an animal's growth. **[2 marks]**

Figure 1

☛ Cell differentiation produces ....

This makes it possible for the organism to ....

(c) Describe the main purpose of cell division in tissues of mature animals. **[1 mark]**

....

---

⑤ **Growth in plants** **Grades 5–7**

3. **Figure 2** shows the tip of a root of a garlic plant.

(a) State whether meristem cells are specialised or unspecialised. **[1 mark]**

....

(b) Describe what happens to cells that divide from meristem cells before they differentiate. **[1 mark]**

....

(c) Explain the importance of meristems in plant root tips in relation to plant growth. **[2 marks]**

....

....

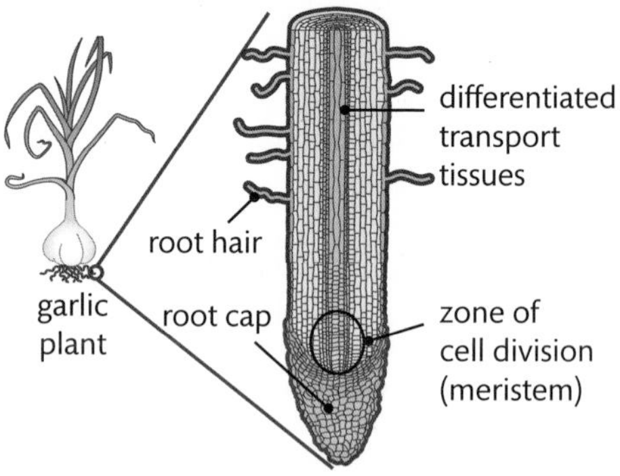

differentiated
transport
tissues

root hair

garlic
plant

root cap

zone of
cell division
(meristem)

Figure 2

---

⑤ **Growth in plants** **Grades 5–7**

4. A child's growth is plotted on a percentile chart, which shows growth curves for boys or girls with different birth weights.

(a) State what the 50th percentile growth curve indicates. **[1 mark]**

....

(b) Explain the advantage of plotting a child's growth on a percentile chart. **[2 marks]**

....

....

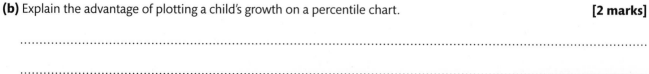

✓ **Made a start** ✓ **Feeling confident** ✓ **Exam ready**

Stem cells

② Quick quiz

Draw **one** line from each key word to its definition.

Key word	Definition
embryonic stem cell	plant cells that divide and differentiate into any type of plant cell
adult stem cell	unspecialised cell that can give rise to most of the different types of cells in a human body
meristem	unspecialised cell in tissue that can produce some types of differentiated cell

⑩ Therapeutic cloning   Grade 5

1. Blood cells are not able to divide. Explain how new blood cells are produced in bone marrow tissue to replace damaged cells. **[2 marks]**

New blood cells are produced by division of .... in bone marrow tissue.

2. Stem cell therapies are being developed to help people with type 1 diabetes. The therapy begins by taking a cell from the person and causing it to change so that it develops as an embryo.

(a) Explain why the cell from the person must first be treated to make it behave as an embryo. **[2 marks]**

....

....

(b) Describe how stem cell therapy may one day help cure someone of type 1 diabetes. **[2 marks]**

....

....

> Remember that type 1 diabetes is caused by pancreas cells not producing the protein insulin.

(c) Explain the importance of using stem cells from an embryo that contains the genes of the person with the disorder. **[2 marks]**

....

....

> Remember the response of the immune system to foreign cells in the body.

(d) Describe one possible risk of inserting embryonic stem cells into a person's body to cure a disorder. **[1 mark]**

....

⑩ Plant stem cell uses   Grades 5–7

3. Banana plants are dying because of a viral disease. New banana plants are produced using stem cells from mature plants.

(a) Name the special tissue that contains plant stem cells. .... **[1 mark]**

(b) Describe one benefit of using stem cells to produce new banana plants. **[1 mark]**

....

(c) Explain why, when producing genetically modified crop plants, new plants are produced from stem cells. **[2 marks]**

....

....

The human nervous system

② Quick quiz

Number the following steps to give the correct order for the response of a reflex arc in the nervous system.

receptor cells	1
relay neurone in spinal cord	
effector cells	
motor neurone	
sensory neurone	

⑤ Synapses   Grade 7

1. Figure 1 is a partly labelled diagram of events at a synapse. Describe what is happening at each numbered step.   **[3 marks]**

1 The electrical impulse reaches ....

2 The impulse causes the axon terminal to ....
....

3 The neurotransmitter ....
....

4 This causes a new ....
....

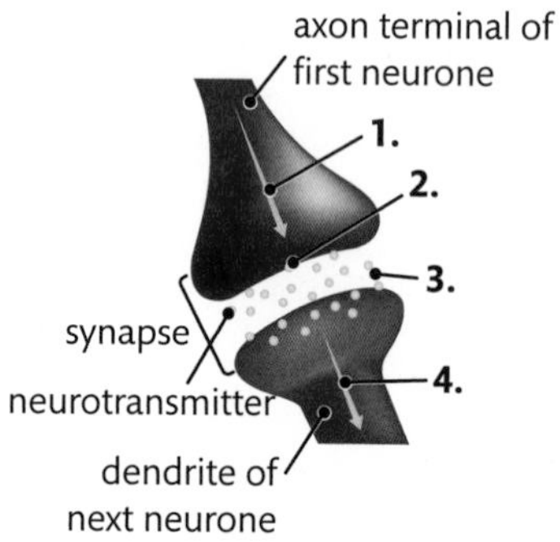

axon terminal of first neurone

1.
2.
3.
synapse
neurotransmitter
4.
dendrite of next neurone

Figure 1

⑤ Reflex actions   Grade 7

2. Blinking when something comes close to our eyes is a reflex action controlled by a reflex arc.

Explain the importance of reflex actions.   **[2 marks]**

....

....

⑮ Features of the nervous system   Grades 5–7

3. Figure 2 shows a sensory neurone.

(a) Explain how the structure of a sensory neurone is related to its function.
[2 marks]

....

....

....

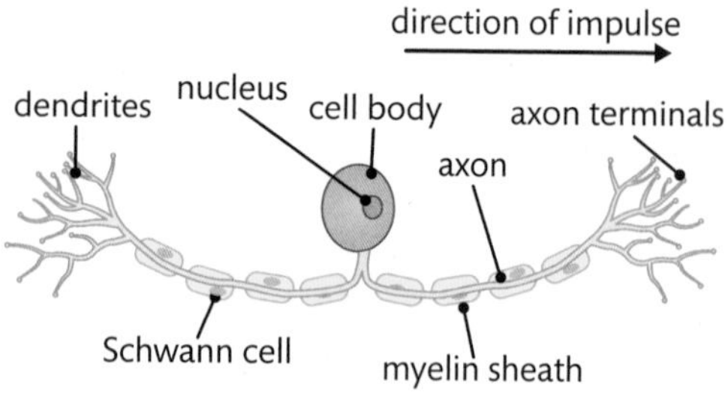

direction of impulse

dendrites   nucleus   cell body   axon terminals
axon
Schwann cell   myelin sheath

Figure 2

(b) Motor neurone disease is a disease of motor neurones. Suggest **one** effect of this disease. Give a reason for this effect.   **[2 marks]**

....

....

 Made a start   ✓ **Feeling confident**   ✓ **Exam ready**

Meiosis

② Quick quiz

True or false?

Meiosis happens in cells in reproductive organs.	**True / False**
Gametes are produced by mitosis.	**True / False**
Fertilisation is when the male and female sex cells fuse together.	**True / False**
Meiosis produces cells that are haploid (contain only one set of chromosomes).	**True / False**

⑩ Process of meiosis   Grades 5–6

1. A body cell from a cat contains 38 chromosomes.

> Remember, gametes are produced by meiosis.

(a) State the number of chromosomes found in an egg cell from a female cat.   **[1 mark]**

....

(b) Explain why meiosis is needed to produce gametes for sexual reproduction.   **[2 marks]**

As two gametes fuse during .... their chromosomes are collected into the new nucleus.

Halving the chromosome number in gametes ....

....

> Think about what happens to the chromosome number during fertilisation.

2. A sperm-forming cell divides to form sperm.

(a) Describe what must happen in the sperm-forming cell before division.   **[1 mark]**

....

(b) State how many sperm cells are produced from each sperm-forming cell.   **[1 mark]**

....

⑩ Comparison of mitosis and meiosis   Grade 8

3. Compare mitosis and meiosis.   **[4 marks]**

....

....

....

....

....

....

....

> **Exam focus**
> When you are asked to 'compare' two different things, you need to write about their similarities and differences.

The structure of DNA

② Quick quiz

Draw **one** line from each stage in the extraction of DNA from fruit to link it to the reason it is done.

Mash up the fruit very thoroughly	causes the DNA to precipitate out of the mixture
Mix the fruit mash with salt, detergent and water and warm for 15 minutes.	separates out the proteins that surround the DNA in the chromosomes
Add two drops of protease enzyme	makes sure you will be able to get as much DNA out of the fruit as possible
Pour ice-cold ethanol down the inside of the tube very carefully	breaks down membranes surrounding cells and nuclei

⑩ DNA structure   Grade 8

1. **Figure 1** shows a small section of DNA.

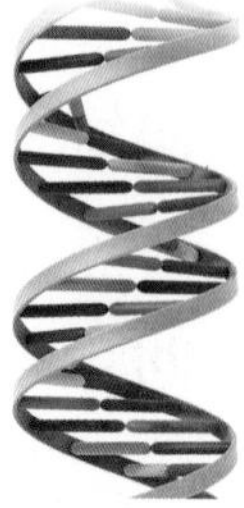

   (a) Which term scientifically describes the shape of a DNA molecule? Tick **one** box. **[1 mark]**

   spiral ☐   double helix ☐   double coil ☐   double twist ☐

   (b) The strands of DNA are linked by complementary base pairs. State what complementary means in this case. **[1 mark]**

   🚩 A particular base will only pair with ....

   [Use the coloured bars in the figure to help you answer this.]

   (c) The bases in a pair are held together by weak hydrogen bonds. Give a reason why it is not easy to pull the DNA strands apart. **[1 mark]**

   ....

   ....

Figure 1

[One bond may be weak, but think about what happens if you have lots of them.]

⑩ DNA bases   Grade 8

2. **Figure 2** shows a very short section of DNA.

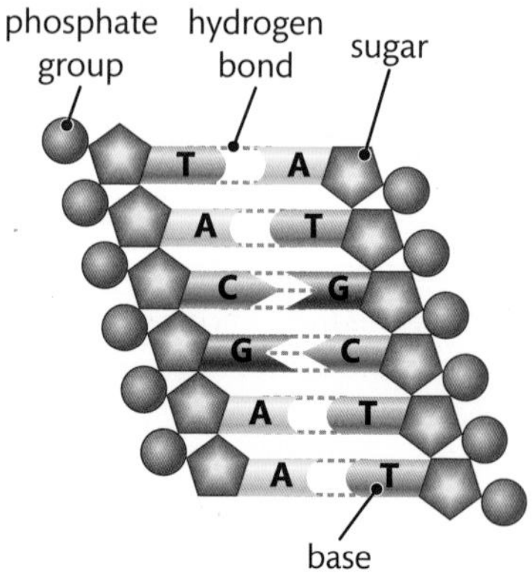

   (a) Name the units that are formed from one sugar, one phosphate group and one base. **[1 mark]**

   ....

   (b) Give a reason why DNA can be described as a polymer. **[1 mark]**

   ....

   (c) Before cell division occurs, DNA is copied by separating the strands and then adding new units to make double strands again. Use **Figure 2** to explain the importance of complementary base-pairing during this process. **[2 marks]**

   ....

   ....

phosphate group   hydrogen bond   sugar

base

Figure 2

 Made a start   **Feeling confident**   ☑ **Exam ready**

DNA and the genome

② Quick quiz

Complete the following sentences. Use words from the box.

| chromosomes | DNA | helix | nucleus | polymer | two | genetic |

The .... material in a cell is composed of a chemical called ....

This chemical is a .... because it is made of repeating units.

The units are joined together to make .... strands, which twist round each other forming a double

.... The strands combine with other molecules to form structures called ....

⑤ Genes and genome   Grade 4

1. The human genome consists of about 20 000 genes.

(a) Give the meaning of the term 'human genome'.   **[1 mark]**

....

(b) Give the meaning of the term 'gene'.   **[2 marks]**

A small section of DNA that ....

....

> Remember that genes are found on chromosomes.

⑩ The human genome   Grades 7–8

2. Many complete human genomes have been mapped to show their DNA structure.

(a) This work has shown many small differences between the genomes of different people caused by mutations. Give the meaning of the term 'mutation'.   **[1 mark]**

....

(b) Analysis of genomes from people all over the world indicates that all non-African people today are descendants of one small group of humans who left Africa around 70 000 years ago. Suggest the evidence for this from genome analysis.   **[2 marks]**

....

....

(c) Once the genome has been mapped, the genes can then be identified. Explain how looking at the detail of a gene can help identify people who are at risk of developing an inherited disorder.   **[2 marks]**

....

....

(d) Describe **one** advantage for a person of knowing their risk of developing a particular disease.   **[1 mark]**

....

(e) Suggest **one** disadvantage for a person of knowing their risk of developing a particular disease.   **[1 mark]**

....

 Made a start   **Feeling confident**   **Exam ready**

Genetic inheritance

② Quick quiz

The diagram shows a pair of chromosomes found in a body cell. Add the following labels to the diagram.

- different genes
- heterozygous allele pair
- homozygous recessive allele pair
- alleles of gene A
- homozygous dominant allele pair

A _____

B _____

A• a•
•b •b
•c •c
•D d•

C _____

D _____

E _____

⑩ Genetic cross and Punnett squares   Grade 6

1. What do most phenotype features result from? Tick **one** box.   **[1 mark]**

   a single gene ☐   multiple interacting genes ☐

   a recessive allele ☐   a dominant allele ☐

   > Phenotype is the observable characteristics of an organism, or its appearance.

2. **(a)** Cystic fibrosis is a disorder of cell membranes caused by a recessive allele.

   State what is meant by the term 'recessive disorder'.   **[1 mark]**

   ➤ A recessive disorder is caused by
   ....

   (b) Complete the Punnett square to show the possible genotypes of offspring from parents who are both heterozygous for the gene related to cystic fibrosis.   **[2 marks]**

   > Start by identifying the father's alleles using information from the question.

   (c) Use your Punnett square to calculate the probability of a child of these parents developing cystic fibrosis.   **[1 mark]**

   probability = ...

   > What proportion of the offspring genotypes could develop the disease?

   Table 1

		Father's alleles	
Mother's alleles	F		
	f		

   > **Maths skills**
   > Probability is a measure of how likely something is to happen. Probabilities can be written as ratios, fractions, decimals and percentages.

⑩ Inheritance   Grade 6

3. Being able to taste bitter Phenylthiocarbamide (PTC) is caused by a dominant allele, **T**. Having two copies of the recessive allele, **t**, makes a person unable to taste PTC.

   (a) Complete the Punnett square to show the genotypes of the offspring from a father who is heterozygous for the PTC gene and a mother who cannot taste PTC.   **[2 marks]**

   (b) Use your completed square to calculate the probability of a child inheriting the inability to taste PTC from these parents. Give the probability as a percentage.   **[1 mark]**

   Table 2

	Father's alleles	
Mother's alleles		

   .... %

☐ **Made a start**   ☐ **Feeling confident**   ☐ **Exam ready**

Inherited disorders

② Quick quiz

Draw **one** line from each word to link it to its meaning.

inherited disorder	affects the phenotype only when there are two copies in the genotype
recessive allele	inheriting a phenotype caused by a single gene
dominant allele	a disorder caused by a faulty allele
monohybrid inheritance	affects the phenotype when only one copy is present in the genotype

⑩ Family pedigree — Grade 9

1. **Figure 1** shows a family pedigree identifying which family members have an inherited disorder caused by a dominant allele.

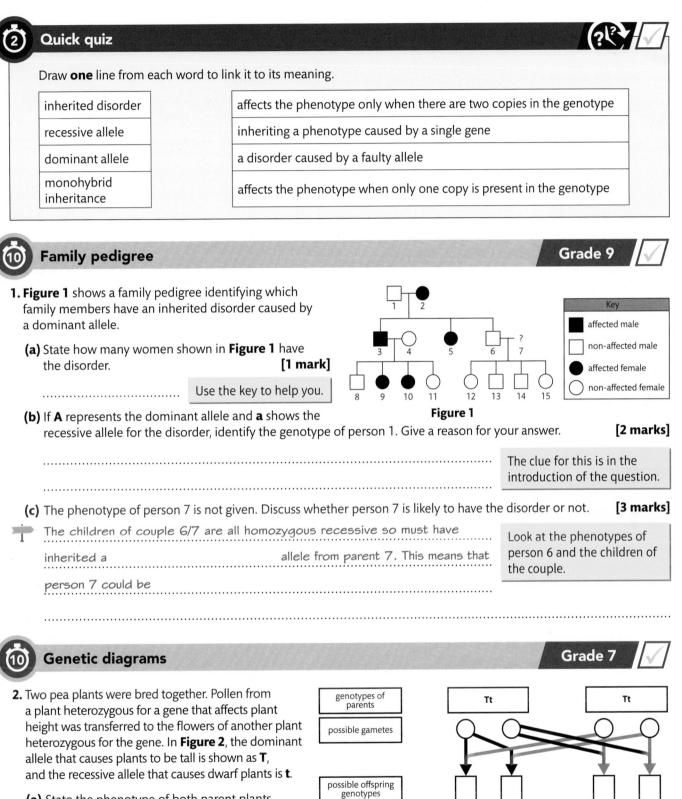

Figure 1

Key
- ■ affected male
- □ non-affected male
- ● affected female
- ○ non-affected female

(a) State how many women shown in **Figure 1** have the disorder. **[1 mark]**

.... Use the key to help you.

(b) If **A** represents the dominant allele and **a** shows the recessive allele for the disorder, identify the genotype of person 1. Give a reason for your answer. **[2 marks]**

....

....

The clue for this is in the introduction of the question.

(c) The phenotype of person 7 is not given. Discuss whether person 7 is likely to have the disorder or not. **[3 marks]**

The children of couple 6/7 are all homozygous recessive so must have

inherited a .... allele from parent 7. This means that

person 7 could be ....

....

Look at the phenotypes of person 6 and the children of the couple.

⑩ Genetic diagrams — Grade 7

2. Two pea plants were bred together. Pollen from a plant heterozygous for a gene that affects plant height was transferred to the flowers of another plant heterozygous for the gene. In **Figure 2**, the dominant allele that causes plants to be tall is shown as **T**, and the recessive allele that causes dwarf plants is **t**.

(a) State the phenotype of both parent plants. **[1 mark]**

....

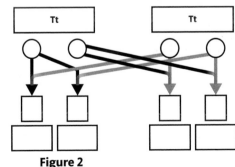

genotypes of parents

possible gametes

possible offspring genotypes

possible offspring phenotypes

Tt | Tt

Figure 2

(b) Complete the genetic diagram in **Figure 2** to show the alleles in the possible gametes, and the genotypes and phenotypes in the possible offspring. **[3 marks]**

(c) Use your completed diagram to identify the percentage of seeds produced from this cross that will produce

dwarf plants. .... **[1 mark]**

✓ **Made a start** ✓ **Feeling confident** ✓ **Exam ready**

Sex determination

② Quick quiz

Complete each sentence by choosing the correct terms from the box below.

| DNA | fertilisation | gametes | pairs | parent | XX | XY | YY | genes | zygote |

The sex of an individual is determined at .... when the two .... fuse to form a

...........................One of the chromosome pairs in each cell carries .... that determine the sex

of the individual.

In human females, the two sex chromosomes are ....

In males, the two sex chromosomes are ....

⑤ Sex chromosomes   Grade 5

1. (a) Name the type of cell division that gives rise to the formation of sex cells.   **[1 mark]**

....

(b) State what proportion of the following gametes contain an X chromosome.

(i) egg cell .... **[1 mark]**   Remember that only one chromosome from each

(ii) sperm cell .... **[1 mark]**   pair enters the gamete during cell division.

(c) The sex of a baby is determined by the inheritance of sex chromosomes. State and explain which parent's sex
chromosome determines whether the baby is a girl or a boy.   **[3 marks]**

Egg cells from the mother contain
....

Sperm cells contain
....

So it is the .... whose gamete determines the sex of the baby.

⑧ Sex determination   Grade 6

2. (a) Complete the Punnett square diagram to show the inheritance   **Table 1**
of sex. Use the symbols **X** and **Y** for the chromosomes. **[2 marks]**

(b) A couple are having a baby. Using your Punnett square, determine
the chance of the baby being a girl. Tick **one** box.   **[1 mark]**

0% ☐   25% ☐   50% ☐   75% ☐

		Sperm cells from father	
		X	
Egg cells from mother	X		

(c) A different couple already have two boys and a girl, and the woman is pregnant. State the probability that the baby
will be a girl.   **[1 mark]**

....

(d) Explain your answer to part **(c)**.   **[2 marks]**

....

....

☑ **Made a start**   ☑ **Feeling confident**   ☑ **Exam ready**

Variation and mutation

② Quick quiz

Each statement below describes an example of variation. Circle the correct word after each statement to show if it describes genetic or environmental variation.

Seeds from tall plants usually produce plants that grow to be tall. **environmental / genetic**

Seeds from tall plants may not grow tall because they cannot get enough water. **environmental / genetic**

Seeds from green-leaved plants may occasionally produce plants with very pale leaves that contain little chlorophyll. **environmental / genetic**

Plants that usually have green leaves may develop pale leaves if grown in the dark. **environmental / genetic**

⑩ Variation and mutations   Grade 6 ☑

1. (a) Give the meaning of the term 'variation'. **[1 mark]**

....

(b) Give the meaning of the term 'mutation'. **[1 mark]**

➤ A mutation is a change in ....

(c) Explain how mutations may lead to variation. **[3 marks]**

....

....

....

> Phenotype is the appearance of an organism. Genotype is the genetic makeup of an organism – its genes.

(d) A baby may have around 100 mutations in its genes that its parents do not have. Give a reason why the baby still looks like its parents. **[1 mark]**

➤ Most or all of the mutations will have no ....

....

⑩ Cause of variation   Grades 6–7 ☑

2. Human hair colour is inherited through the effects of two interacting genes.

(a) Suggest why there is a wide range of different inherited hair colours in humans. **[2 marks]**

....

....

(b) Explain why children of the same parents may have different hair colour to each other. **[2 marks]**

....

....

(c) Occasionally, parents with fair, brown or black hair have a child who has very pale or white hair. Suggest a reason for the pale-coloured hair. **[1 mark]**

....

(d) People with light brown hair may develop paler, fair hair if they spend a lot of time in bright sunshine. Explain why this is an example of environmental variation. **[2 marks]**

....

....

Evolution by natural selection

② Quick quiz

Complete the following sentences on Darwin's theory. Use words from the box.

| adapted | characteristics | evolution | genes | natural selection | phenotypes | simple | offspring |

Darwin's theory of .... describes how organisms may change over time through

.... This explains how changes in the environment can lead to changes in ....

of species as only the best .... individuals survive and breed, passing on their characteristics to

their .... in their ....

⑩ Evolution of resistance   Grade 7

1. One example of evidence for evolution by natural selection is the evolution of antibiotic-resistant bacteria.
Label the diagrams in **Figure 1** to show how this evolution occurs. Each shape is a bacterium.   **[3 marks]**

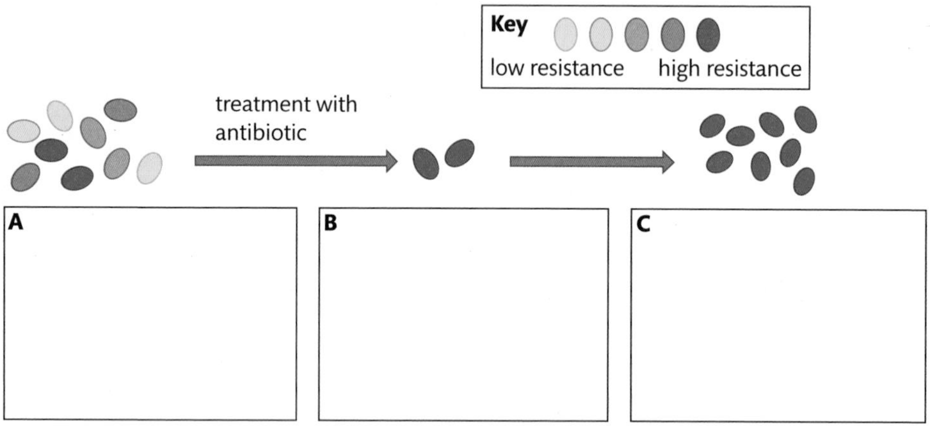

Key
low resistance   high resistance

treatment with antibiotic

A

B

C

Label **A** should say why there is variation in the population. Label **B** should describe the impact of using antibiotics on the population. Label **C** should say how the population of antibiotic-resistant bacteria then develops.

Figure 1

⑮ New species   Grade 6

2. Bonobos and chimpanzees are thought to have evolved from a common ancestor around 2 million years ago.
Bonobos live south of the wide Congo river in Africa, while chimpanzees live north of the river. Neither bonobos nor chimpanzees are good swimmers.

Explain how the formation of the Congo river around 2 million years ago could have led to the evolution of the bonobo and chimp species.   **[6 marks]**

....

....

....

....

....

....

....

This answer needs to describe why the DNA of the two groups changed once they were separated from each other.

Exam focus
Remember some marks in a 6-mark question are for the ordering and coherence of your argument.

Continue your answer on your own paper.

 Made a start   **Feeling confident**   **Exam ready**

Evidence for human evolution

② Quick quiz

True or false?

The Leakey family found fossils of human-like species that lived in Africa 1.6 million years ago.	**True / False**
'Lucy' is an example of the human-like species *Homo habilis*.	**True / False**
Ardi belongs to the human-like species *Ardipithecus ramidus* and lived 4.4 million years ago.	**True / False**
Evidence from fossil bones and stone tools helps to show how human-like species evolved.	**True / False**

⑩ Fossil evidence   Grades 6–7

1. **Figure 1** shows the upper leg bone of two living species (human and chimp) and of the fossil skeleton known as 'Lucy'. The position of each bone shows its alignment in the whole skeleton.

   (a) Use evidence from **Figure 1** to suggest how Lucy's height compares with that of a modern human and chimp.   **[2 marks]**

   Lucy's leg bone is nearer in length to a ....

   than .... This suggests she was a

   similar height to a modern ....

   (b) Use evidence from **Figure 1** to suggest whether Lucy walked upright or on four legs.   **[2 marks]**

   The alignment of Lucy's leg bone indicates that her knees .... when she walked.

   This suggests that ....

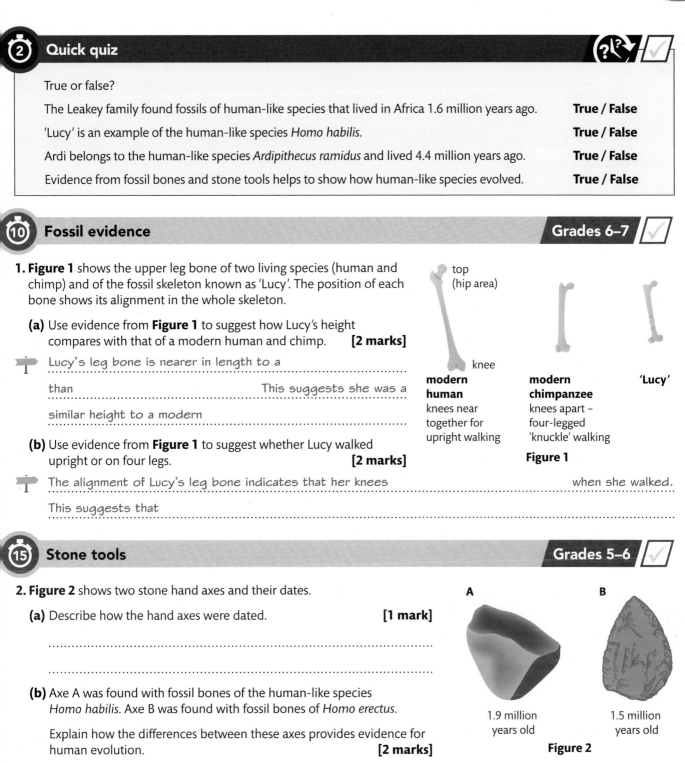

top
(hip area)

knee

**modern
human**
knees near
together for
upright walking

**modern
chimpanzee**
knees apart –
four-legged
'knuckle' walking

'Lucy'

Figure 1

⑮ Stone tools   Grades 5–6

2. **Figure 2** shows two stone hand axes and their dates.

   (a) Describe how the hand axes were dated.   **[1 mark]**

   ....

   ....

   (b) Axe A was found with fossil bones of the human-like species *Homo habilis*. Axe B was found with fossil bones of *Homo erectus*.

   Explain how the differences between these axes provides evidence for human evolution.   **[2 marks]**

   ....

   ....

   ....

   ....

   ....

A

B

1.9 million
years old

1.5 million
years old

Figure 2

Exam focus 📌

When a question asks you to use evidence given, make sure you refer to the evidence in your answer.

Classification

② Quick quiz

Use lines to link each kingdom with a characteristic feature shared by organisms in that kingdom.

kingdom	feature
prokaryotes	usually multi-celled organisms that are able to photosynthesise
protists	usually multi-celled organisms that digest food outside their bodies
fungi	single cells with genetic material free in cytoplasm
plants	multi-celled organisms that digest food inside their bodies
animals	usually single cells with nucleus and other sub-cellular structures

⑤ Classification systems   Grade 4

1. Complete each of the following sentences about classification systems with one word from the box. Note: not all words in the box are used.

characteristics	domains	genetics	genus	kingdoms	order	species

(a) In the 18th century Carl Linnaeus developed a classification system for organisms based on ...characteristics....................
                                                                                          [1 mark]

(b) The largest groups in Linnaeus' system are the ....   **[1 mark]**

(c) The smallest group in Linnaeus' system is the ....   **[1 mark]**

(d) In the 20th century Carl Woese developed a new classification for organisms based on ....
                                                                                          [1 mark]

(e) This new classification groups all organisms into ....   **[1 mark]**

⑤ Classification by domains   Grade 7

2. The three-domain classification consists of three main groups: Bacteria, Archaea and Eukaryota.

(a) Name **two** kingdoms from the old classification that are now placed in the Eukaryota.   **[2 marks]**

....

....

(b) Name the kingdom from the old system that is now classified within the domain Bacteria.   **[1 mark]**

....

(c) Explain why Archaea are placed between Bacteria and Eukaryota in the domain system.   **[2 marks]**

....

....

....

> Think about how position indicates relationships between groups.

 Made a start   Feeling confident   Exam ready

Selective breeding

Suggest **one** feature of each organism shown below that has been selectively bred.

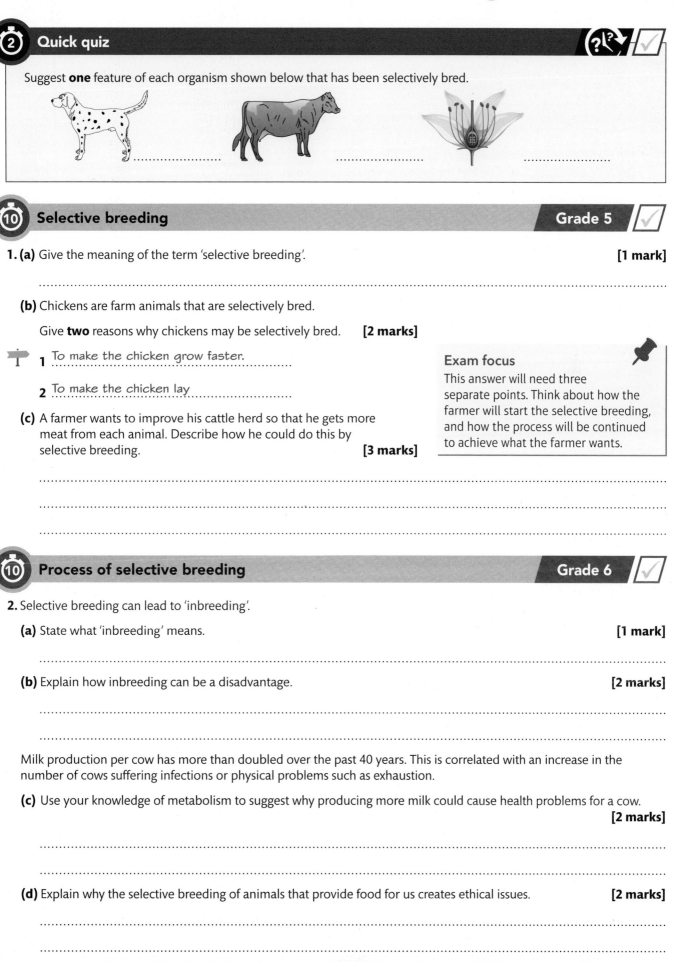

....

⑩ **Selective breeding**   Grade 5

1. (a) Give the meaning of the term 'selective breeding'.   **[1 mark]**

....

(b) Chickens are farm animals that are selectively bred.

Give **two** reasons why chickens may be selectively bred.   **[2 marks]**

1 To make the chicken grow faster. ....

2 To make the chicken lay ....

(c) A farmer wants to improve his cattle herd so that he gets more meat from each animal. Describe how he could do this by selective breeding.   **[3 marks]**

> **Exam focus**
> This answer will need three separate points. Think about how the farmer will start the selective breeding, and how the process will be continued to achieve what the farmer wants.

....

....

....

⑩ **Process of selective breeding**   Grade 6

2. Selective breeding can lead to 'inbreeding'.

(a) State what 'inbreeding' means.   **[1 mark]**

....

(b) Explain how inbreeding can be a disadvantage.   **[2 marks]**

....

....

Milk production per cow has more than doubled over the past 40 years. This is correlated with an increase in the number of cows suffering infections or physical problems such as exhaustion.

(c) Use your knowledge of metabolism to suggest why producing more milk could cause health problems for a cow.   **[2 marks]**

....

....

(d) Explain why the selective breeding of animals that provide food for us creates ethical issues.   **[2 marks]**

....

....

Genetic engineering

② Quick quiz

Complete the following sentences using selected words from the box.

| bacteria | ligase enzyme | restriction enzymes | sticky ends | vectors |

(a) In genetic engineering the required gene is cut from a chromosome using ....

(b) A few bases on one strand of the gene are left unpaired, creating ....

(c) Similar cuts are made in plasmids taken from ....

(d) Copies of the gene are joined with the DNA of the plasmids using a ....

(e) The plasmids are put into bacteria, which are used as .... to insert the gene into the cells of another organism.

⑧ Genetic engineering of cells   Grades 5–7

1. Bacteria have been genetically engineered to produce human insulin.

(a) Describe how bacteria are genetically engineered to produce human insulin.
[2 marks]

> Insulin is a protein. Remember how cells are instructed to produce a particular protein.

➤ The gene for human insulin
....

The gene is then inserted into
....

(b) Suggest how genetic modification could be used to overcome inherited disorders, such as cystic fibrosis, which affects cells lining the lungs. **[2 marks]**

> Think about how inserting a gene into the cells of an early embryo will affect all the cells of the individual that grows from that embryo.

....

....

⑩ Genetic modification of crops   Grade 8

2. Maize (sweetcorn) has been genetically modified to contain a gene that codes for a poison that kills caterpillars which eat the plant. The gene comes from a bacterium.

(a) Describe the stages of genetic engineering used to produce genetically modified maize.   **[4 marks]**

....

....

....

....

(b) Explain why growing this type of genetically modified maize can increase the yield (amount of food harvested) from each plant.   **[2 marks]**

....

....

(c) Explain why some people are concerned about how growing genetically modified maize might affect the environment.   **[2 marks]**

....

....

     Made a start   **Feeling confident**   ☑ **Exam ready**

Health issues

(2)
Quick quiz

The following are examples of communicable and non-communicable diseases. Draw a circle around the diseases that are **non-communicable**.

HIV   chalara dieback   cholera   lung cancer   cardiovascular disease   tuberculosis   malaria

(5)
Health and disease   Grade 7

1. One definition of health is a state of physical and mental well-being.

   Give **one** reason why health is considered to be more than just being free of disease.   **[1 mark]**

   ....

2. Explain why some diseases are described as communicable and others are non-communicable diseases.   **[2 marks]**

Communicable diseases are caused by a pathogen and

....

Non-communicable diseases have other causes, such as genes or faults in the way cells work, and

....

....

(10)
Non-communicable disease   Grade 6

3. Alcohol is a drug that slows down the nervous system. Some people become dependent on alcohol for its effects.

   The cost of treating 100 alcohol-dependent people so they are no longer dependent is estimated at £40 000. The cost of treating 100 alcohol-dependent people in hospital for alcohol-related injury and illness is estimated at £60 000.

   Justify the argument for increasing the availability of treatment for alcohol dependency.   **[2 marks]**

> **Exam focus**
> The 'justify' command word means you should use evidence from the information you have been given to support your answer.

   ....

   ....

4. Asthma is an allergic reaction to a trigger, such as pollen, dust mites, or many other factors. The trigger causes airways to narrow and produce more mucus.

   (a) Explain why a severe asthma attack can be very harmful. **[2 marks]**

   ....

   ....

   ....

   ....

Years
--- asthma   — flu
Figure 1

   (b) Flu is a communicable disease of the nose, throat and lungs. **Figure 1** shows the number of people in hospital for either flu infection or asthma attack between 2002 and 2012.

   Use **Figure 1** to identify if there is a relationship between flu infection and asthma attack. Give a reason for your answer.   **[2 marks]**

   ....

   ....

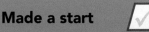

Communicable diseases

---

② Quick quiz

Cross out the incorrect **bold** words to make each sentence correct.

Disease-causing microorganisms are called **archaea / pathogens**. For example, chalara ash dieback is caused by a **protist / fungus**, chlamydia is caused by a **bacterium / virus** and malaria is caused by a **protist / virus**.

---

⑩ Preventing the spread of disease | **Grade 5** ✓

1. (a) Flu is caused by a virus. The virus irritates the skin lining the nose and throat making it itchy and causing it to produce more fluid than normal. Suggest how these effects of the virus help to spread flu. **[2 marks]**

👉 The irritation will cause

.... spreading the viruses though the air in ....

....

> **Exam focus**
> Some exam questions will expect you to apply what you have learnt to examples that you may not know. In this case, use your knowledge of how pathogens that affect the nose and mouth can be spread to other people.

(b) Explain the health advice 'catch it, bin it, kill it'. **[2 marks]**

....

....

2. TMV is a virus that causes disease in many plant species by killing cells. It is spread by sap-sucking insects. Suggest reasons for each of the following recommendations on how to protect plants from infection.

(a) Clear away all damaged plant parts and burn them. **[1 mark]**

....

(b) Spray plants to kill any insect pests that suck plant sap. **[2 marks]**

....

....

> You may not have learnt how TMV is spread, but you should have learnt about how malaria is spread by insects. Use that knowledge to help you here.

---

⑩ Tuberculosis | **Grade 6** ✓

3. Tuberculosis (TB) is one of the top 10 causes of death worldwide.

(a) Describe **one** effect of a tuberculosis infection. **[1 mark]**

....

People who have been treated successfully for tuberculosis may develop the disease again. **Table 1** shows the results of an investigation into the relationship between smoking and developing tuberculosis a second time.

(b) Complete the table by calculating the percentage of those who smoked more than 10 cigarettes a day who developed tuberculosis again. **[1 mark]**

(c) Comment on the results shown in the table. **[3 marks]**

Table 1

Number of cigarettes smoked each day	Total number in group	Number with recurrent tuberculosis	Percentage of group (%)
0	4280	55	1.3
1–10	250	3	1.2
>10	602	19	

....

....

....

....

 Made a start **Feeling confident** ✓ **Exam ready**

Viral diseases

BBC

② Quick quiz

True or false?

Some viral infections can make a person more likely to catch other infections.	**True / False**
Cholera is caused by a virus.	**True / False**
Some viral pathogens are spread in droplets through air when someone sneezes.	**True / False**
Diseases caused by viruses can be cured using antibiotics.	**True / False**

⑤ HIV   Grade 5

1. HIV is a human pathogen.

(a) State which type of microorganism HIV is. **[1 mark]**

....

(b) Describe **one** way in which HIV can be spread. **[1 mark]**

....

(c) Describe **one** way in which the risk of spreading HIV can be reduced. **[1 mark]**

....

(d) Name the type of cell that HIV infects. **[1 mark]**

....

(e) Explain the role of the type of cell you named in part **(d)** in keeping people healthy. **[2 marks]**

White blood cells are part of the ....

and attack and destroy ....

⑩ HIV   Grade 7

2. Figure 1 shows the proportion of people with HIV and the proportion of people with a bacterial disease, TB, for 50 different countries.

(a) Describe the trend shown in the scatter diagram. **[1 mark]**

....

....

(b) TB is one of the diseases that people catch in the AIDS stage of an HIV infection. Use your knowledge of HIV to explain the relationship shown in the scatter diagram. **[2 marks]**

....

....

....

....

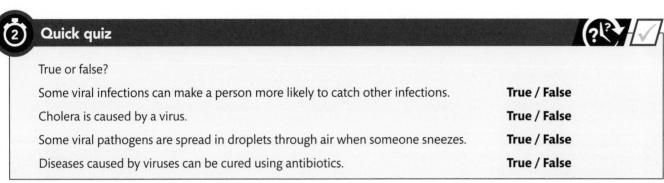

Figure 1

(y-axis: Proportion of people with TB; x-axis: Proportion of people with HIV)

Bacterial diseases

Quick quiz

Draw a circle round the infections caused by bacteria.

chlamydia   cholera   malaria   chalara dieback   tuberculosis   HIV

Chlamydia infections   Grade 6

1. Chlamydia is a sexually transmitted infection (STI).

Figure 1 shows how the number of chlamydia infections per 100 000 men in different age groups has changed between 2009 and 2017 in England.

(a) Compare the infection rate in men under-25 and over-25. **[1 mark]**

The infection rates in the two under-25 age groups are .... than in the three over-25 groups.

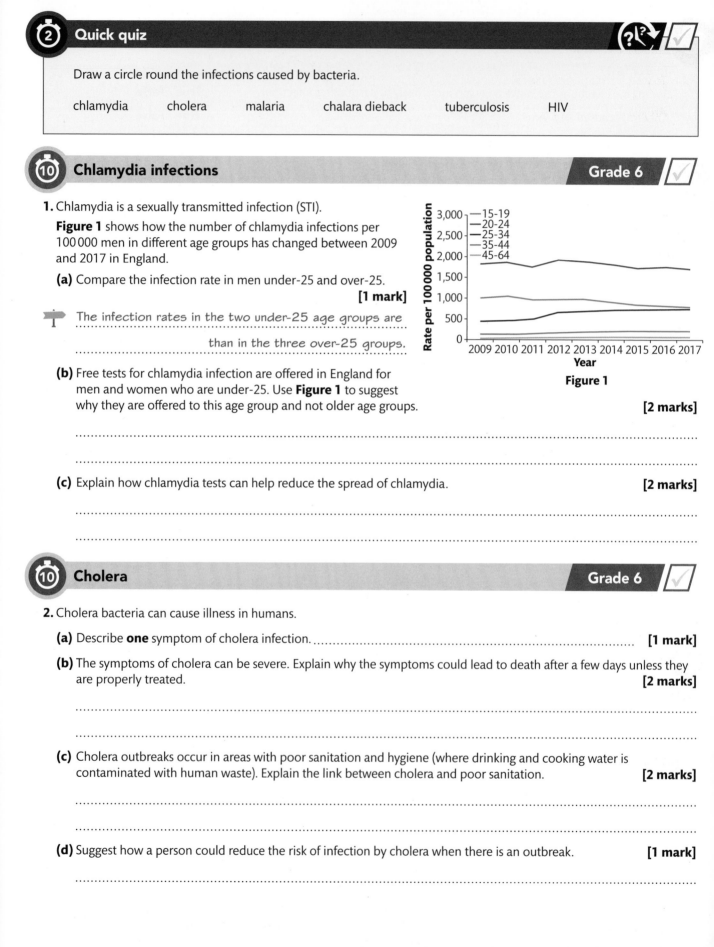

Figure 1

(b) Free tests for chlamydia infection are offered in England for men and women who are under-25. Use **Figure 1** to suggest why they are offered to this age group and not older age groups. **[2 marks]**

(c) Explain how chlamydia tests can help reduce the spread of chlamydia. **[2 marks]**

Cholera   Grade 6

2. Cholera bacteria can cause illness in humans.

(a) Describe **one** symptom of cholera infection. .... **[1 mark]**

(b) The symptoms of cholera can be severe. Explain why the symptoms could lead to death after a few days unless they are properly treated. **[2 marks]**

(c) Cholera outbreaks occur in areas with poor sanitation and hygiene (where drinking and cooking water is contaminated with human waste). Explain the link between cholera and poor sanitation. **[2 marks]**

(d) Suggest how a person could reduce the risk of infection by cholera when there is an outbreak. **[1 mark]**

Made a start   Feeling confident   Exam ready

Fungal diseases

②ⁱ Quick quiz

To which classification domain do fungi belong? Circle **one** word.

Archaea　　　Bacteria　　　Eukaryota

⑩ Impact of chalara　　　　　　　　　　　　　　　　　　**Grade 6**

1. Chalara dieback is an infection of ash trees. **Figure 1** shows how infection spreads.

   (a) Describe the symptoms of chalara ash dieback.　　　**[1 mark]**

   ....

   ....

   (b) The fungus blocks the xylem tubes in the leaves and stems. Explain how this could cause the symptoms you described in **(a)**.　　**[2 marks]**

   If water and nutrients cannot reach the leaf and stem cells, ...

   .... carry out ....

   ....

   > Remember that xylem carries water and dissolved minerals from the roots to the leaves.

healthy ash tree　　　　infected ash tree

summer

spring　　　　　　　　　　　　　　autumn

winter

spores released from　　　dying leaves fall
fruiting bodies on　　　　　to the ground
infected leaf stalks

Figure 1

   (c) The disease has destroyed many ash trees in Europe since 1992, but was first seen on young trees in a UK tree nursery in 2012. Use **Figure 1** to suggest two ways in which the disease has spread across the UK since 2012.　　　　　　　**[2 marks]**

   ....

   ....

   ....

⑩ Controlling chalara　　　　　　　　　　　　　　　　**Grade 6**

2. **(a)** Advice to tree owners is to cut down infected ash trees and clear fallen ash leaves. Give a reason for this advice.
   　　　　　　　　　　　　　　　　　　　　　　　　　[1 mark]

   ....

   (b) Suggest **one** problem with following this advice in natural woodland where a high proportion of the trees are ash.
   　　　　　　　　　　　　　　　　　　　　　　　　　[2 marks]

   ....

   ....

   ....

   ....

   > Use your knowledge of the interdependence of organisms to answer this question.

Protist diseases

② Quick quiz

True or false?

Malaria is a disease caused by a protist pathogen.	**True / False**
Protists are a type of bacteria.	**True / False**
Mosquitoes are pathogens that cause malaria.	**True / False**
An animal vector is an animal that carries pathogens from infected people to others.	**True / False**

⑩ Malaria   Grade 5

1. Figure 1 shows how malaria is spread.

person
with malaria   A   B

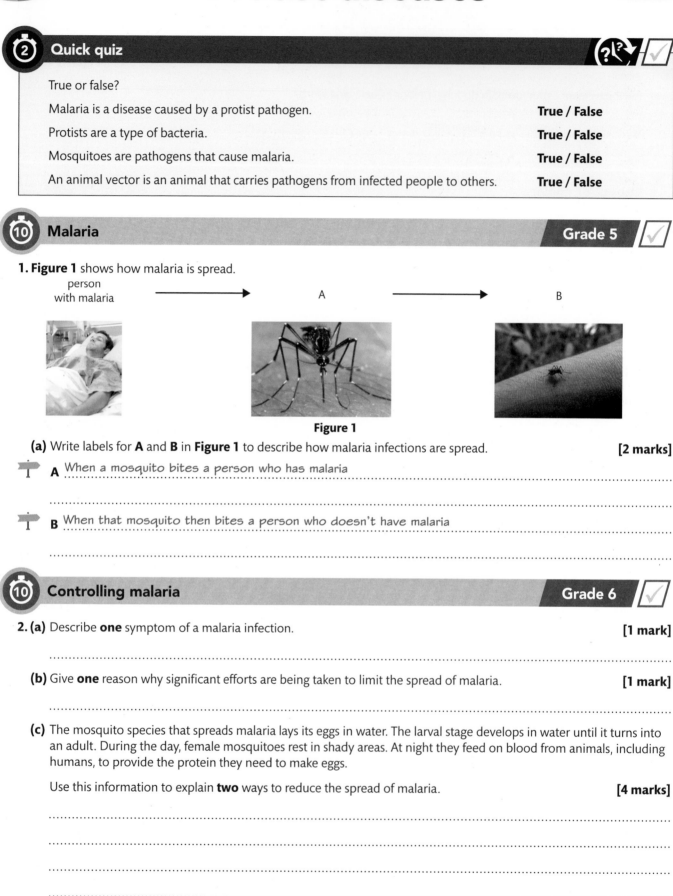

Figure 1

(a) Write labels for **A** and **B** in **Figure 1** to describe how malaria infections are spread.   **[2 marks]**

A When a mosquito bites a person who has malaria
....

B When that mosquito then bites a person who doesn't have malaria
....
....

⑩ Controlling malaria   Grade 6

2. (a) Describe **one** symptom of a malaria infection.   **[1 mark]**
....

(b) Give **one** reason why significant efforts are being taken to limit the spread of malaria.   **[1 mark]**
....

(c) The mosquito species that spreads malaria lays its eggs in water. The larval stage develops in water until it turns into an adult. During the day, female mosquitoes rest in shady areas. At night they feed on blood from animals, including humans, to provide the protein they need to make eggs.

Use this information to explain **two** ways to reduce the spread of malaria.   **[4 marks]**
....
....
....
....
....
....

| Made a start | ✓ Feeling confident | Exam ready |

Human defence systems

② Quick quiz

True or false?

The human body produces antibiotics to fight off disease.	**True / False**
Phagocytes are white blood cells that engulf and destroy invading pathogens.	**True / False**
Antitoxins are produced by bacteria.	**True / False**
The immune system is a non-specific defence system of the body.	**True / False**

⑩ Defence against infection   Grades 4–5

1. (a) The human body has defence systems that help to prevent pathogens entering.

For each feature give a reason why it defends the body.   **[4 marks]**

Thick skin makes it difficult ....

Sticky mucus in the nose traps ....

Cells lining the trachea and bronchi have cilia (tiny hairs) on their surface that ....

Stomach acid ....

(b) Describe how **one** other chemical defence helps to prevent infection.   **[2 marks]**

....

....

⑮ Specific defence against disease   Grade 6

2. (a) Name the defence system that protects against disease once a pathogen enters the blood.   **[1 mark]**

....

(b) Name the blood cells which are part of the defence system you named in **(a)**.   **[1 mark]**

....

(c) Describe **three** ways in which the blood cells named in part **(b)** protect against disease.   **[3 marks]**

....

....

....

3. The graph shows how the concentration of antibodies in the blood changes after an infection.

(a) Describe what is happening to pathogen numbers up to time A on the graph.   **[1 mark]**

....

(b) Add a label on the graph at the point where you think the person would feel most ill.
                                                                        [1 mark]

(c) Explain your answer to **(b)**.   **[2 marks]**

....

....

infection by pathogen

Concentration of antibodies in blood

A

Time

Figure 1

Pathogen numbers are not shown on the graph. You will need to use your knowledge about bacteria to answer this.

Immunisation

② Quick quiz

Complete the following sentences, using the words in the box.

| specific | antigens | illness | communicable |

Vaccines used in immunisation contain the .... of a pathogen.

Immunisation has been used to prevent the spread of .... diseases such as polio.

A vaccine is .... to the pathogen that causes a particular disease.

Immunisation is used to prevent .... in an individual.

⑩ Vaccinations   Grade 7

1. Almost all children in the UK are immunised against polio, a disease caused by the polio virus.

(a) Suggest how the polio vaccine was produced.   **[1 mark]**   Use the term 'antigen' in your answer.

....

....

(b) Explain how immunisation using the polio vaccine protects a child against developing polio.   **[3 marks]**

The vaccine triggers the immune system to produce

....

This means that if the child is infected later with the polio virus

....

This will prevent the child developing

....

⑩ Widespread immunisation   Grade 7

2. Smallpox was an infectious viral disease with serious symptoms, including death. In 1966, 10–15 million people in more than 50 countries had smallpox, and 1.5–2 million people died of the disease.

(a) Immunisation against smallpox began in 1853 in the UK. Suggest **two** reasons why smallpox immunisation was made compulsory.   **[2 marks]**

Reason 1 ....

Reason 2 ....

(b) Worldwide smallpox immunisation was carried out from 1965. The last case of smallpox occurred in 1971. Give a reason why children in the UK are no longer immunised against smallpox.   **[1 mark]**

....

(c) The cost of smallpox vaccination between 1967 and 1979 was £18 million each year. Evaluate the cost of the smallpox eradication campaign.   **[4 marks]**

....

....

....

....

....

> **Exam focus**
>
> In an 'evaluate' question, you need to use the information in the question, as well as your knowledge and understanding, to consider evidence for and against.

> Continue your answer on your own paper.

 Made a start   **Feeling confident**   **Exam ready**

Biology	Health and disease	Development of medicine

Antibiotics

(2) Quick quiz

Draw **one** line from each word to link it with its definition.

antibiotic	stimulates the immune system to attack a pathogen
antibody	medicine used to cure bacterial disease
painkiller	produced by immune system in response to infection
antigen	medicine used to reduce some symptoms of disease

(15) Choosing the right medicine   Grade 6

1. Flu is a viral disease that causes a high temperature, aches, a runny nose and sore throat.

(a) Explain why someone who has flu is not given antibiotics such as penicillin to treat their infection.   **[2 marks]**

Antibiotics only kill .... so they will have no effect
....

....

> Think about what antibiotics can or cannot kill.

(b) Rarely, a person with flu may then develop a bacterial infection such as pneumonia. Explain why pneumonia can be treated with antibiotics.   **[2 marks]**

....

....

> For the second mark, consider why antibiotics can be used safely in humans.

(5) Drawbacks of antibiotic use   Grade 6

2. Figure 1 shows how the number of deaths from infectious disease per 100 000 people per year changed between 1900 and 1996 in the US.

(a) Using **Figure 1** to help you, comment on the importance of antibiotics in the control of infectious disease.   **[3 marks]**

....
....
....
....
....
....

Figure 1

(b) Suggest why doctors are concerned about the development of antibiotic-resistant strains of bacteria.   **[2 marks]**

....

....

 Made a start   Feeling confident   Exam ready

39

Development of drugs

② Quick quiz

Draw **one** line from each term to link it with its definition.

cell culture	unintended harm caused by a drug
side effect	how much drug to use at a time
dose	cells grown in the lab for testing a new drug

⑤ Discovery and development — Grade 5

1. Complete the text using words from the box. **[4 marks]**

antibiotics	development	discovery	computers	plants

The first stage of the process in producing a new medicine is 'discovery'. The source of many old medicines was from

.... Today, scientists are looking at soil and nasal mucus to find possible new .... to

treat bacterial infections. When they have a possible new medicine, there is a stage of .... when the

structure of the molecule is often studied using ....

⑮ Drug trials — Grade 8

2. One important stage in drug development is **pre-clinical testing**.

(a) Describe **two** possible stages of pre-clinical testing. **[2 marks]**

1 ....

2 ....

(b) Give a reason why pre-clinical testing is done before the drug is tested on people. **[1 mark]**

....

(c) The clinical stage of drug trialling involves at least two main phases.

Describe how each phase is carried out and what it tests for. **[4 marks]**

Phase 1 Test the drug on a small group of healthy volunteers

....

....

Phase 2 Test the drug on a large number

....

....

(d) Describe **one** advantage and **one** disadvantage of taking many years to develop a new drug. **[2 marks]**

Advantage ....

Disadvantage ....

3. Large-scale clinical trials may test the effect of a new medicine by giving one group of patients the new medicine and another
similar group of patients a placebo. (A placebo is something that looks like the drug but contains none of the new medicine.)

Explain why a placebo may be used in clinical trials. **[2 marks]**

....

....

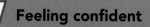 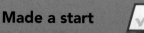

Made a start   Feeling confident   Exam ready

Biology | Health and disease | Non-communicable diseases

Non-communicable diseases

② Quick quiz

True or false?

All cancers are inherited.	**True / False**
Cancer is caused by controlled cell division and growth.	**True / False**
Lung cancer may be caused by drinking large amounts of alcohol.	**True / False**
Cardiovascular diseases are non-communicable.	**True / False**

⑤ Waist : hip ratio and disease | Grade 7

1. Figure 1 shows the results of a study into how risk of death from cardiovascular disease is related to waist : hip ratio.

(a) Describe how waist : hip ratio is measured. **[1 mark]**

Waist : hip ratio is a person's .... measurement

divided by their .... measurement.

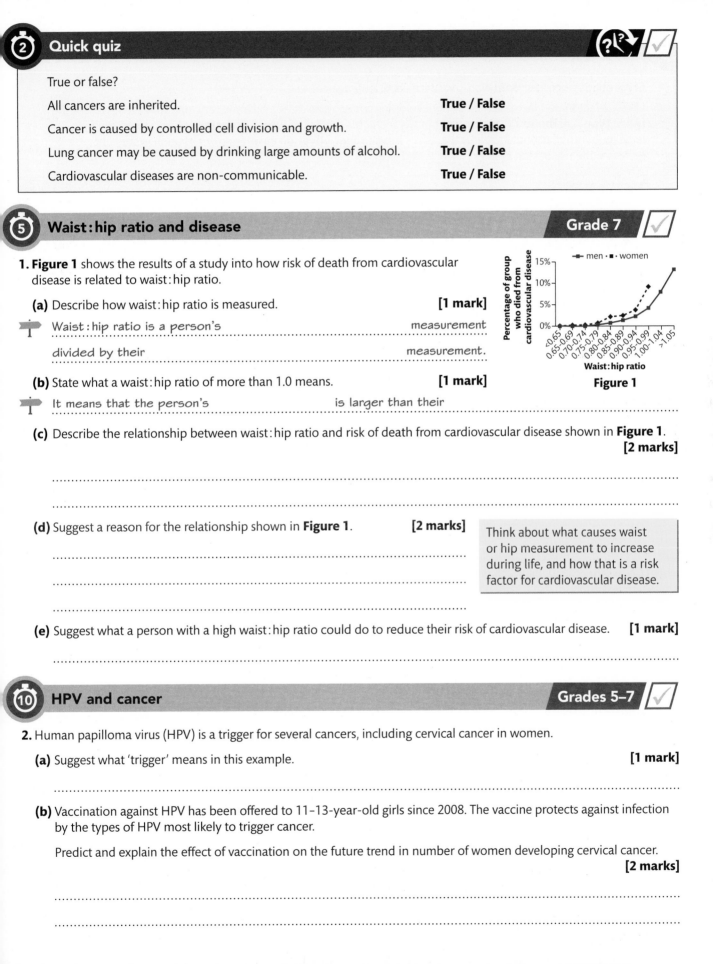

Figure 1

(b) State what a waist : hip ratio of more than 1.0 means. **[1 mark]**

It means that the person's .... is larger than their ....

(c) Describe the relationship between waist : hip ratio and risk of death from cardiovascular disease shown in **Figure 1**.
[2 marks]

....

....

(d) Suggest a reason for the relationship shown in **Figure 1**. **[2 marks]**

....

....

....

> Think about what causes waist or hip measurement to increase during life, and how that is a risk factor for cardiovascular disease.

(e) Suggest what a person with a high waist : hip ratio could do to reduce their risk of cardiovascular disease. **[1 mark]**

....

⑩ HPV and cancer | Grades 5–7

2. Human papilloma virus (HPV) is a trigger for several cancers, including cervical cancer in women.

(a) Suggest what 'trigger' means in this example. **[1 mark]**

....

(b) Vaccination against HPV has been offered to 11–13-year-old girls since 2008. The vaccine protects against infection by the types of HPV most likely to trigger cancer.

Predict and explain the effect of vaccination on the future trend in number of women developing cervical cancer.
[2 marks]

....

....

✓ **Made a start** ✓ **Feeling confident** ✓ **Exam ready**

Effects of lifestyle

② Quick quiz

Cross out the incorrect **bold** words to make each sentence correct.

Lifestyle factors can increase the risk of developing some diseases. For example, smoking tobacco increases the risk of **type 2 diabetes / lung cancer**, obesity increases the risk of **type 2 diabetes / skin cancer**, drinking large amounts of alcohol increases the risk of **lung cancer / liver disease**, and UV radiation in sunlight increases the risk of **skin cancer / type 2 diabetes**.

⑤ Smoking and cardiovascular disease   Grades 5–7

1. **Table 1** shows the results of a study into the relationship between smoking and cardiovascular disease in a group of over 13 000 men in Copenhagen, Denmark.

Table 1

Risk of heart attack compared with never smoked (1.0)	Mass tobacco smoked (g per day)		
	1–14	15–24	>24
	1.60	1.75	2.09

(a) Explain what the risk for someone who smokes 1–14 g tobacco per day means.   **[2 marks]**

Smoking 1–14 g/day has a risk of .... of having a heart attack compared with a risk of ....

for someone who never smoked. This means their risk of heart attack is .... times greater.

(b) Use the information in **Table 1** to describe the relationship between risk of having a heart attack and the amount of tobacco smoked per day.   **[1 mark]**

As the mass of tobacco smoked per day .... the risk of having a heart attack ....

(c) Explain why smoking tobacco affects the risk of having a heart attack.   **[2 marks]**

Substances inhaled in smoke are absorbed .... Some of these substances cause ....

....

(d) Comment on how the study was carried out and how this could affect whether other scientists might get similar results.   **[2 marks]**

The study included 13 000 men which means the results ....

The study was carried out only with men from Copenhagen, which means the results ....

....

⑩ Alcohol and liver disease   Grade 6

2. **Figure 1** shows how the amount of alcohol consumed per person per year and number of deaths from liver disease in the UK changed between 1970 and 2009.

(a) Describe the change in alcohol consumption and deaths shown in **Figure 1**.   **[2 marks]**

....

....

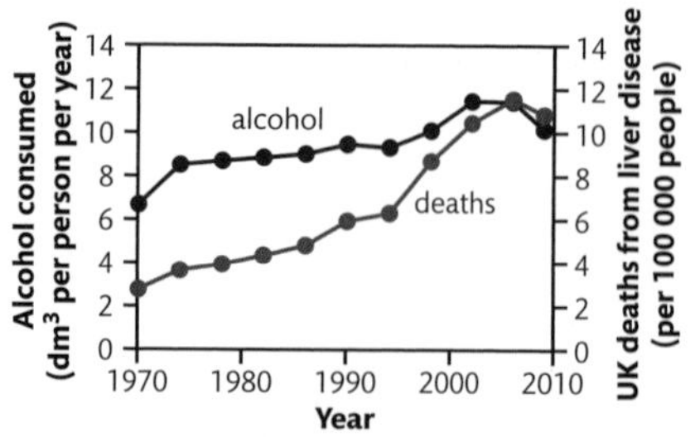

Figure 1

(b) Suggest a reason for the relationship between the changes in alcohol consumption and deaths shown in **Figure 1**.   **[2 marks]**

....

....

✓ Made a start   ✓ Feeling confident   ✓ Exam ready

Cardiovascular disease

② Quick quiz

Cross out the incorrect **bold** words to make each sentence correct.

Cardiovascular disease (CVD) is a general term for conditions affecting the **digestive / circulatory** system. CVD can be caused when coronary **arteries / capillaries** in the heart muscle become narrowed. Deposits of **fat / protein** on the walls of these blood vessels reduce blood flow to the muscle cells beyond the blockage. The cells receive less **carbon dioxide / oxygen**, which they need for respiration, and so may die.

⑤ Treatment of heart disease   Grade 7

1. A faulty heart valve can be replaced during surgery with either a mechanical valve or a biological valve. Explain why a faulty heart valve may need to be replaced.   **[2 marks]**

🖝 If blood flow through the heart is affected
....
.... This will reduce the amount of energy ....
....
....

⑤ Comparing data   Grade 6

2. **Figure 1** compares the performance of mechanical and biological valves. The left graph shows the risk of death after surgery. The right graph shows the risk that the replaced valve will need to be replaced again.

Compare the information about the valves in the graphs to suggest which type of valve is the most successful over 15 years.   **[3 marks]**

....
....
....
....

Left graph — y-axis: Risk of death (%), values 0, 20, 40, 60, 80, 100; x-axis: Time from surgery in years, values 0, 5, 10, 15.

Right graph — y-axis: Risk of aortic valve redo replacement (%), values 0, 2, 4, 6, 8, 10; x-axis: Time from surgery in years, values 0, 5, 10, 15.

—— mechanical   ···· biological

Figure 1

⑩ Heart disease treatment   Grade 6

3. **(a)** Suggest, with reasons, two lifestyle changes that a doctor might advise for a patient who is recovering from cardiovascular disease.   **[4 marks]**

....
....
....
....

(b) Statins are drugs that can reduce blood cholesterol concentration when it is high and a risk factor for cardiovascular disease. Give a reason why someone at risk of a heart attack might take statins for the rest of their life.   **[1 mark]**

....
....

 Made a start   **Feeling confident**   **Exam ready**   43

Photosynthesis

② Quick quiz

Choose the correct word equation for photosynthesis. Tick **one** box.

water + carbon dioxide → oxygen + glucose ☐

oxygen + water → carbon dioxide + glucose ☐

carbon dioxide + glucose → oxygen + water ☐

glucose + oxygen → carbon dioxide + water ☐

⑩ Photosynthesis reaction   Grade 6 ☑

1. (a) Describe the importance of photosynthesis in food chains.   **[2 marks]**

🚩 Plants are producers that use photosynthesis to make ....

This is the source of .... in the food chain.

(b) Explain why photosynthesis is an example of an endothermic reaction.   **[2 marks]**

🚩 More energy is transferred .... the reaction from ....

than is transferred from ....

(c) Explain why plants produce less glucose on a cloudy day than on a sunny day.   **[3 marks]**

🚩 There is less light .... so less energy

.... so the rate of photosynthesis is ....

....

⑩ The site of photosynthesis   Grade 7 ☑

2. Figure 1 shows the structure of a leaf.

(a) Name the sub-cellular structure in plant cells where photosynthesis occurs.   **[1 mark]**

....

(b) Name the pigment in plant cells that captures energy from light.   **[1 mark]**

....

(c) Use **Figure 1** to identify the leaf tissue in which most photosynthesis occurs. Give a reason for your answer.   **[2 marks]**

....

....

(d) Explain the importance for photosynthesis of the position of the tissue you identified in **(c)**.   **[2 marks]**

....

....

....

....

cuticle (waxy coating)

upper epidermis

chloroplast

palisade tissue

spongy tissue

lower epidermis containing stomata

guard cell

Figure 1

 Made a start   **Feeling confident**   **Exam ready**

Rate of photosynthesis

---

② **Quick quiz** **⏱** **✓**

Draw a circle around the **three** factors that can affect the rate of photosynthesis.

soil water content   intensity of light   temperature

biomass   oxygen concentration   carbon dioxide concentration

---

⑩ **Light intensity** **Grade 7** **✓**

1. Give the meaning of the term 'limiting factor' in relation to photosynthesis.   **[1 mark]**

....

2. Figure 1 shows how increasing the concentration of carbon dioxide affects the rate of photosynthesis.

   (a) Identify, with a reason, whether carbon dioxide concentration is a limiting factor at point X or point Y in **Figure 1**.   **[2 marks]**

   👉 Point .... because on this part of the graph, as carbon dioxide concentration

   increases rate of photosynthesis ....

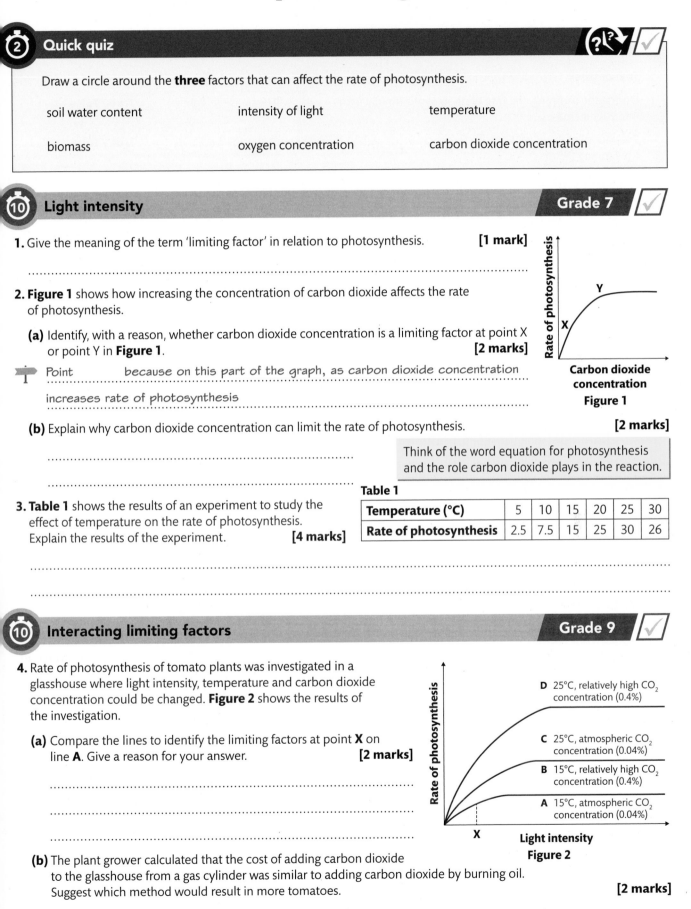

Figure 1 (right): axes labelled "Rate of photosynthesis" (vertical) and "Carbon dioxide concentration" (horizontal), with points X and Y marked. **Figure 1**

   (b) Explain why carbon dioxide concentration can limit the rate of photosynthesis.   **[2 marks]**

....

....

> Think of the word equation for photosynthesis and the role carbon dioxide plays in the reaction.

3. Table 1 shows the results of an experiment to study the effect of temperature on the rate of photosynthesis. Explain the results of the experiment.   **[4 marks]**

Table 1

Temperature (°C)	5	10	15	20	25	30
Rate of photosynthesis	2.5	7.5	15	25	30	26

....

....

---

⑩ **Interacting limiting factors** **Grade 9** **✓**

4. Rate of photosynthesis of tomato plants was investigated in a glasshouse where light intensity, temperature and carbon dioxide concentration could be changed. **Figure 2** shows the results of the investigation.

   (a) Compare the lines to identify the limiting factors at point **X** on line **A**. Give a reason for your answer.   **[2 marks]**

....

....

....

Figure 2 (right): axes labelled "Rate of photosynthesis" (vertical) and "Light intensity" (horizontal), point X marked. Lines labelled:
D 25°C, relatively high CO_2 concentration (0.4%)
C 25°C, atmospheric CO_2 concentration (0.04%)
B 15°C, relatively high CO_2 concentration (0.4%)
A 15°C, atmospheric CO_2 concentration (0.04%)
Figure 2

   (b) The plant grower calculated that the cost of adding carbon dioxide to the glasshouse from a gas cylinder was similar to adding carbon dioxide by burning oil. Suggest which method would result in more tomatoes.   **[2 marks]**

....

....

 Made a start   **Feeling confident**   **Exam ready**

Practical: Photosynthesis

BBC

② Quick quiz

True or false?

During the morning, the rate of photosynthesis in a garden plant will decrease as light intensity increases. **True / False**

The rate then levels off because temperature or carbon dioxide concentration becomes the limiting factor. **True / False**

⑳ Investigating photosynthesis — Grades 7–9

1. A student investigated the effect of light intensity on the rate of photosynthesis in algal balls. **Figure 1** shows the equipment used.

   (a) Name the gas absorbed by the algal balls that causes a change in indicator colour. **[1 mark]**

   ....

   (b) Name the independent variable and a suitable dependent variable in this investigation. **[2 marks]**

   Independent variable ....

   Dependent variable ....

   (c) Another student suggested placing a beaker of water between the lamp and the tube. Explain this suggestion. **[2 marks]**

   This reduces ....

   which helps because ....

   (d) Suggest **two** other control variables for this investigation. **[2 marks]**

   ....

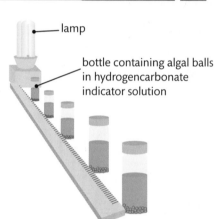

lamp

bottle containing algal balls in hydrogencarbonate indicator solution

Figure 1

Water is a good thermal insulator.

2. **Table 1** shows results from an investigation that measured the number of bubbles of oxygen released from pondweed at different distances from a lamp. It also shows inverse square values for some of the distances.

Table 1

Distance from lamp (cm)	10	15	20	25	40
Inverse square distance (1/cm^2)		0.0044	0.0025	0.0016	0.0006
Number of bubbles produced in 1 min	22	9	5	4	2

   (a) Complete the table by calculating the inverse square of 10 cm. **[1 mark]**

   (b) Draw a graph of the results to show number of bubbles against inverse square of distance. **[2 marks]**

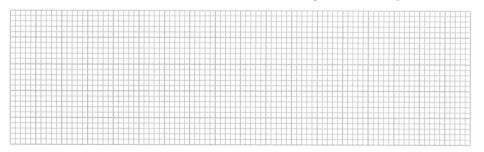

   (c) Use your graph to draw a conclusion from this investigation. **[1 mark]**

   ....

 Made a start **Feeling confident** 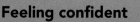 **Exam ready**

Specialised plant cells

② Quick quiz

The list shows some tissues of a plant leaf.

☐ upper epidermis   ☐ lower epidermis   ☐ palisade mesophyll

(a) Write A in the box beside the tissue which contains most stomata.

(b) Write B in the box beside the tissue that carries out the most photosynthesis.

⑤ Adaptations of root hair cells   Grade 6

1. Figure 1 is a photo of a germinating seed, showing a young root with many root hairs. Each hair is a single cell.

(a) Describe the function of root hair cells.   **[1 mark]**

....

(b) Explain how the structure of root hair cells is related to their function.   **[2 marks]**

☞ Root hair cells have a large .... This increases the rate

....

Figure 1

(c) The solute concentration of soil water is lower than the solute concentration of cell cytoplasm. Explain why root hair cells contain many mitochondria.   **[2 marks]**

☞ Mitochondria are where .... is carried out.

This provides the energy the cell needs for ....

⑩ Xylem and phloem   Grade 7

2. Figure 2 is a diagram of part of a xylem vessel.

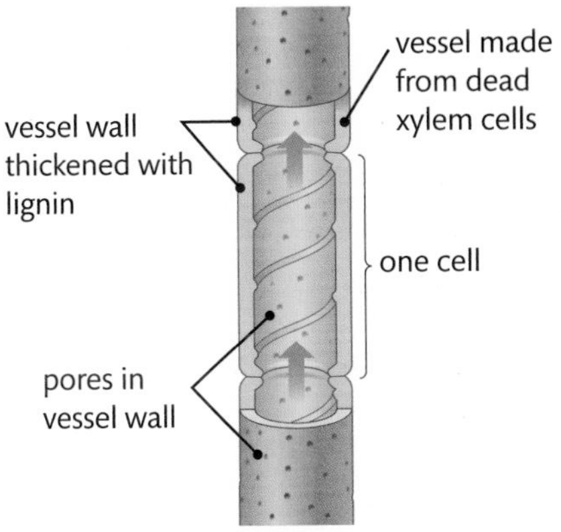

(a) Describe the function of xylem tissue in plants.   **[1 mark]**

....

(b) Use the features in **Figure 2** to describe **three** ways in which xylem vessels are adapted for their function.   **[3 marks]**

....

....

....

....

....

vessel made from dead xylem cells

vessel wall thickened with lignin

one cell

pores in vessel wall

Figure 2

3. (a) Describe the function of phloem tissue in relation to translocation.   **[1 mark]**

....

(b) Explain why phloem tissue is formed from living cells.   **[2 marks]**

....

....

✓ **Made a start**   ✓ **Feeling confident**   ✓ **Exam ready**   **47**

Transport in plants

② Quick quiz

Cross out the incorrect **bold** words to make each sentence correct.

Transpiration transports **sucrose / water and dissolved mineral ions** around the plant in **phloem / xylem** tissue.

Translocation is the transport of dissolved **sucrose / water and dissolved mineral ions** around the plant in **phloem / xylem** tissue.

⑤ Transport of water   Grade 7

1. Complete the sentences using words from the box.

| active transport | diffusion | evaporation | leaves | osmosis | roots | translocation | transpiration |

(a) Water enters a plant through its _roots_ ....   **[1 mark]**

(b) The uptake of water occurs by the process of ....   **[1 mark]**

(c) Water moves through the plant by the process of ....   **[1 mark]**

(d) Water is returned to the environment from the .... by the process of

....   **[2 marks]**

⑧ Transport of mineral ions   Grade 8

2. Explain how plants absorb mineral ions from the environment.   **[3 marks]**

....

....

....

....

⑩ Stomata   Grade 8

3. **Figure 1** shows a single stoma surrounded by two guard cells.

(a) Describe the function of stomata.   **[1 mark]**

....

(b) Stomata open during the day and close at night. Describe the role of the guard cells in opening and closing a stoma.   **[2 marks]**

....

....

(c) Explain the importance of the opening and closing of stomata at different times of the day.   **[2 marks]**

guard cells swollen with water and rigid
chloroplast
cell membrane
vacuole
stoma
thin cell wall
mitochondrion
thick cell wall
nucleus

stoma open
Figure 1

....

....

....

Made a start   Feeling confident   Exam ready

Water uptake in plants

---

② Quick quiz

True or false?

The transport of water through a plant is called translation.	**True / False**
Sugars made in leaf cells are transported to other plant organs in phloem.	**True / False**
Water is lost from plant leaves to the environment through stomata.	**True / False**

---

⑤ Environmental effects   Grade 7

1. Explain the following effects of the environment on the rate of water loss from a plant's leaves.

(a) The rate of water loss from a plant is faster on a sunny day than on a cloudy day. **[2 marks]**

Stomata open more as .... so more water molecules

can evaporate from the leaf at the same time when it is ....

(b) The rate of water loss from a plant is faster on a windy day than on a still day.

[2 marks]

....

....

> Think about the effect of air movement on the concentration gradient of water vapour around the leaf.

---

⑩ Rate of water uptake   Grade 8

2. Figure 1 shows apparatus used for measuring the rate of water uptake by a plant. The results for the distance travelled by the meniscus in the tube in 5 minutes are shown in **Table 1**.

Table 1

Test	1	2	3	mean
Distance in 5 min (mm): no wind, 25 °C	39.5	36.8	40.4	38.9
Distance in 5 min (mm): no wind, 15 °C	28.5	26.4	29.1	

(a) Complete the table by calculating the mean value for the last row.

[1 mark]

(b) Calculate the mean rate of water uptake per minute at 25 °C. **[1 mark]**

....

(c) Explain the difference in results shown in the table. **[2 marks]**

....

....

(d) Explain why the surface area of leaves (if using different plants) must be controlled in the experiment. **[2 marks]**

....

....

(e) Suggest **one** other factor that should be controlled during the experiment. **[1 mark]**

....

water evaporates from the plant

leafy shoot cut under water

airtight seals   capillary tube

plastic tubing

graduated scale   movement of meniscus is measured over time

Figure 1

Human endocrine system

② Quick quiz

Label the diagram to show the position of the following endocrine glands.

| pituitary | thyroid | adrenal glands | pancreas |

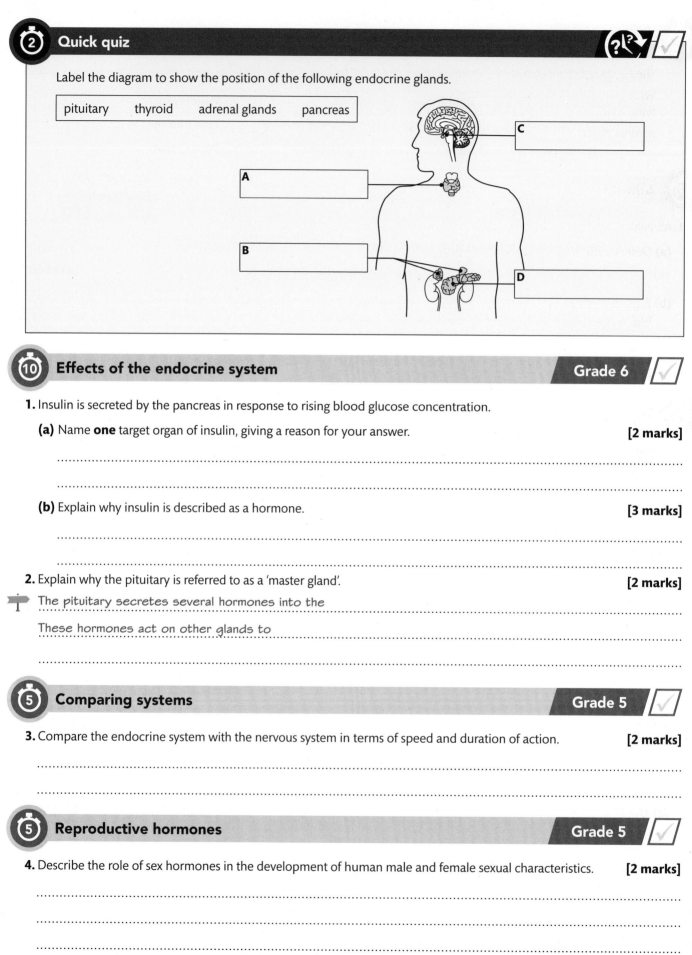

A

B

C

D

⑩ Effects of the endocrine system   **Grade 6**

1. Insulin is secreted by the pancreas in response to rising blood glucose concentration.

(a) Name **one** target organ of insulin, giving a reason for your answer.   **[2 marks]**

....

....

(b) Explain why insulin is described as a hormone.   **[3 marks]**

....

....

2. Explain why the pituitary is referred to as a 'master gland'.   **[2 marks]**

🚩 The pituitary secretes several hormones into the ....

These hormones act on other glands to ....

....

⑤ Comparing systems   **Grade 5**

3. Compare the endocrine system with the nervous system in terms of speed and duration of action.   **[2 marks]**

....

....

⑤ Reproductive hormones   **Grade 5**

4. Describe the role of sex hormones in the development of human male and female sexual characteristics.   **[2 marks]**

....

....

....

✓ **Made a start**   ✓ **Feeling confident**   ✓ **Exam ready**

Adrenalin and thyroxine

② **Quick quiz**

The list shows some endocrine glands in the human body.

Write A in the box beside the gland that releases adrenalin, and T in the box beside the gland that releases thyroxine.

adrenal gland ☐   pituitary gland ☐   ovary ☐   thyroid gland ☐

⑩ **Adrenalin**   **Grade 6**

1. Adrenalin is a hormone that is released suddenly in large amounts in particular situations.

(a) Describe the effect of adrenalin on heart rate.   **[1 mark]**

....

(b) Explain how the effect of adrenalin on the heart helps to prepare the body to respond to a stressful or frightening situation.   **[2 marks]**

Increasing heart rate pumps blood containing ....

Increased blood flow to the brain and muscles ....

⑩ **Thyroxine production and control**   **Grade 8**

2. Thyroxine is a hormone that controls basal metabolic rate.

(a) Suggest **one** effect of a low blood concentration of thyroxine, giving a reason for your answer.   **[2 marks]**

....

....

Figure 1 is a simplified diagram of the control of thyroxine release. Green arrows show stimulation, the red arrow shows inhibition (slowing down). TRH and TSH are also hormones.

```
                        low thyroxine concentration
              ┌──────────────────────────────────────────────┐
              │                                              │
              ▼         TRH              TSH        thyroxine
         ┌──────────┐ in blood ┌──────────┐ in blood ┌──────────┐ in blood  ╭────────╮
         │hypothalamus├────────►│ pituitary├─────────►│ thyroxine├──────────►│ target │
         └──────────┘          └──────────┘          └──────────┘           │ organs │
              ▲                                                              ╰────────╯
              │              high thyroxine concentration                     │
              └──────────────────────────────────────────────────────────────┘
```

Figure 1

(b) Use **Figure 1** to explain how TSH concentration would change if the thyroid gland was releasing too little thyroxine.   **[2 marks]**

....

....

(c) Use **Figure 1** to explain why the control of thyroxine release is an example of negative feedback.   **[3 marks]**

....

....

....

....

Hormones in reproduction

② Quick quiz

Draw **one** line from each word to link it with its definition.

puberty	male hormone that stimulates sperm production
oestrogen	female hormone that causes development of breasts and start of menstrual cycle
testosterone	features that develop in response to increasing sex hormone concentrations
secondary sexual characteristics	time when the body starts developing in ways that will allow reproduction

⑤ Hormones and the menstrual cycle   Grade 5

1. Describe the function of each of the following hormones in the control of the female menstrual cycle.   **[3 marks]**

Follicle-stimulating hormone (FSH) *causes an egg* ....

Luteinising hormone (LH) *causes an egg* ....

Oestrogen and progesterone ....

....

⑤ Details of the menstrual cycle   Grade 5

2. (a) State the meaning of the term 'ovulation'.   **[1 mark]**

....

(b) Give the total number of days in the average menstrual cycle.   **[1 mark]**

....

(c) Name the endocrine gland that produces oestrogen and progesterone.   **[1 mark]**

....

⑩ Interpreting data   Grades 7–9

3. Figure 1 shows how concentrations of four hormones change during the menstrual cycle. Use **Figure 1** to help you answer the following questions.

(a) Identify the role of oestrogen and LH in ovulation.   **[2 marks]**

....

....

....

(b) Identify what causes menstruation to begin.   **[1 mark]**

....

....

Figure 1

 Made a start   **Feeling confident**   **Exam ready**

Contraception

② **Quick quiz**

Which of the following are hormonal methods of contraception? Tick **two** boxes.

Condom ☐ Sterilisation ☐ Implant ☐

Oral contraceptive (the Pill) ☐ Spermicide ☐

---

⑩ **Evaluating contraceptives** **Grade 7** ☑

1. The cards show facts about the use of implants or male condoms as contraceptives.

Implant	Male condom
• >99% effective	• perfect use is 98% effective, typical use 82% effective
• minor surgery to insert implant, lasts for up to 3 years	• protects against transmission of sexually transmitted disease
• hormones can cause side-effects, e.g. irregular menstrual periods, depression, nervousness	• needs to be put on when penis is erect
• can be removed at any time	

(a) An implant, or patch, contains progesterone. Explain how an implant works as a contraceptive. **[2 marks]**

Progesterone inhibits the release of ....

Keeping a constant high level of progesterone in the body means that ....

....

(b) >99% effective means that less than 1 woman in 100 during a year will get pregnant. Calculate the number of women in 100 who may get pregnant with typical use of a male condom. **[1 mark]**

100 – 82 =

(c) Use the cards to identify **one** advantage of using a male condom rather than an implant as a contraceptive. **[1 mark]**

....

---

⑩ **How non-hormonal contraception works** **Grades 6–7** ☑

2. Give a reason why each of the following non-hormonal methods acts as a contraceptive.

(a) female diaphragm **[1 mark]**

....

(b) surgery that seals the tubes that carry sperm from the testes **[1 mark]**

....

(c) avoiding sexual activity during the middle of the menstrual cycle **[1 mark]**

....

(d) using an intra-uterine device **[1 mark]**

....

Hormones to treat infertility

② Quick quiz

Write down the word for each definition.

Hormone that triggers release of an egg from an ovary. ....

When the nucleus of an egg cell fuses with the nucleus of a sperm cell. ....

Treatment where egg cells and sperm cells are mixed outside the woman's body. ....

Name for the ball of cells produced after a few divisions of a fertilised egg. ....

⑩ IVF treatment   Grades 8–9

1. IVF treatment is an example of Assisted Reproductive Therapy (ART). **Figure 1** shows some stages in IVF treatment.

```
woman given  →  woman given  →  eggs removed
hormone A       hormone B        from woman
                                              ↘
                                               egg and sperm    →   one or two healthy
                                               mixed to allow        embryos placed in
                              sperm taken  →    fertilisation        woman's uterus to
                              from man                               develop
```
Figure 1

(a) Name the hormones in **Figure 1**, giving a reason for each answer.   **[4 marks]**

Hormone A is FSH because ....

Hormone B is ....

(b) Suggest with a reason which hormone might be given to the woman before the healthy embryo is placed in her uterus.   **[2 marks]**

....

....

(c) Identify one stage in IVF treatment when a microscope may be used, and give a reason for its use.   **[2 marks]**

....

....

⑩ Clomifene   Grades 8–9

2. Clomifene is a medication given to women who are having difficulty getting pregnant because they rarely or never ovulate.

(a) Explain how clomifene treatment increases the chances of the woman becoming pregnant.   **[2 marks]**

....

....

(b) Explain why clomifene treatment increases the chance of having more than one baby at the same time.   **[2 marks]**

....

....

(c) Suggest a reason why research continues for a treatment like clomifene that has a lower risk of having twins or triplets.   **[1 mark]**

....

....

Control of blood glucose

② Quick quiz

Complete the text using words from the box.

| blood glucose | cells | constant | external | internal |

Homeostasis is the control of the .... environment of the body in response to internal and

.... change. Homeostasis makes sure that conditions, such as temperature, water levels

and .... concentration are kept relatively .... so that processes

inside .... continue to work well.

⑩ Blood glucose and insulin   Grade 8

1. Figure 1 shows how blood glucose and insulin concentrations change over 24 hours. The graphs show the range of values for people who do not have diabetes.

(a) Use **Figure 1** to describe the effect of food on blood glucose concentration.   **[1 mark]**

Figure 1 shows that after each meal the ....

blood glucose concentration ....

(b) Use **Figure 1** to describe how insulin concentration changes in response to blood glucose changes after meals.   **[1 mark]**

Figure 1 shows an .... in blood ....

glucose concentration is accompanied by ....

....

(c) Explain the change in blood insulin concentration after a meal.   **[2 marks]**

....

....

(d) Explain why the control of blood glucose concentration by insulin is important.   **[2 marks]**

....

....

Figure 1

⑩ Glucagon   Grade 8

2. (a) Explain why blood glucagon concentration might rise in someone who has been exercising for a while.   **[3 marks]**

....

....

....

(b) Explain the importance of controlling blood glucose concentration by the two hormones, insulin and glucagon. **[2 marks]**

....

....

Diabetes

② Quick quiz

True or false?

Blood glucose concentration is controlled by the hormones insulin and glucagon.	**True / False**
The organ that monitors blood glucose concentration is the pancreas.	**True / False**
Type 2 diabetes occurs when a person does not produce their own insulin.	**True / False**
People with type 1 diabetes must control their intake of vitamins.	**True / False**

⑩ Obesity and diabetes   Grades 7–8

1. Figure 1 shows how mean body mass and percentage of people with type 2 diabetes changed between 1990 and 2000.

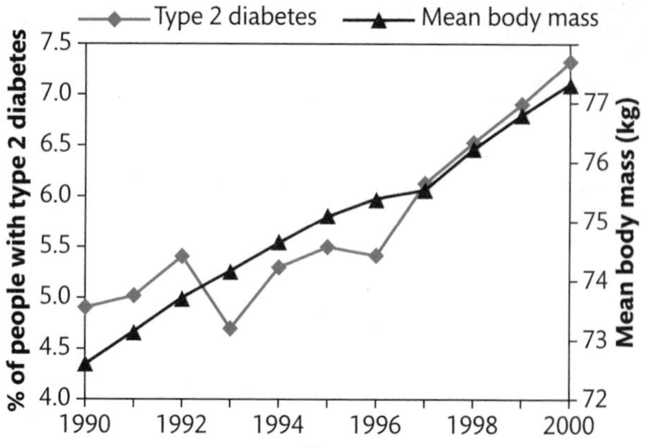

(a) Use **Figure 1** to identify any correlation between body mass and the risk of developing type 2 diabetes. **[2 marks]**

Between 1990 and 2000, mean body mass and the

percentage of people with type 2 diabetes

.... This means that

....

....

(b) One measure of body mass is body mass index (BMI). Give a reason why doctors often use BMI to assess a person's risk of developing type 2 diabetes rather than simple body mass. **[2 marks]**

....

....

> Think about how height can affect body mass.

(c) Another measure of body mass is waist:hip ratio. Explain what a waist:hip ratio of 0.9 indicates compared with a waist:hip ratio of 1.1. **[2 marks]**

....

....

....

> Remember that waist:hip ratio is the waist circumference divided by the hip circumference.

(d) Suggest advice that a doctor might give to a man with a waist:hip ratio of 1.05 and explain how it would help the man's health. **[2 marks]**

....

....

Figure 1 shows a graph with legend: ◆ Type 2 diabetes, ▲ Mean body mass. Left y-axis: % of people with type 2 diabetes (4.0 to 7.5). Right y-axis: Mean body mass (kg) (72 to 77). X-axis: Year (1990 to 2000).

Figure 1

⑩ Cause and effect of diabetes   Grade 7

2. Explain why the treatment of type 1 diabetes differs from that of type 2 diabetes. **[4 marks]**

....

....

....

....

....

 Made a start   **Feeling confident**   **Exam ready**

Transport in animals

 Quick quiz

Cross out the incorrect **bold** words to make each sentence correct.

The waste product from amino acid breakdown that is transported out of the body by the kidneys is **urea / urine**.

Plants and animals must transport **oxygen / carbon dioxide** into all their cells for respiration.

If too much water is absorbed from food and drink, the excess must be transported **into / out of** the body to protect cells from swelling.

Gases are exchanged between the human body and the environment through the **lungs / small intestine**.

 Surface area and volume | **Grade 7**

1. Table 1 calculates the surface area and volume of three cubes.

Table 1

Length (cm)	Surface area of cube (cm²)	Volume of cube (cm³)	Surface area : volume ratio
1	$6 \times 1^2 = 6$	$(1 \times 1 \times 1 =) 1$	$\left(\frac{6}{1} =\right) 6$
2	24	8	3
4			

(a) Calculate the values to complete the bottom row of the table. **[3 marks]**

Surface area = 6×4^2 =

Volume = 4^3 =

Surface area : volume ratio = $\dfrac{\text{surface area}}{\text{volume}}$ =

(b) Describe the relationship between surface area : volume ratio and length shown in the table. **[1 mark]**

As length increases, surface area : volume ratio

 Adaptations for exchange | **Grade 9**

2. Figure 1 shows how the small intestine is lined with folds called villi.

(a) Describe the function of the small intestine. **[1 mark]**

(b) Explain the importance of villi in the small intestine. **[2 marks]**

(c) Explain the importance of **one** other adaptation shown in **Figure 1** that helps the small intestine carry out its function well. **[3 marks]**

short section of small intestine

network of capillaries

inner surface has many folds called villi

section through one villus

blood supply

Figure 1

Alveoli

BBC

② Quick quiz

Complete the text using words from the box.

| air | alveoli | carbon dioxide | capillaries | kidneys | lungs | oxygen |

The human organs in which gas is exchanged with the air are called the ....

Air passes into the body through the nose and mouth and reaches tiny sacs in these organs called

.... The gas ...., which is needed for cellular respiration, passes into the blood

from these tiny sacs. The gas ...., which is a waste product of respiration, passes from the blood

into the .... in the tiny sacs.

⑩ Structure of alveolus   Grade 8

1. **Figure 1** shows gas exchange in one alveolus.

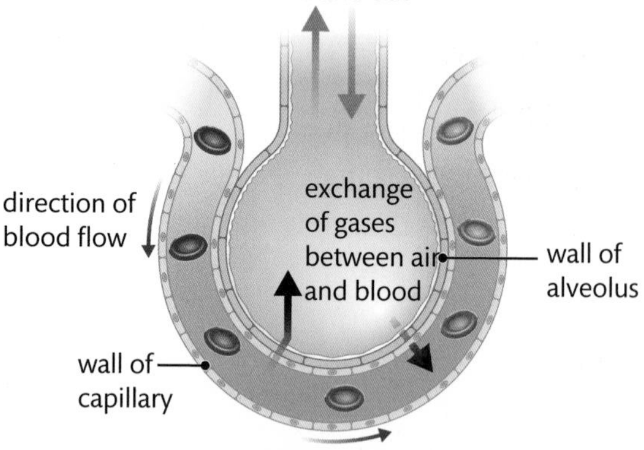

   (a) Which method of transport is used to exchange gases between air and blood? Tick **one** box. **[1 mark]**

   active transport ☐   diffusion ☐

   osmosis ☐   phagocytosis ☐

   (b) State and explain whether the concentration of carbon dioxide is higher in the blood coming to the alveolus or in the air in the alveolus. **[2 marks]**

   ⚐ Higher in the blood because the blood is ....

   ....

   (c) Explain the importance of there being millions of alveoli surrounded by many capillaries in the lungs. **[2 marks]**

   ....

   ....

in and out

direction of blood flow

exchange of gases between air and blood

wall of alveolus

wall of capillary

Figure 1

> Think about where the carbon dioxide is coming from.

> Think about the effect of surface area on exchange of substances across a surface.

⑩ Adaptations for exchange   Grade 8

2. Look at **Figure 1**.

   (a) Explain the importance of the structure of the alveolus and capillary walls in the exchange of gases in the lungs. **[2 marks]**

   ....

   ....

   (b) Explain the role of ventilation of the lungs (breathing), and the continual flow of blood through capillaries, in the exchange of gases between the body and air. **[4 marks]**

   ....

   ....

   ....

   ....

   Continue your answer on your own paper.

☑ **Made a start**   ☑ **Feeling confident**   ☑ **Exam ready**

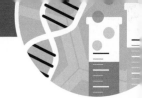

The blood

② Quick quiz

Draw **one** line from each part of the blood to link it to its function.

red blood cell	attacks and destroys pathogens
white blood cell	carries dissolved substances
plasma	causes blood to clot where blood vessels are damaged
platelet	carries oxygen

⑩ Erythrocyte structure **Grade 7**

1. Figure 1 shows an erythrocyte.

(a) State why erythrocytes are red. **[1 mark]**

☞ The red colour is caused by the pigment ....

(b) Give a reason why the red colour of erythrocytes is an adaptation to their function. **[1 mark]**

☞ The red pigment binds to ....

Figure 1

(c) Erythrocytes contain no nucleus. State **one** advantage of this adaptation. **[1 mark]**

☞ This means there is .... space for ....

....

(d) Erythrocytes have an unusual dimpled shape. Explain how this shape is an adaptation to their function. **[2 marks]**

☞ The shape gives the cell ....

This means that exchange of ....

⑩ Mending a blood vessel **Grade 7**

2. The different components of blood have important roles in mending skin and blood vessels at the site of a wound. First a clot is formed, then new skin grows beneath the clot.

(a) Explain the role of platelets in the formation of the clot. **[2 marks]**

....

....

(b) Explain the importance of a rapid increase in the numbers of phagocytes and lymphocytes at the site of the wound soon after the damage happens. **[3 marks]**

....

....

....

(c) Explain why there continues to be a high rate of blood flow to the wound site once the clot is formed. **[3 marks]**

....

....

....

Blood vessels

② Quick quiz

Circle the correct blood vessel name in each description.

The type of blood vessel that is about the diameter of a single red blood cell. **artery / capillary / vein**

The type of blood vessel with the widest diameter tube. **artery / capillary / vein**

The type of blood vessel where substances are exchanged between blood and tissues. **artery / capillary / vein**

The type of blood vessel that has the most elastic and muscle fibres in its wall. **artery / capillary / vein**

⑤ Adaptations of blood vessels   Grade 7

1. Explain **two** ways in which veins are adapted for their function in the circulatory system.   **[4 marks]**

Veins have a wide space inside which allows

....

....

Veins also have valves on the inside of their walls that

....

....

⑩ Functions of blood vessels   Grade 7–8

2. Table 1 shows the blood pressure in some human blood vessels.

(a) Give a reason why there is such a wide variation in blood pressure in the aorta, as shown in the table.   **[2 marks]**

Table 1

Blood vessel	Blood pressure (kPa)
aorta	11–16
capillaries	3.3–1.5
veins	0.7–1.3

....

....

....

(b) Explain how the structure of arteries affects the variation in pressure as blood flows through them.   **[2 marks]**

....

....

....

....

(c) Capillaries would be damaged by high blood pressure because their walls are only one cell thick. Explain how this structure is related to their function.   **[2 marks]**

> Blood pressure is affected by the size of the vessel it flows through.

....

....

....

....

(d) Give a reason for the difference in blood pressure between capillaries and veins.   **[1 mark]**

....

....

✓ **Made a start**   ✓ **Feeling confident**   ✓ **Exam ready**

The heart

Quick quiz

Label the parts of the heart marked on the diagram.

Exam focus
Labelling of the heart is as viewed, so the left side of the heart is shown on the right of the diagram and vice versa.

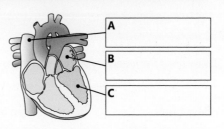

A

B

C

Blood flow through the heart   Grade 5

1. Complete the sentences using words from the box. Note: not all words are used.

aorta	left atrium	left ventricle	pulmonary arteries
pulmonary veins	right atrium	right ventricle	vena cava

(a) Blood from the body enters the heart through the *vena cava* .... **[1 mark]**

(b) This blood flows into the chamber of the heart called the .... **[1 mark]**

(c) Contraction of the muscle of that chamber pushes blood into the .... **[1 mark]**

(d) From there the blood is pumped into blood vessels that go to the lungs called the .... **[1 mark]**

(e) Blood returns from the lungs to the heart through the .... **[1 mark]**

(f) It is pumped from the atrium to the ventricle on that side of the heart, then pumped out to the rest of the body

through the .... **[1 mark]**

Heart adaptations   Grade 7

2. (a) Explain the role of valves in the openings between the atria and ventricles, and where ventricles connect to
blood vessels.   **[2 marks]**

....

....

(b) Explain why the muscle of the atrial walls is thinner than the muscle of the ventricle walls.   **[2 marks]**

....

....

(c) Explain why the muscle of the left ventricle wall is thicker than the muscle of the right ventricle wall.   **[2 marks]**

....

....

(d) Explain why the aorta has the thickest muscular walls and largest diameter of any blood vessel in the body. **[2 marks]**

....

....

....

Aerobic and anaerobic respiration

⏱ Quick quiz

Draw lines from each type of respiration in muscle cells to the correct reactants and products. Some products/reactants may be used more than once.

Reactants	**Type of respiration**	**Products**
oxygen	aerobic	carbon dioxide
glucose	anaerobic (in muscle cells)	lactic acid
		water

⏱ Cellular respiration   Grades 5–7

1. (a) Name the sub-cellular structures in which respiration occurs.   **[1 mark]**

....

(b) Write a word equation to describe the process of aerobic respiration.   **[2 marks]**

....

(c) Give a reason why respiration is described as an exothermic reaction.

[1 mark]

> Most of the exothermic reactions you study in chemistry give out heat, but the term is defined a little differently here.

....

(d) Explain why cellular respiration must occur continuously in cells.   **[2 marks]**

🪧 *Cellular respiration releases* .... *for* ....

If this doesn't happen continuously ....

⏱ Anaerobic respiration   Grades 5–7

2. (a) Anaerobic respiration can take place in muscle cells. Give the word equation for anaerobic respiration in muscle cells.   **[1 mark]**

....

(b) The process of anaerobic respiration in yeast is called fermentation. Complete the word equation to show the products of fermentation.   **[2 marks]**

glucose → ....

⏱ Comparing respiration   Grade 7

3. Compare aerobic and anaerobic respiration in muscle cells in terms of when they occur and how much energy each process releases.   **[4 marks]**

....

....

....

....

 Made a start   **Feeling confident**   **Exam ready**

Practical: Rate of respiration

 Quick quiz

True or false?

Aerobic respiration can only occur when there is enough oxygen available. **True / False**

A product of anaerobic respiration in muscle cells is carbon dioxide. **True / False**

Aerobic respiration releases more energy from each glucose molecule than anaerobic respiration. **True / False**

 Respirometer investigation | Grade 6

1. Figure 1 shows a simple respirometer for measuring the rate of respiration in living organisms.

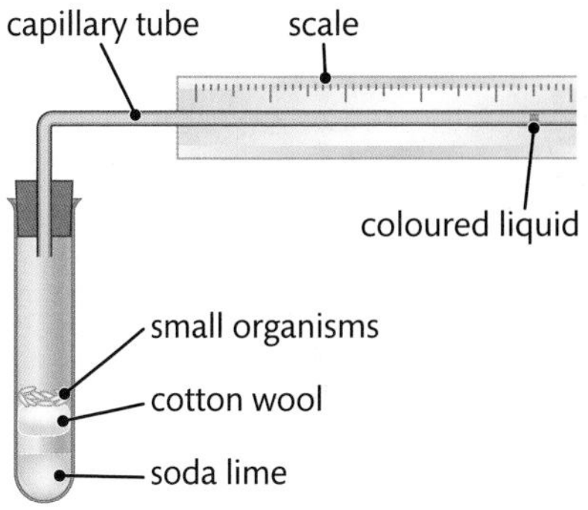

(a) State what happens to the blob of coloured liquid during the investigation. **[1 mark]**

It moves to the ....

(b) State the function of the soda lime in the respirometer. **[1 mark]**

Soda lime absorbs ....

(c) Explain how the change you described in part **(a)** is related to respiration in the organisms. **[2 marks]**

....

....

(d) Describe **one** way in which temperature could be controlled during this investigation. **[1 mark]**

....

capillary tube   scale

coloured liquid

small organisms

cotton wool

soda lime

Figure 1

Think about what is happening to the oxygen and carbon dioxide inside the respirometer.

 Effect of temperature on respiration rate | Grades 7–8

2. Table 1 shows results from an investigation into the effect of temperature on the respiration of mealworms.

(a) State and explain whether any measurements were anomalous. **[2 marks]**

....

....

(b) Calculate the rate of movement of the liquid in mm/min at 25 °C. **[2 marks]**

Table 1

Temperature (°C)	Distance liquid moves in 5 min (mm)
10	8
15	14
20	15
25	22

(c) Draw a conclusion from the table about the effect of temperature on the rate of respiration in mealworms. **[2 marks]**

....

....

(d) Explain why temperature affects rate of respiration as you have described in your conclusion in part **(c)**. **[2 marks]**

....

....

(e) Describe **one** way in which the investigation could be improved so that the conclusion is repeatable. **[1 mark]**

....

 Made a start **Feeling confident** **Exam ready**

63

Response to exercise

② Quick quiz

The table shows one set of data for a person at rest and one set during exercise. Identify the correct column headings by circling the appropriate word in each case.

Organ	Blood flow during rest / exercise (cm³/min)	Blood flow during rest / exercise (cm³/min)
Heart	300	890
Muscles	1500	2500

⑤ The body's response to exercise — Grade 5

1. Explain why each of the following changes during exercise.

🚩 Breathing rate _increases so that_ .... **[2 marks]**

....

🚩 Breath volume _increases which means that_ .... **[2 marks]**

....

🚩 Heart rate .... _so that_ .... **[2 marks]**

....

⑤ Cardiac output — Grade 9

2. At rest, an athlete's heart was beating at 55 beats per minute and the volume of blood pumped out of their heart in each pulse was 0.081 litres.

> Cardiac output is calculated using the equation: cardiac output = stroke volume × heart rate

(a) Calculate the athlete's resting cardiac output in litres/min to 2 decimal places.

[2 marks]

.... litres/min

(b) An unfit person had the same cardiac output in litres/min as the athlete, but their heart rate was 69 beats per minute. Calculate the stroke volume of the unfit person in litres to 3 decimal places. **[2 marks]**

.... litres

(c) Suggest why the stroke volume of the athlete and unfit person differed. **[2 marks]**

....

....

⑩ Anaerobic respiration in muscles — Grade 7

3. Anaerobic respiration takes place in muscles during vigorous activity, in addition to aerobic respiration.

(a) Explain the importance of anaerobic respiration during vigorous activity. **[2 marks]**

....

....

(b) Describe **one** effect of muscle fatigue after a long period of activity. **[1 mark]**

....

 Made a start **Feeling confident** **Exam ready**

Communities

---

② Quick quiz

Cross out the incorrect **bold** words to make each sentence correct.

A population is all the organisms of **the same / different** species living in **the same area / different areas**.

A community is all the populations of **the same / different** species living in **the same area / different areas**.

---

⑩ Interdependence   **Grade 6**

1. State the term that describes all the organisms within a community and the environment that affects that community.   **[1 mark]**

....

2. Read the text, then answer the questions.

Blackberry plants form large bushes in hedges. Blackbirds nest in the hedges in the summer. During the autumn they eat blackberry fruits. Seeds from the fruits may be dropped far from the hedge, in the blackbirds' faeces.

(a) Describe how blackberry plants and blackbirds are interdependent.   **[2 marks]**

Blackbirds depend on blackberry plants for ....

Blackberry plants depend on blackbirds for ....

> **Interdependence** means how different organisms need each other for survival. Look for factors given in the text that indicate what each species is getting from the other.

(b) Explain the importance of interdependence for the populations of blackbirds and blackberry bushes.   **[2 marks]**

If the number of blackberry plants in the area increased, the number of blackbirds might ....

because ....

....

> **Exam focus**
> 'Explain' questions expect a statement or fact with a supporting reason in the answer.

---

⑩ Interdependence in a food web   **Grade 4**

3. Figure 1 shows the feeding relationships between some organisms that live in a woodland. The arrows point to the organisms that eat others. Use the diagram to answer the questions.

(a) Name **two** species eaten by foxes.   **[1 mark]**

....

(b) The diagram shows competition between roe deer and rabbits. State what they are competing for.   **[1 mark]**

....

(c) Explain how the number of rabbits in the wood might change if roe deer numbers increase.   **[2 marks]**

....

....

(d) Explain why the number of foxes might change if rabbit numbers decrease.   **[2 marks]**

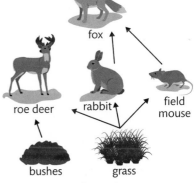

Figure 1

....

....

 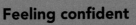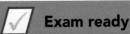

Abiotic factors

② Quick quiz

The list shows some factors that affect organisms in an ecosystem. Draw a circle around each of the abiotic factors.

light intensity   temperature   predation   water availability   competition for food

soil nutrient concentration   pollutants   carbon dioxide concentration in air

⑩ Temperature   Grade 7

1. **Figure 1** shows the change in UK mean air temperature since 1860.

   (a) Describe the trend after 1980 shown in **Figure 1**.   **[1 mark]**

   ....

   Scientists studying the effect of temperature on insects found that a few days of high temperatures can reduce the number of healthy sperm in male insects.

   (b) Suggest how the changing climate in the UK could affect insect populations.   **[2 marks]**

   As the temperature   this could cause more male

   insects to ....

   which could cause insect population sizes to ....

   (c) Explain how the effect of temperature could affect whole communities of organisms.   **[2 marks]**

   ....

Figure 1: graph — Difference from mean temperature 1961–1990 (°C) vs Year (1860–2000), showing Annual average and Five year average.

Figure 1

⑮ Pollution   Grade 6

2. Plastic is becoming a major pollution problem. For example, plastic waste caught on coral reefs increases the risk of coral becoming diseased.

   (a) Give the meaning of the term 'pollution'.   **[1 mark]**

   ....

   (b) Coral reef ecosystems are highly biodiverse. Explain the concern with plastic pollution on coral reefs.   **[2 marks]**

   ....

   ....

⑩ Identifying abiotic factors   Grade 7

3. Ash tree dieback is a disease that causes ash trees to lose many of their leaves. Explain how the disease could affect populations of low-growing plants in woodlands containing many ash trees.   **[4 marks]**

   ....

   ....

   ....

   ....

   Continue your answer on your own paper.

 Made a start   **Feeling confident**   **Exam ready**

Biotic factors

② Quick quiz

Cross out the incorrect **bold** words to make each example correct.

Scabies is caused by mites that lay their eggs in the skin of animals. The mites and their young feed on the skin and cause an intense itch in the animal's skin. This is an example of **parasitism / mutualism**.

Bees feed on nectar in flowers and collect pollen for feeding their young. Pollen on the bee's body is transferred to other flowers, which leads to fertilisation of the plant. This is an example of **parasitism / mutualism**.

⑩ Impact of non-indigenous species   Grade 6

1. Signal crayfish were introduced to the UK in the 1970s. Since then, their numbers have increased rapidly across the country. Signal crayfish are voracious predators, eating a wide range of small aquatic animals, and are having a significant impact on native white-clawed crayfish.

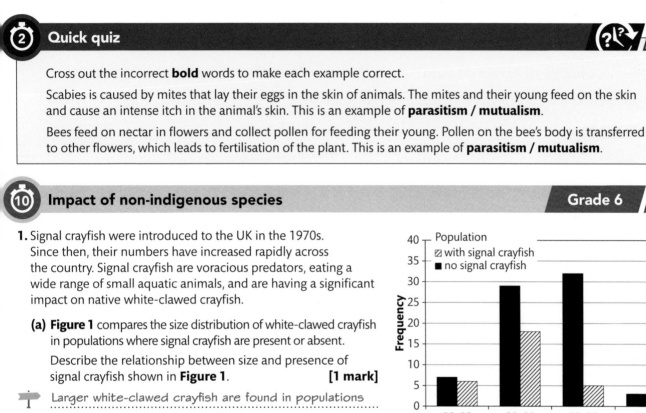

Figure 1

   (a) **Figure 1** compares the size distribution of white-clawed crayfish in populations where signal crayfish are present or absent.

   Describe the relationship between size and presence of signal crayfish shown in **Figure 1**.   **[1 mark]**

   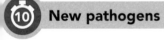 Larger white-clawed crayfish are found in populations

   that contain

   (b) Use the information in the question to suggest **two** possible ways that signal crayfish could affect white-clawed crayfish.   **[2 marks]**

   1 ....

   2 ....

   > Think about how animals in the same habitat may affect each other.

   (c) Using your answer to **(b)**, explain the most likely cause of the relationship shown in **Figure 1**.   **[2 marks]**

   ....

   ....

⑩ New pathogens   Grade 7

2. Grey squirrels were introduced to the UK in the 1870s. Since then, they have spread across most of England, Wales and parts of Scotland. Where the number of grey squirrels has increased, the number of native red squirrels has fallen.

   (a) Grey squirrels eat more than red squirrels. Suggest how this could account for the change in red squirrel abundance.   **[2 marks]**

   ....

   ....

   (b) Grey squirrels can be infected with the squirrel pox virus without suffering from the disease. In areas where grey squirrels have the virus, the decrease in red squirrel abundance is much more rapid than where grey squirrels are not infected. Explain this finding.   **[2 marks]**

   ....

   ....

   > What you learnt about the immune system and evolution of resistance can help you answer this.

   ....

 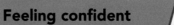

Practical: Population studies

 Quick quiz

Write the correct word for each definition.

How the individuals of a species are spread throughout an area. ....

The number of individuals in a given area. ....

 Calculating population size   **Grades 5–7**

1. Students counted the buttercup plants in quadrat samples in a small field that was 25 m by 34 m.

(a) Give a reason why the quadrats should be placed randomly.   **[1 mark]**

The buttercups are not spread
....

....

Table 1 shows the results of the sampling.

Table 1

Maths skills

To calculate the mean, find the total number of plants and divide that by the number of quadrats sampled.

quadrat	A	B	C	D	E	F
number of buttercup plants in quadrat	3	2	0	0	2	1

(b) Calculate the mean number of buttercup plants per quadrat to 1 decimal place.   **[1 mark]**

mean = ...

(c) Each quadrat had an area of 100 cm². Use your answer to part **(b)** to calculate the population size of buttercups in the field.   **[3 marks]**

total area of field = ... m²

total area of quadrat in m² = 100 cm² = $\dfrac{100}{100 \times 100}$ .... m²

population size = ...

 Using a transect   **Grades 5–7**

2. A transect line was set from under a large tree to out into the open. Students took quadrat measurements of the abundance of daisy plants every 2 m from the tree base. **Table 2** shows their results.

Table 2

distance from tree base (m)	0	2	4	6	8	10
number of daisy plants in quadrat	0	0	2	6	9	7

(a) Describe the distribution of daisy plants along the transect.   **[1 mark]**

....

(b) Name **one** factor that could produce this distribution, explaining your choice.   **[2 marks]**

....

....

 Made a start   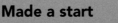 **Feeling confident**   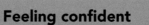 **Exam ready**

Biodiversity

② Quick quiz

Complete the text using words from the box. Not all words are used.

| depend | ecosystem | food | habitats | less | live | more | species |

Biodiversity is all the different .... on Earth or within an ....

A higher biodiversity means that each species may .... on more than one other species for

resources such as .... or shelter. This makes it .... likely that the

community will be harmed if there is a change in the environment.

⑩ Eutrophication   Grade 7

1. **Figure 1** shows the oxygen concentration of water in the River Rhine in Germany between 1955 and 1997, and the number of invertebrate species sampled in the river in a selection of years.

   (a) Describe the changes in oxygen concentration of the water shown in **Figure 1**.   **[2 marks]**

   From 1955 to 1971 oxygen concentration ....

   from .... mg/l to .... mg/l.

   From 1971 to 1997 ....

Figure 1

   (b) Describe the relationship between changes in species number and changes in oxygen concentration.   **[2 marks]**

   As oxygen concentration decreases, the number of species ....

   When oxygen concentration increases, ...

> Make sure you use the correct *y*-axis to read off these values.

   (c) Explain how increased use of fertilisers in farming could lead to the change in species number between 1900 and 1955.   **[4 marks]**

   ....

   ....

   ....

   ....

> Think about how eutrophication affects aquatic environments.

⑩ Fish farming   Grade 7

2. Eating farmed fish is suggested as being better for the environment as it can protect biodiversity.

   (a) Suggest how eating farmed fish could protect biodiversity in the sea.   **[2 marks]**

   ....

   ....

   (b) To help farmed fish grow faster, they are given plenty of food and are treated with chemicals to keep them healthy. Explain how growing farmed fish could harm the environment.   **[2 marks]**

   ....

   ....

Maintaining biodiversity

 Quick quiz

True or false?

Deforestation increases biodiversity.	**True / False**
All human activities have a negative impact on biodiversity.	**True / False**
Conservation is the protection of species or habitats to maintain biodiversity.	**True / False**
Breeding programmes in zoos and conservation areas can help protect endangered species from becoming extinct.	**True / False**

 Conservation of birds Grades 5–6

1. At RSPB Hope Farm, studies are being carried out to find ways of farming that also improve biodiversity. **Table 1** shows the number of breeding territories on the farm for skylarks, a bird species that feed on insects in summer and seeds in winter. In the UK, since the 1970s, skylark numbers have fallen by over 75%.

Table 1

Year	2000	2001	2002	2003	2004	2005	2006	2007	2008	2009	2010	2011
Skylarks	10	18	24	27	27	34	32	30	23	44	41	42

(a) Compare the trends in numbers for skylarks nationally with those on the RSPB farm. **[2 marks]**

The national trend for skylarks is
....
The trend on the farm for skylarks is

(b) One reason for the national decrease is that many crops are now planted in the autumn, and harvested in the early summer. This leaves little food for birds over winter, but produces a greater yield of food than spring-sown crops. Give a reason why many farmers choose to grow autumn-sown crops. **[1 mark]**

More yield means

(c) On Hope Farm, field edges have been planted with wildflowers to attract flying insects all summer long, or planted with seed-bearing species that are left over winter. Explain how these changes could have resulted in the trend in bird numbers seen in **Table 1**. **[2 marks]**

....
....

 Reforestation Grade 7

2. In January 2018, the UK government announced a plan to create a new forest of around 50 million new trees in the north of England. One purpose for this is to increase biodiversity in these areas. Suggest how the new forest should be planned to maximise the benefits it provides. **[6 marks]**

....
....
....
....
....
....
....

 Made a start **Feeling confident** **Exam ready**

Carbon cycle

② Quick quiz

The following processes are involved in the carbon cycle. Identify whether each process causes an increase or a decrease in carbon dioxide in the atmosphere by circling the correct word.

respiration   **increases / decreases**

photosynthesis   **increases / decreases**

decay by microorganisms   **increases / decreases**

⑩ Carbon cycling   Grades 5–6

1. Many substances cycle through the abiotic and biotic components of an ecosystem. One example is carbon.

(a) Name the form of carbon found in the atmosphere.   **[1 mark]**

....

> The carbon in the atmosphere is found in a gas.

(b) Name the process that converts carbon in the atmosphere to large carbon compounds in plants.   **[1 mark]**

....

> The carbon compound made in plants is glucose.

(c) Name **two** other large carbon compounds in living organisms.   **[2 marks]**

1 ....

2 ....

> Think about the substances that are used to build plant and animal cells and tissues.

(d) Name the process in living organisms that breaks down large carbon compounds to the form of carbon in the air.
[1 mark]

....

(e) Large carbon compounds are transferred to the environment in animal faeces and urine. Explain how these carbon compounds are converted to the form of carbon found in air.   **[2 marks]**

It is broken down by .... that release

....

⑩ Carbon and decay   Grade 6

2. A student decided to investigate the production of carbon dioxide during decomposition of leaves in a sealed bag. She used a carbon dioxide sensor and datalogger. The results are shown in **Figure 1**.

Explain the change in concentration of carbon dioxide in **Figure 1**.
[3 marks]

....

....

....

....

....

Figure 1

Water cycle

② Quick quiz

Complete the sentences with words from the box.

| cytoplasm | dissolved | plasma | phloem | reactions | vacuole | xylem |

Water is essential to living organisms. It is a major component of cell .... where many cell

.... take place. Plant cells depend on water to fill their central .... to help support the plant.

Water is essential in transport systems. For example, blood carries many substances around the body

.... in the .... In plants, mineral ions dissolved in water are transported in the

.... and dissolved sucrose is transported around the plant in the ....

⑩ The water cycle   Grade 4

1. (a) Explain the importance of the water cycle to living organisms.   [2 marks]

   ⚐ The water cycle provides fresh water
   ....

   The water also dissolves
   ....

(b) **Figure 1** shows the water cycle. Identify each lettered process in the cycle and describe what happens in each process.   [3 marks]

⚐ **A** Evaporation is when
....

B Condensation
....

C Precipitation
....

> Remember the processes in which water changes from one state to another.

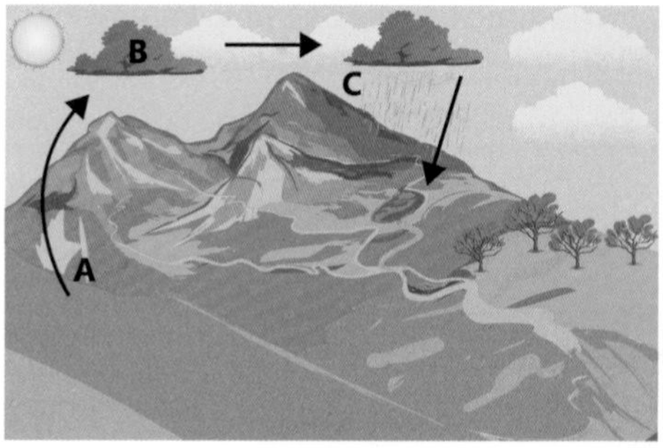

Figure 1

⑩ Desalination   Grade 5

2. **Figure 2** is a diagram of an emergency solar still which might be found in a lifeboat. The still can be used to produce potable water from seawater.

   (a) State what is meant by potable water.   [1 mark]

   ....

   (b) Describe how potable water is produced from seawater in the solar still.
                                                                                   [2 marks]

   ....

   ....

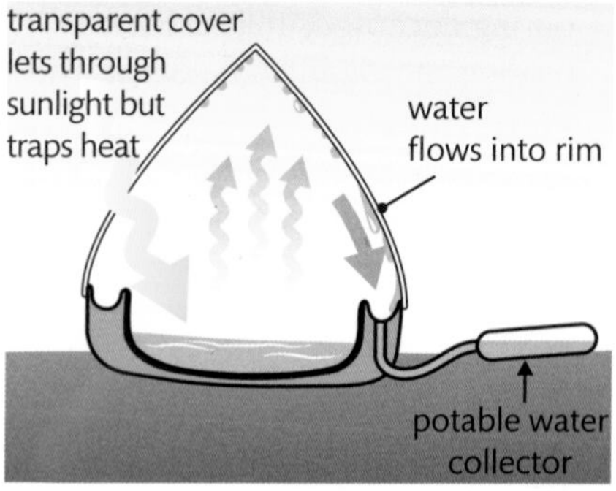

transparent cover lets through sunlight but traps heat

water flows into rim

potable water collector

Figure 2

   (c) Give a reason why this process is an example of desalination.   [1 mark]

   ....

   (d) Give a reason why desalination is an important source of potable water in countries in the Middle East.   [1 mark]

   ....

 Made a start   **Feeling confident**   **Exam ready**

Nitrogen cycle

② Quick quiz

True or false?

Nitrogen is found in proteins and DNA in the biotic components of an ecosystem.	**True / False**
Plants absorb nitrogen from the air through their leaves.	**True / False**
Animals can absorb inorganic nitrogen directly from the environment.	**True / False**
Nitrogen cycles from the biotic components to the abiotic components of an ecosystem by decay.	**True / False**

⑩ The nitrogen cycle   Grades 5–6

1. **Figure 1** shows the effect of mass of nitrogen in fertiliser on the yield (mass of harvested food) of a crop.

   (a) Describe the relationship between mass of nitrogen and yield shown in **Figure 1**.

   [1 mark]

   As the mass of nitrogen is increased, the yield ....

   (b) Explain the relationship shown in **Figure 1**. **[2 marks]**

   ....

   ....

   ....

   ....

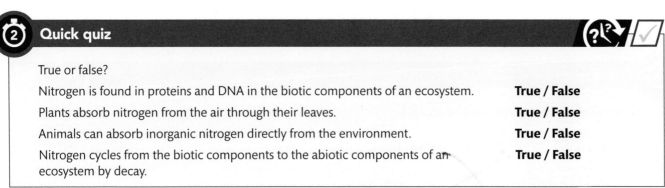

Figure 1

> Think about how plants use nitrogen, and what effect more nitrogen will have on plant growth.

⑩ Different farming practices   Grade 7

2. Farmers use a variety of ways to increase the fertility (concentration of nitrate ions) of the soil of their fields.

   > Each of the practices relies on bacteria in the nitrogen cycle.

   (a) Explain how each of the following practices can increase soil fertility.

   (i) Plough the old crop stalks into the ground and leave the field unplanted for a year. **[2 marks]**

   ....

   ....

   (ii) Crop rotation, where different crops are planted in a field each year, one of which is beans (a legume). **[2 marks]**

   ....

   ....

   (b) Manure is a natural fertiliser made from animal waste (usually cow faeces and urine) mixed with straw.

   Explain why manure must be spread on the field several months before the next crop is planted. **[2 marks]**

   ....

   ....

Atoms, elements and compounds

② Quick quiz

Draw **one** line from each word to match it to its definition.

atom	consists of two or more different elements chemically combined
element	the smallest part of an element that can exist
compound	made of only one type of atom; cannot be broken down into simpler substances by chemical methods

⑤ Chemical equations — Grade 4

1. When calcium reacts with oxygen a compound is formed. Write the word equation for the reaction. **[1 mark]**

calcium + Oxygen → Calcium oxide

2. A sample of water contains magnesium hydrogencarbonate. When this is heated, it decomposes to form magnesium carbonate and water. Carbon dioxide is also given off in the reaction. Write the word equation for the reaction. **[1 mark]**

Magnesium hydrogencarbonate → Magnesium carbonate + water + Carbon dioxide

Exam focus

Quite often, all, or most, of the information will be provided in this type of question. The challenge of the question is to see if you can understand what is happening during the reaction.

⑩ Atoms, elements and compounds — Grades 4–5

3. Use the periodic table (on page 283) to complete **Table 1**. **[6 marks]**

4. Which of these is a compound? Tick **one** box. **[1 mark]**

Mg ☐   Au ☐   carbon dioxide ☑ O_2 ☐

Table 1

Element name	Element symbol
Sodium	Na
bromine	Br
lead	Pb
iron	Fe
Chlorine	Cl
potassium	K

⑤ Reactions and compounds — Grade 5

5. Which compound is produced when barium and chlorine react? **[1 mark]**

chlorine baride ☐   barium chlorate ☐   chlorine barate ☐   barium chloride ☑

6. Determine the number of different elements present in Fe_2O_3. **[1 mark]**

5

7. When copper carbonate is heated, it decomposes to form copper oxide and carbon dioxide. Write the word equation for the reaction. **[1 mark]**

Copper Carbonate → Copper oxide + Carbon dioxide

☑ **Made a start**   ☑ **Feeling confident**   ☑ **Exam ready**

The model of the atom

② Quick quiz

Number the events from 1 to 5, in the order in which they occurred, from earliest to latest.

Chadwick proves the existence of neutrons within the nucleus. ☐

Electrons are discovered. ☐

Alpha particle scattering experiments, carried out by Rutherford, Geiger and Marsden, led to the nuclear model of the atom. ☐

Dalton proposed that atoms cannot be broken down. ☐

The plum pudding model of the atom was developed. ☐

⑩ Atomic models   Grade 8

1. **Figure 1** shows two suggested models for the atom. The current understanding of the structure of the atom is the nuclear model. Compare and contrast the plum pudding model and the nuclear model.   **[6 marks]**

Plum pudding model

ball of positive charge

electrons

Nuclear model

electrons

Figure 1

In both models, the atom contains positive charges. However, the plum pudding model describes a ball of positive charge whereas the nuclear model contains separate positive charges within a central nucleus. Both models have negative particles called

Electrons   The plum pudding model has electrons arranged randomly whereas the nuclear model has electrons in shells

The plum pudding model has no nucleus unlike the nuclear model

The plum pudding model has no nucleus

⑩ Evidence for the nuclear model   Grade 8

2. Positively charged alpha particles were aimed at a very thin sheet of gold foil. Most particles passed through undeflected, but some particles were repelled. Explain how this experiment provided evidence for the nuclear model.   **[4 marks]**

The observation that particles were repelled and their relative numbers are both important.

The protons in the nucleus repelled the alpha Positively charged alpha particles; showing that

Subatomic particles

What are the parts of the atom shown by labels **A**, **B** and **C**?

A ..Electron...

B ..Neutron...

C ..Proton...

What is the name of the part of the atom where **B** and **C** are located?

..Nucleus...

(10) **Subatomic particles** | **Grade 6**

1. Complete **Table 1** to show the names of the three subatomic particles and their position in an atom. **[3 marks]**

Table 1

Name of subatomic particle	Position in the atom
proton	nucleus
neutron	~~proton~~ nucleus
electron	shell

2. Name the subatomic particle that gives an element its atomic number. **[1 mark]**

..Proton..

3. Give a reason why atoms have no overall electrical charge. **[1 mark]**

.neutrons are neutral and electrons cancel out the positive charge on the protons

(10) **Atomic structure** | **Grade 5**

4. The radius of an atom is 1×10^{-10} m, and the radius of the nucleus of an atom is 1×10^{-14} m. Calculate how many times greater the radius of an atom is than the radius of its nucleus. Give your answer in standard form. **[2 marks]**

$$\frac{\text{radius of atom}}{\text{radius of nucleus}} =$$

5. The radius of an atom is about 0.1 nm.

What is the radius of an atom in m? Tick **one** box. **[1 mark]**

0.0001 m ☐

0.0000001 m ✓

0.000 000 000 1 m ☐

0.000 000 000 000 1 m ☐

Exam focus

You will need to use a scientific calculator in your exams. You need to be able to convert answers to standard form and back.

Maths skills

Examples of standard form:
0.000 52 is shown as 5.2×10^{-4}
3 500 000 is shown as 3.5×10^{6}

✓ **Made a start**   ✓ **Feeling confident**   ✓ **Exam ready**

Size and mass of atoms

② Quick quiz

True or false?

Most of the mass of an atom is located in the nucleus.	**True / False**
The mass of the atom is made up by the protons and electrons.	**True / False**
The number of neutrons is always equal to the number of protons.	**True / False**

⑩ Atomic number and mass number   Grade 6

1. State the meaning of the terms 'atomic number' and 'mass number'.   **[2 marks]**

Atomic number is the number of   particles   in   the   nucleus

Mass number is   the   number of   protons   in   the   atom

2. An atom of gold is represented by this symbol: $^{197}_{79}Au$

Calculate the number of each type of subatomic particle in this atom. Explain your reasoning for each answer.   **[4 marks]**

There are 79 protons because the atomic number is   79

There are   79   electrons because   there are 79 protons

There are   118   neutrons because   the   ~~mass~~   mass number is the   amount of protons and neutrons so you subtract the atomic number from the mass number

⑤ Ions and subatomic particles   Grade 8

3. An atom of iron has a mass number of 56 and an atomic number of 26. The ion Fe^{3+} forms when iron reacts with oxygen. Calculate the number of protons, neutrons and electrons in an Fe^{3+} ion.   **[3 marks]**

....

....

....

Exam focus 📌

Ions have a charge because they are formed when atoms, or groups of atoms, have gained or lost electrons. You will need to take this into account if asked to calculate numbers of subatomic particles in an ion. A positive charge means loss of electrons and a negative charge means gain of electrons.

⑩ Nucleus numbers   Grade 5

4. An atom of beryllium has 4 protons and 5 neutrons. Determine the atomic number and mass number for this atom.   **[2 marks]**

Atomic number ....4........................   Mass number ....9....................

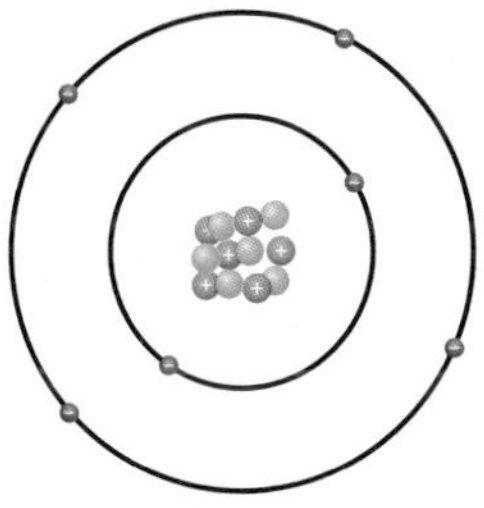

5. (a) Name the atom shown in **Figure 1** ....Carbon................................   **[1 mark]**

(b) Explain how you identified the atom in **(a)**.   **[2 marks]**

By counting the number of Protons and Neutrons

(c) An atom of fluorine can be represented as $^{19}_9F$. Describe how this atom is different from the atom in **Figure 1**.   **[3 marks]**

........It   has   1   more   neutron   in   its   nucleus........................

....

Figure 1

Isotopes and relative atomic mass

Quick quiz

True or false?

Isotopes of an element have the same mass number but different atomic number.	**True / False**
Isotopes of an element have the same chemical properties.	**True / False**
Isotopes of an element have the same number of protons and neutrons, but a different number of electrons.	**True / False**
You need the mass number and relative abundance of each isotope to work out the relative atomic mass of an element.	**True / False**

Isotopes and relative atomic mass   Grade 7

1. An isotope of oxygen, oxygen-16, is represented as $^{16}_{8}O$.

(a) Deduce the number of each subatomic particle present in an atom of oxygen-16.   **[3 marks]**

protons ....   neutrons ....   electrons ....

> For all atoms other than hydrogen-1, $^{1}_{1}H$, mass number is greater than atomic number. Check your periodic table to find the atomic number for atoms of an element.

(b) Explain in terms of subatomic particles why oxygen-16 and oxygen-18 are isotopes of the same element.   **[3 marks]**

....

....

....

(c) **Table 1** shows the percentage abundances of the two natural isotopes of copper.

Calculate the relative atomic mass of copper. Give your answer to three significant figures.   **[3 marks]**

relative atomic mass = $\dfrac{(63 \times 69.2) + (65 \times 30.8)}{100}$

Table 1

Isotope	Percentage abundance
$^{63}_{29}Cu$	69.2%
$^{65}_{29}Cu$	30.8%

= ....   relative atomic mass of copper = ...

Isotopes   Grade 5

2. One of the isotopes of helium is $^{3}_{2}He$.

(a) Deduce the number of each type of subatomic particle found in an atom of this isotope.   **[3 marks]**

....

(b) Suggest an explanation for why the relative atomic mass of helium is shown as 4 on the periodic table.   **[1 mark]**

....

 Made a start   **Feeling confident**   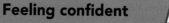 **Exam ready**

Developing the periodic table

② Quick quiz

Fill in the gaps using words from the box.

| Mendeleev   periods   different   similar   elements   groups   atomic mass   atomic number |

.... arranged elements in order of their relative .... He put

elements with .... properties into .... He changed the order

of some .... to fit the trend better.

⑩ Early periodic tables   Grade 6

1. In an early version of the periodic table, a scientist arranged the elements in atomic weight order in groups of three as shown in **Figure 1**.

   (a) Suggest and explain **two** reasons why this periodic table was not correct.   **[2 marks]**

Li	7
Na	23
K	39

S	32
Se	79
Te	128

Cl	35.5
Br	80
I	127

Figure 1

   ➤ Metals and non-metals
   ....

   ....

   (b) Describe **two** ways in which Mendeleev's table was better arranged than the table in **Figure 1**.   **[2 marks]**

   ➤ Elements with similar properties
   ....

   ....

⑩ Mendeleev's periodic table   Grade 5

2. Mendeleev was a Russian chemist who developed an early periodic table.
   Give **three** features of Mendeleev's periodic table.   **[3 marks]**

   ....

   ....

   ....

3. (a) Explain how Mendeleev was able to predict the existence of elements that had not been discovered at that time.
                                                                              [2 marks]

   ....

   ....

   (b) Give a reason why Mendeleev changed the order of some elements in his periodic table.   **[1 mark]**

   ....

 Made a start   **Feeling confident**   **Exam ready**

The periodic table

② Quick quiz

Match each element to its group number.

potassium	Group 0
nitrogen	Group 1
argon	Group 5

True or false?

A column in the periodic table is a group. **True / False**

A row in the periodic table is a period. **True / False**

Elements in the same group have similar reactions. **True / False**

Elements in the same group have the same number of electron shells. **True / False**

⑩ Periodic table positions   Grade 6

1. (a) Name an element in Group 7. .... **[1 mark]**

   (b) Give the symbol of the element named in **(a)**. .... **[1 mark]**

2. (a) Give the atomic number of the element in Group 4, Period 2. **[1 mark]**

   ....

   (b) Give the number of electrons in the outer shell of the element in **(a)**.   **[1 mark]**

   ....

> Remember, the period number tells you the number of electron shells and the group number tells you the number of electrons in the outer shell.

3. An element has 3 electron shells and 13 electrons.

   (a) Deduce the group and period it occupies in the periodic table.   **[2 marks]**

   ....

   (b) Name the element in **(a)**.   **[1 mark]**

   ....

> **Exam focus**
>
> Use your periodic table to help you answer these types of questions.

⑩ Group 1   Grade 7

4. Hydrogen is sometimes positioned above lithium in the periodic table.

   (a) Give **one** similarity between hydrogen and Group 1 elements such as lithium.   **[1 mark]**

   Hydrogen and the Group 1 elements all have one electron

   (b) Give **two** differences between hydrogen and the Group 1 elements.   **[2 marks]**

   Hydrogen is a non-metal, but Group 1 elements are ....

   At room temperature, hydrogen is a ....

   (c) Rubidium is an element in Group 1. It forms an oxide that dissolves in water to give an alkaline solution. Francium is also in Group 1. Predict whether francium oxide will form an acidic or alkaline solution. Explain your answer.   **[2 marks]**

   ....

   ....

   (d) Rubidium (Rb) reacts with chlorine to form rubidium chloride. Predict the formula of rubidium chloride.   **[1 mark]**

   ....

 Made a start   **Feeling confident**   ☑ **Exam ready**

Electronic structure

② Quick quiz

Complete the table to show the maximum number of electrons in the first three shells.

Shell	Maximum number of electrons
1	
2	
3	

To which group does an element with electronic configuration 2.8.6 belong?

....

In which period is this element found?

....

Use your periodic table to identify the element.

....

⑤ Electronic structure   Grade 6

1. (a) Complete **Figure 1** to show the electronic configuration of potassium. Use the periodic table on page 283.   **[2 marks]**

  (b) Explain what other information you can determine from the electronic configuration of the element.   **[1 mark]**

➤ If there are 19 electrons there must be
....

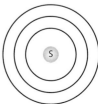

Figure 1

⑮ Using electronic structure   Grade 5

2. The electronic configuration of an atom of an element is 2.8.3. Explain, using this electronic configuration, in which group and in which period in the periodic table this element is found.   **[4 marks]**

....

....

....

....

3. (a) Write the electronic configuration of the following elements.

  (i) oxygen ....   **[1 mark]**

  (ii) hydrogen ....   **[1 mark]**

  (b) State the link between the number of electrons in the outer shell and the group in which the element is placed.   **[1 mark]**

....

  (c) An element has two occupied electron shells. The outermost shell contains four electrons. Give the electronic configuration for the element. Use the periodic table to identify the element.   **[2 marks]**

....

....

4. Complete **Figure 2** to show the electronic configuration of a sulfur atom.   **[2 marks]**

S

Figure 2

Metals and non-metals

② **Quick quiz**

Place a tick in one box in each row of the table to show whether each property is typical of metals or of non-metals.

Property	Metals	Non-metals
poor conductor of electricity		
good conductor of heat		
strong		
brittle		
dull		
malleable		

⑩ **Reactivity of metals and non-metals**   **Grade 7**

1. Selenium is a non-metal element. Describe where in the periodic table you would expect to find selenium. **[1 mark]**

....

2. Mercury is a dense metal. In the past, it was used in electrical switches that responded to being tilted. Explain what is unusual about mercury. **[2 marks]**

....

....

> Think about the properties of mercury and the typical properties of metals.

3. Explain, in terms of electrons, what happens when a metal reacts with a non-metal. **[4 marks]**

Metals lose electrons (to gain a full outer shell), forming .... ions.

Non-metals gain ....

....

....

....

> **Exam focus**
> When substances react with each other, outer electrons are either transferred between atoms or ions or shared between atoms.

⑩ **Properties of metals and non-metals**   **Grade 7**

4. Graphite is a form of carbon, a non-metal. Graphite is used in the manufacture of aluminium. Graphite electrodes remain solid when dipped in a liquid at around 1000 °C, and conduct electricity to this liquid. Explain what is unusual about this form of carbon. **[4 marks]**

....

....

....

....

 Made a start   **Feeling confident**   **Exam ready**

Chemical bonds

② Quick quiz

Which statements are true? Rewrite the false statements so they are correct.

Ionic bonding occurs between a metal and a non-metal element. ☐

Two types of metal are needed to form a metallic bond. ☐

Covalent bonding involves transfer of electrons. ☐

Metallic bonding and ionic bonding both involve delocalised electrons. ☐

Covalent bonds form in non-metals only. ☐

....

....

....

⑩ Covalent bonding   Grade 5

1. Hydrogen chloride (HCl) is an example of a compound that contains covalent bonds.

(a) Explain how this type of bonding can be identified from the chemical formula.   **[1 mark]**

🚏 Both hydrogen and chlorine are non-metals and so can only
....

(b) Explain how a covalent bond forms between a hydrogen atom and a chlorine atom.   **[2 marks]**

🚏 Hydrogen has 1 electron in its outer shell and shares one electron to obtain
....

Chlorine has 7 electrons in its outer shell
....

2. Complete **Table 1** by placing a tick against each pair of elements that will form covalent bonds together.   **[3 marks]**

Table 1

Pair of elements	Tick if they form covalent bonds together
oxygen and carbon	
phosphorus and oxygen	
calcium and phosphorus	
carbon and chlorine	
sodium and chlorine	
iron and sulfur	

⑩ Ionic and metallic bonding   Grade 6

3. Ionic bonds form between metals and non-metals. State what is meant by the term 'ionic bond'.   **[2 marks]**

....

....

4. Describe the type of bonding present in magnesium.   **[3 marks]**

....

....

....

Ionic bonding

② Quick quiz

Give the symbol for the ion that each element forms. (For example, lithium forms Li^+.)

magnesium ....   oxygen ....   sodium ....

aluminium ....   fluorine ....   calcium ....

⑩ Losing and gaining electrons   Grade 7

1. Give the number of electrons an atom from a Group 2 element will lose when it reacts. Explain your answer. **[3 marks]**

👉 All atoms of elements in Group 2 have

....

....

To be stable, they

....

....

2. **(a)** A reaction takes place between lithium and chlorine to make the ionic compound lithium chloride. Explain how ions form during the reaction. **[4 marks]**

👉 Lithium is in Group 1 so when it reacts it loses its outer electron to form a

....

Chlorine

....

....

(b) Using dot and cross diagrams, draw the outer shell of the ions formed in **(a)**. Give the charge on each ion. **[2 marks]**

$$\Big[\qquad\Big] \; + \; \Big[\qquad\Big]$$

⑩ Forming an ionic compound   Grade 6

3. Magnesium reacts with chlorine to form an ionic compound, magnesium chloride, $MgCl_2$.

Draw dot and cross diagrams to show the electronic configurations of a magnesium atom, a chlorine atom and the ions formed when magnesium and chlorine react. Give the charge on each ion. **[4 marks]**

Remember that elements in Groups 1–3 form positive ions in which the number of charges is equal to the group number. Elements in Groups 5–7 form negative ions in which the number of charges is equal to eight minus the group number.

Ionic compounds

(2) Quick quiz

Name **four** different ways of representing the structure of ionic compounds.

....

....

(10) Three-dimensional diagrams of ionic compounds | Grade 8

1. Describe the advantages and disadvantages of using a three-dimensional diagram to represent the structure of an ionic compound. **[4 marks]**

Advantages: The different sizes of the ions can be seen. ....

....

Disadvantages: ....

....

(10) Ball and stick vs dot and cross | Grade 7

2. Compare and contrast the use of ball and stick models with that of dot and cross models to represent the structure of compounds. **[6 marks]**

....

....

....

....

....

....

Exam focus

When you are asked to compare and contrast something, you should use your knowledge and understanding to consider similarities and differences.

Continue your answer on your own paper.

(5) Ionic lattice | Grades 7–8

3. The ionic lattice structure for magnesium oxide is shown in **Figure 1**.

(a) Describe the structure of an ionic lattice. **[2 marks]**

....

....

(b) Deduce the formula for magnesium oxide. **[1 mark]**

....

....

Figure 1

(c) Compare and contrast the ratio of ions in the diagram and the ratio of ions in the formula in **(b)**. Suggest an explanation for the difference. **[2 marks]**

....

....

Properties of ionic compounds

② Quick quiz

Select the correct answers.

Ionic compounds:

conduct electricity when solid ☐

conduct electricity when liquefied ☐

cannot conduct electricity when molten ☐

cannot conduct electricity in solution. ☐

Ionic compounds have a high melting point because:

they can conduct electricity ☐

there are strong forces of attraction between ions ☐

they do not melt easily. ☐

⑩ Ionic compounds   Grade 6 ✓

1. Describe the structure of an ionic compound such as sodium chloride. **[3 marks]**

➤ A giant ionic ....

held together by ....

....

2. Explain why the ionic compound calcium chloride does **not** conduct electricity when solid. **[2 marks]**

➤ The ions in a solid are in fixed positions. In order to conduct electricity, ...

....

⑩ Properties of ionic compounds   Grade 5 ✓

3. Explain why an aqueous solution of sodium chloride can conduct electricity. **[2 marks]**

....

....

....

4. Describe **two** simple tests which could be carried out on a solid compound to show that it is an ionic compound. **[4 marks]**

....

....

....

....

....

> You need to choose two typical properties of ionic compounds that are different from the typical properties of covalent compounds.

 Made a start   **Feeling confident**   **Exam ready**

Covalent bonding

② Quick quiz

Draw **one** line from each word to match it with the correct statement.

covalent	a bond formed by the transfer of electrons between atoms
ion	a bond formed when a pair of electrons is shared between atoms
ionic	a group of atoms bonded together
molecule	an atom or group of atoms with a positive or negative charge

⑩ Sharing electrons   Grade 6

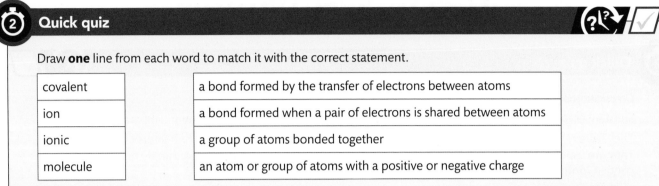

1. The structural formulae of some covalent substances are shown in **Figure 1**. They are labelled A, B, C, and D.

(a) Describe how the covalent bonds form in C. **[2 marks]**

Oxygen has six electrons in its outer shell so it can share

Each hydrogen atom has one electron in its outer shell

Figure 1

(b) Give the letter of the molecule which represents methane. **[1 mark]**

Methane has the formula CH_4.

(c) Give the formula of molecule D. **[1 mark]**

(d) Give the letter of a diatomic molecule. **[1 mark]**

Diatomic means there are two atoms in the molecule.

(e) Give the name of molecule C. **[1 mark]**

⑩ Dot and cross diagrams   Grade 6

2. Oxygen is a simple molecular, covalent substance. The electronic configuration of an atom of oxygen is 2.6. Draw the dot and cross diagram of an oxygen molecule, O_2. Show outer electrons only. **[2 marks]**

3. Carbon dioxide molecules contain double and single bonds. Draw the dot and cross diagram of a carbon dioxide molecule, CO_2. Show outer electrons only. **[2 marks]**

Exam focus

Use your periodic table to work out the number of outer shell electrons in each atom that forms the molecule.

Chemistry | **Key concepts** | **Types of substance**

Properties of simple molecular substances

(2) Quick quiz

Cross out the incorrect **bold** words to make each sentence correct.

Substances that consist of small molecules are usually **solids / liquids** or gases at room temperature.

They have relatively **low / high** melting and boiling points. They are **good / poor** conductors of electricity. They are usually **soluble / insoluble** in water. Simple molecular substances consist of simple molecules that contain **ionic / covalent** bonds and have intermolecular forces between molecules.

(10) Intermolecular forces 　　　　　　　　　　　Grade 7

1. Carbon dioxide exists as simple molecules. Explain why it is a gas at room temperature. **[2 marks]**

Carbon dioxide is a gas at room temperature because the forces of attraction between the molecules are

....

....

2. **Table 1** shows the molecular formula and boiling points of some alkenes.

Table 1

Name	Molecular formula	Boiling point in °C
ethene	C_2H_4	−104
propene	C_3H_6	−48
butene	C_4H_8	−6
pentene	C_5H_{10}	30
hexene	C_6H_{12}	63
heptene	C_7H_{14}	

> Be careful when dealing with negative values. Remember the larger the number the lower the value.

> Use the term 'intermolecular forces' in your answer to part **(c)**.

(a) Describe how the size of alkene molecules affects their boiling points. **[1 mark]**

As the size of the molecule increases,

....

(b) Complete **Table 1** to predict the boiling point of heptene. **[1 mark]**

(c) Explain the trend in boiling points of the alkenes. **[2 marks]**

....

....

(10) Simple molecular substances 　　　　　　　　　　　Grade 7

3. Explain why carbon dioxide gas does not conduct electricity. **[2 marks]**

....

....

4. Methane is a simple molecular, covalent substance. Explain, in terms of structure and bonding, why methane has a very low melting point. **[2 marks]**

....

....

88 Made a start 　 Feeling confident 　 Exam ready

Giant covalent structures

② Quick quiz

Label each diagram to show whether it is a giant covalent structure or a simple molecular structure.

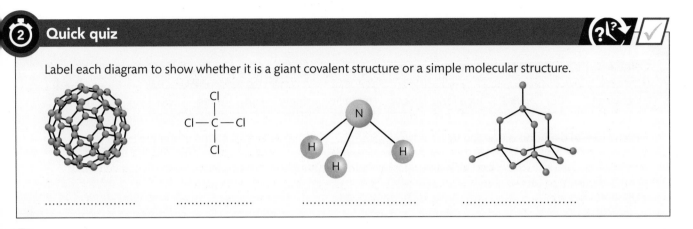

....

⑩ Giant covalent structures   Grade 6

1. Glass is made from silicon dioxide and other compounds. Silicon dioxide (**Figure 1**) is an example of a substance with a giant covalent structure. It has a structure similar to that of diamond.

   (a) Describe how the bonds are formed in a giant covalent structure.   **[1 mark]**

   ☞ Covalent bonds are formed between atoms by
   ....

   (b) Suggest and explain **three** physical properties you would expect silicon dioxide to have.   **[3 marks]**

   ☞ 1 Very high ....

   ....

   2 ....

   ....

   3 ....

   ....

Si ●
O ●

Figure 1

⑩ Structure and properties   Grades 8–9

2. Which is a correct description of the properties of graphite, a giant covalent substance? Tick **one** box.   **[1 mark]**

   It has a high melting point and is a poor conductor of electricity. ☐

   It has a high melting point and is a good conductor of electricity. ☐

   It has a low melting point and is a good conductor of electricity. ☐

   It has a low melting point and is a poor conductor of electricity. ☐

3. Diamond and carbon dioxide both contain covalent bonds. Diamond has a high melting point but carbon dioxide has a low melting point. Explain, in terms of the structure and bonding of these substances, the difference in melting points.
          [5 marks]

   ....

   ....

   ....

   ....

   ....

Diamond

1 **Quick quiz**

Use words from the box to complete the sentences.

| covalent | four | hard | high | ionic | low | metallic | shiny | soft | three | two |

Each atom in diamond is bonded to .... other atoms. All the atoms are joined by

.... bonds. Diamond is suitable for cutting tools because it is ....

Diamond has a .... melting point.

10 **Properties of diamond**   **Grade 6**

1. Diamond is made from carbon atoms.

(a) Explain, with reference to structure and bonding, why diamond is used in cutting tools.   **[4 marks]**

↪ Diamond has a giant covalent structure with many
....

....

....

....

Figure 1 Diamond is used in cutting tools.

(b) Give a reason why diamond is unable to conduct electricity.   **[1 mark]**

....

(c) Give **two** further properties of diamond.   **[2 marks]**

1 ....

2 ....

(d) Explain how the structure of diamond determines its melting point.   **[3 marks]**

....

....

....

10 **Structure of diamond**   **Grade 7**

2. Figure 2 shows the structure of diamond. Describe its structure and bonding.   **[4 marks]**

....

....

....

....

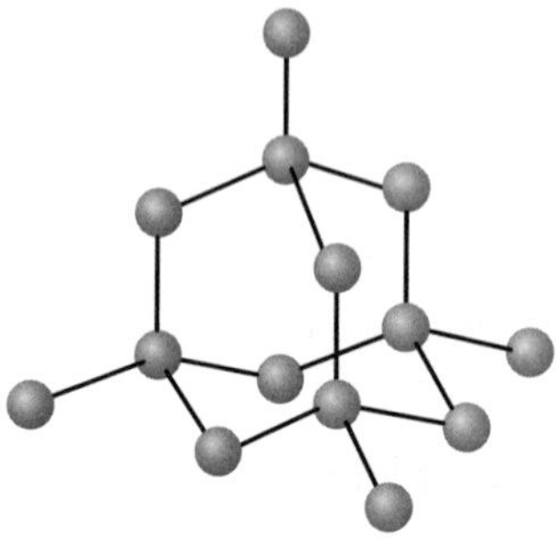

Figure 2

 Made a start   **Feeling confident**   **Exam ready**

Polymers

① Quick quiz

Cross out the incorrect **bold** words to make each sentence correct.

Polythene is a **large / small** molecule.

The intermolecular forces between polythene molecules are **stronger / weaker** than the intermolecular forces between ethene molecules.

Polythene has a relatively **high / low** melting point.

⑤ Formation of polymers   Grade 6

1. (a) State what is meant by the term 'polymer'.   **[1 mark]**

A polymer is a large molecule made from

(b) Name the type of bonds which hold together the atoms in a polymer.   **[1 mark]**

....

> Are the atoms made from metals or non-metals?

(c) Explain why polymers are solids at room temperature.   **[2 marks]**

....

....

....

⑮ Polymer properties   Grade 6

2. Polypropene is a polymer with many uses. The displayed structural formula of propene is shown in **Figure 1**.

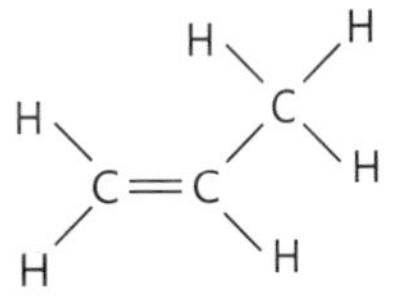

Figure 1

(a) Give the molecular formula of propene.   **[1 mark]**

....

(b) Name the type of bonds formed between the atoms in propene.   **[1 mark]**

....

(c) Explain why polypropene has a higher melting point than propene.   ·**[2 marks]**

....

....

3. PVC is a polymer. It does not conduct electricity. Give a reason, in terms of its structure and bonding, why PVC does not conduct electricity.   **[1 mark]**

....

> Think about the type of particles in the polymer.

....

Metallic bonding

② Quick quiz

(a) Label the diagram to show an electron and a metal atom.

(b) What charge do electrons have? ....

(c) How are the atoms arranged? ....

(d) Why are the electrons shown in a random arrangement?

....

⑩ Properties from metallic bonding   Grade 6

1. (a) Explain, in terms of structure and bonding, why the bonding in metals is strong.   **[3 marks]**

☞ Metals consist of a regular arrangement of metal atoms surrounded by delocalised electrons.
....

There is strong attraction between the positive metal nuclei and
....

....

(b) Describe the bonding in magnesium and sodium metal. State any differences in the bonding.   **[4 marks]**

....

....

....

....

| Refer to the number of delocalised electrons available. |

⑩ Metallic bonding   Grade 8

2. (a) State which electrons in a metal atom can become delocalised.   **[1 mark]**

....

(b) Give the number of delocalised electrons per aluminium atom. Explain your answer.   **[2 marks]**

....

....

....

3. Which one of the following describes the structure of a metal? Tick **one** box.   **[1 mark]**

Layers of metals with weak forces between the layers.

Layers of positive metal nuclei attracted to delocalised electrons.

Layers of atoms covalently bonded.

Regular arrangement of metal atoms and delocalised ions.

 Made a start   **Feeling confident**   **Exam ready**

Properties of metals

② Quick quiz

Draw and label a diagram to show the arrangement of particles in a metal and use it to explain why metals conduct electricity.

⑩ Metallic properties   Grade 5

1. Metals are malleable. Which of the following correctly explains the meaning of malleable? Tick **one** box.   **[1 mark]**

Malleable means that metals can be drawn into a wire. ☐

Malleable means that metals can be hammered into shape without breaking. ☐

Malleable means that metals can conduct electricity. ☐

Malleable means that metals can be shiny when freshly cut. ☐

2. X is a metal found in Group 2 in the periodic table. State **three** properties of metal X.   **[3 marks]**

1 X has a high melting point. ....

2 It is a good ....

3 ....

3. Y is a red-brown liquid which does not conduct electricity. State **two** reasons why Y is thought to be a non-metal.
[2 marks]

....

....

⑩ Metallic properties   Grade 7

4. Explain why metals are malleable.   **[3 marks]**

....

....

....

5. Explain why most metals have high melting points.   **[4 marks]**

....

....

....

....

> Think about the type of bonds present in metals.

Relative formula mass

(2) Quick quiz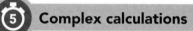

True or false?

The symbol for relative formula mass is M_r.	**True / False**
Relative formula mass is the mass of one atom of an element.	**True / False**
Relative formula mass is found by adding the atomic numbers of the elements together.	**True / False**
Relative formula masses have the unit grams.	**True / False**

(5) Simple calculations | Grade 5

1. (a) Give the relative atomic mass of the following elements. **[3 marks]**

Carbon .... 12 ....

Sodium ....

Mercury ....

(b) Calculate the relative formula mass of the following elements. **[3 marks]**

Oxygen (O_2) $2 \times 16 =$ ....

Fluorine (F_2) ....

Chlorine (Cl_2) ....

> You can find relative atomic masses and atomic numbers in the periodic table on page 283.

(5) Complex calculations | Grade 7

2. Calculate the relative formula mass of the following compounds. **[5 marks]**

$CuSO_4$ $Cu + S + (4 \times O) =$ ....

Na_2CO_3 $2 \times$ ....

NaCl ....

NH_4OH ....

$Ca(NO_3)_2$ ....

> If there are brackets within the formula, you need to multiply the contents of the brackets by the number that follows, e.g. $(NO_3)_2$ means $2 \times NO_3$ (two units of NO_3) = 2N and 6O.

(15) Calculating M_r | Grade 7

3. Calculate the relative formula mass of the following compounds.

(a) $FeSO_4$ .... **[1 mark]**

(b) $KMnO_4$ .... **[1 mark]**

(c) NH_4NO_3 .... **[1 mark]**

(d) $Cu(NO_3)_2$ .... **[1 mark]**

(e) $Al_2(SO_4)_3$ .... **[1 mark]**

4. Describe how relative formula masses can be used to show that an equation is balanced. **[1 mark]**

....

5. A compound XNO_3 has a relative formula mass of 101. Deduce the identity of element X. **[3 marks]**

....

....

....

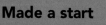 **Made a start** 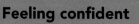 **Feeling confident** **Exam ready**

Empirical formulae

② Quick quiz

Write down the empirical formula for each of the compounds below.

C_6H_6 .... CH_4 .... C_2H_6 ....

C_2H_6O .... C_6H_{12} .... $CaCl_2$ ....

⑩ Empirical formulae   Grade 6

1. A compound has an empirical formula of CH_2O and a relative formula mass of 180. Deduce the molecular formula of the compound.   **[3 marks]**

M_r of $CH_2O = 12 + (2 \times 1) + 16 =$ ....

then divide 180 by this value
....

2. A compound contained 55.5% mercury Hg and 44.5% bromine. Calculate the empirical formula of the compound.   **[3 marks]**

$Hg = \dfrac{55.5}{201} = $ ....

Relative atomic masses: Hg 201   Br 80

⑩ Experimental determination of empirical formulae   Grade 8

3. A student carried out an experiment to determine the empirical formula of titanium oxide.

titanium + oxygen → titanium oxide

The student obtained the following results:

mass of titanium reacted = 1.020 g, mass of titanium oxide formed = 1.700 g

(a) Describe an experimental method which could be used to produce these results.   **[6 marks]**

....
....
....
....
....
....
....
....

(b) Use the results given to calculate the empirical formula of titanium oxide.   **[3 marks]**

Balancing equations

② **Quick quiz**

Balance each equation by writing the correct numbers in the equations.

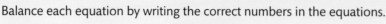

......Na + Cl$_2$ → ......NaCl   ......Mg + O$_2$ → ......MgO

⑩ **Balancing equations**   **Grade 6**

1. Balance the following equations.

 (a) BaO + 2HCl → BaCl$_2$ + H$_2$O   **[1 mark]**

(b) ......Na + Br$_2$ → ......NaBr   **[1 mark]**

(c) ...... Mg + ...CuSO$_4$ → ......MgSO$_4$ + ...Cu   **[1 mark]**

(d) ...... Li$_2$CO$_3$ + ...HNO$_3$ → ......LiNO$_3$ + ...H$_2$O + ...CO$_2$ **[1 mark]**

(e) ...... N$_2$ + ...H$_2$ → ......NH$_3$ **[1 mark]**

(f) ......Al + ...O$_2$ → ......Al$_2$O$_3$ **[1 mark]**

(g) ......Fe + ...CuSO$_4$ → ......Fe$_2$(SO$_4$)$_3$ + ...Cu   **[1 mark]**

> 2H$_2$ + O$_2$ → 2H$_2$O
> 2 × 2 = 4H   2 × 2 = 4H
> 1 × 2 = 2O   2 × 1 = 2O
>
> It can help to write the number of atoms of each element underneath the equation. Remember, each of these numbers must be the same on the left of the arrow as on the right of it.

⑩ **Balancing symbol equations**   **Grade 8**

2. Write the balanced symbol equation for each of the reactions.

(a) copper oxide + hydrogen → copper + water   **[2 marks]**

....

(b) sulfur dioxide + oxygen → sulfur trioxide   **[2 marks]**

....

(c) iron oxide (Fe$_2$O$_3$) + carbon monoxide → iron + carbon dioxide   **[2 marks]**

....

(d) carbon dioxide + water → glucose (C$_6$H$_{12}$O$_6$) + oxygen   **[2 marks]**

....

(e) butane (C$_4$H$_{10}$) + oxygen → carbon dioxide + water   **[2 marks]**

....

✓ **Made a start**   ✓ **Feeling confident**   ✓ **Exam ready**

Conservation of mass

---

① Quick quiz

Which of the following reactions give off a gas? Tick all of the correct answers.

Heating copper carbonate ☐   Reacting hydrochloric acid and magnesium ☐

Reacting sodium hydroxide and sulfuric acid ☐   Reacting magnesium and oxygen ☐

---

⑩ Changes in mass   Grade 7 ☑

1. Silver oxide, Ag_2O, decomposes when heated. Two products form, silver and oxygen.

(a) Write a balanced equation for the reaction.   **[2 marks]**

🚩 $2Ag_2O \rightarrow \quad\quad Ag + O_2$

(b) When 6.22 g of silver oxide decomposes, 5.79 g of silver is produced. Calculate the expected mass of oxygen produced in the reaction.   **[1 mark]**

🚩 $6.22g - 5.79g =$ expected mass of oxygen =   g

(c) Explain why the actual mass of products produced in an experiment may appear to be less than the expected (calculated or theoretical) mass.   **[2 marks]**

....

....

---

⑮ Mass changes   Grade 5 ☑

2. A 500 g pack of iron nails is left uncovered in a shed. The iron reacts with oxygen and water to form rust.

(a) State what happens to the mass of the pack of nails.   **[1 mark]**

....

(b) Explain why this happens.   **[2 marks]**

....

....

3. A student weighed some magnesium in a crucible, covered it with a lid and then heated it. The results are as follows:

crucible + lid = 30.10 g   magnesium + crucible + lid = 30.34 g   magnesium oxide + crucible + lid = 30.50 g

Calculate the mass of magnesium, magnesium oxide and oxygen used in the experiment.   **[2 marks]**

4. A teacher weighs a strip of copper, then heats it in a boiling tube containing iodine vapour. A layer of yellow-brown copper iodide forms on the surface of the copper. The teacher weighs the strip again.

(a) Write a word equation for the reaction that takes place.   **[1 mark]**

....

(b) Suggest an explanation for what happens to the mass of the strip. Explain your answer.   **[2 marks]**

....

....

☑ **Made a start**   ☑ **Feeling confident**   ☑ **Exam ready**

Calculating masses in reactions

② Quick quiz

192 g of magnesium reacts with oxygen to produce 320 g of magnesium oxide. How much oxygen has been used?

132 g ☐   512 g ☐   128 g ☐   1.67 g ☐

⑩ Conservation of mass in reactions   **Grade 6**

1. Two students added a weighed sample of solid calcium carbonate to a weighed open beaker of hydrochloric acid. They weighed the beaker and its contents after the reaction finished. Before they carried out the experiment, each student made a prediction about the results.

   Student 1 wrote: When the reaction is finished, the mass of the products will be less than the mass of the reactants.

   Student 2 wrote: When the reaction is finished, the mass of the products will be equal to the mass of the reactants.

   (a) Suggest a reason for each student's prediction.   **[3 marks]**

   Student 1 ...The reaction produces a gas,...

   ....

   Student 2 ....

   ....

   (b) Write a balanced equation to show the reaction between calcium carbonate and hydrochloric acid. Include state symbols.   **[3 marks]**

   $CaCO_3(s) + $ .... $\rightarrow CaCl_2(aq) + $ .... $+$ ....

   (c) Explain why the students found that the mass measured after the reaction was less than the total mass measured before the reaction.   **[2 marks]**

   ....

   ....

2. Magnesium reacts with hydrochloric acid to produce magnesium chloride and hydrogen.

   $Mg + 2HCl \rightarrow MgCl_2 + H_2$

   Explain, using calculation of the relative formula masses, that mass is conserved in this reaction.   **[2 marks]**

   ....

   ....

⑩ Law of conservation of mass   **Grade 5**

3. Give the meaning of the 'law of conservation of mass'.   **[1 mark]**

   | You do not need to explain this law in your answer. |

   ....

4. Give the meaning of the term 'closed system'.   **[1 mark]**

   ....

5. When heated, 50 g of calcium carbonate decomposes to form carbon dioxide and 28 g of solid calcium oxide. Calculate the percentage mass loss of carbon dioxide. Give your answer to 2 significant figures.   **[3 marks]**

   percentage mass loss of carbon dioxide = ... %

 Made a start   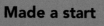 Feeling confident   Exam ready

Concentrations of solutions

---

② Quick quiz

Write down the units used for:

concentration ....   mass ....   volume ....

What is the equation for calculating concentration of solutions?

concentration = ...

---

⑩ Concentration calculations　　　　　　　　　　　　　　　**Grade 7**

1. Give the volume of the following solutions in dm^3.

  (a) 20 cm^3 of sodium chloride solution .... **[1 mark]**

  (b) 150 cm^3 of sulfuric acid solution .... **[1 mark]**

  (c) 25 cm^3 of hydrochloric acid solution .... **[1 mark]**

> Remember that 1000 cm^3 = 1 dm^3.

2. 3.7 g of a compound is dissolved in water to make 100 cm^3 of solution.

  (a) Give the volume of the solution in dm^3. **[1 mark]**

  ....

  (b) Calculate the concentration of the solution. **[3 marks]**

> Rearrange the concentration equation.

                                  concentration of solution = ... $g\,dm^{-3}$

3. Calculate the mass of solute present in 2.5 dm^3 of 65 $g\,dm^{-3}$ solution. **[3 marks]**

  mass = concentration × volume

  mass = ... × ....

> Don't forget to include units if none are supplied in the answer line.

                                  mass of solute = ... g

---

⑩ Mass and volume calculations　　　　　　　　　　　　　　　**Grade 7**

4. A student wants to make 5 cm^3 of a 0.2 $g\,dm^{-3}$ sodium chloride solution. Calculate the mass of sodium chloride that she must dissolve. Give your answer in standard form. **[4 marks]**

                                mass of sodium chloride = ... g

> Standard form means to put a number in the form $A \times 10^x$ where A is a number between 1 and 10.

5. A student prepares a solution of concentration 20 $g\,dm^{-3}$. He uses 2 g of the solute. Calculate the volume of solution that he makes. **[3 marks]**

                                volume of solution = ... dm^3

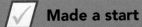

Moles

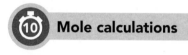 **Quick quiz**

Write the equation used to calculate the number of moles of a substance.

What is the mass of one mole of oxygen gas O_2? Tick **one** box.

8 g ☐

16 g ☐

32 g ☐

64 g ☐

> Use the periodic table to find A_r

 Mole calculations   **Grade 7** ✓

1. Calculate the mass, in grams, of 2 mol of carbon dioxide.   **[2 marks]**

> Remember to use your periodic table to obtain A_r and then work out M_r

> mass = moles × M_r

mass of carbon dioxide = ... g

2. The relative formula mass of propanol, C_3H_7OH, is 60. Calculate the number of moles of propanol particles in 15 g of propanol.
   [2 marks]

 15 g = number of moles × 60

number of moles = $\dfrac{15}{........}$

number of moles = ...

3. Give the mass of one mole of sulfuric acid, H_2SO_4.   **[1 mark]**

....

> The mass of one mole is equal to the relative formula mass expressed in grams.

 Mole calculations   **Grade 8** ✓

4. Calculate the number of moles of sodium carbonate present in 5.3 g of anhydrous sodium carbonate, Na_2CO_3.   **[2 marks]**

number of moles = ...

5. Calculate the mass of ammonium sulfate particles present in 2 mol of ammonium sulfate, $(NH_4)_2SO_4$.   **[2 marks]**

mass of ammonium sulfate = ...g

✓ **Made a start**   ✓ **Feeling confident**   ✓ **Exam ready**

Amounts of substances

② Quick quiz

Draw lines to match the units and symbols to their meanings.

M_r	relative atomic mass
mol	relative formula mass
A_r	unit for amount of matter
g	unit for mass

Which is the correct value for Avogadro's constant?

602×10^{23} ☐

6.02×10^{23} ☐

6.02×10^{-23} ☐

602×10^{-23} ☐

⑩ Mole calculations   Grade 7 ☑

1. (a) Give the number of atoms in one mole of carbon.   **[1 mark]**

🚩 6.02×10^{23}

(b) Use the answer to **(a)** to calculate the number of atoms in 0.83 mol of carbon. Give your answer to 2 decimal places.   **[2 marks]**

> Multiply the answer to part **(a)** by the value given in part **(b)**.

2. Calculate the number of moles of CH_4 molecules in 6.4 g of methane CH_4.   **[2 marks]**

 $moles = \dfrac{mass}{M_r}$

number of moles of molecules = ...

⑩ Rearranging mole calculations   Grade 8 ☑

3. Use Avogadro's constant to calculate the number of atoms in 12.0 g of water.
Give your answer in standard form and to 3 significant figures.   **[4 marks]**

number of atoms in 12.0 g of water = ...

4. 3 mol of substance X has a mass of 480 g. Calculate the relative formula mass of X.   **[2 marks]**

relative formula mass of substance X = ...

Using mass to balance equations

Quick quiz

Draw **one** line from each substance to match it to its relative formula mass.

F_2		38
$SrCO_3$		208
$BaCl_2$		170
$AgNO_3$		148

Which of these equations is correct? Tick **one** box.

$$moles = \frac{M_r}{mass}$$ ☐

$$mass = \frac{M_r}{moles}$$ ☐

$$M_r = \frac{mass}{moles}$$ ☐

Look at the periodic table to find the relative atomic masses needed.

Using mass in calculations

Grade 7

1. A sample of 5.08 g of copper is heated in air to form 6.36 g of copper oxide.

(a) Calculate the mass of oxygen that reacted with the copper. **[1 mark]**

mass of oxygen = mass of copper oxide − mass of copper

mass of oxygen = ... g

(b) Deduce the balanced equation for the reaction. **[4 marks]**

Calculate the M_r of the reactants and product.

M_r is the atomic mass of the atoms added together.

....

....

Divide the mass (g) of each substance by its A_r or M_r to get the number of moles.

....

....

Find the simplest whole number ratio of moles.

....

....

Use the ratio to produce the balanced equation.

....

....

Divide all values by the smallest one first.

Balancing an equation using reacting masses

Grade 8

2. 1.76 g of methane, CH_4, burns completely in air. The products formed are 4.85 g of CO_2 and 3.96 g of H_2O. Deduce the balanced equation for this reaction and justify your answer. **[5 marks]**

....

....

....

....

....

 Made a start   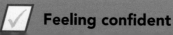 Feeling confident   Exam ready

States of matter

② Quick quiz

Fill in the gaps in the table about the states of matter.

State	Particle arrangement	Particle movement	Forces of attraction
solid	close together regular lattice arrangement		
liquid	close together random arrangement	move around each other	weak
gas		move around freely in all directions	

⑤ Changes of state and state symbols
Grade 6

1. **(a)** Describe **three** changes which take place when energy is transferred to a solid. Refer to the particle model in your answer. **[3 marks]**

🚩 1 The particles move further apart. ....

2 The strength of the forces between the particles ....

3 ....

(b) An element has melting point –7 °C and boiling point 59 °C. What state is it in at room temperature (20 °C)? **[1 mark]**

....

2. The equation for the reaction of hydrochloric acid with sodium carbonate solution is:

$Na_2CO_3(aq) + 2HCl(aq) \rightarrow 2NaCl(aq) + H_2O(l) + CO_2(g)$

Look at the state symbols.

Explain how the equation shows that sodium carbonate is dissolved in water. **[1 mark]**

....

⑮ States of matter
Grade 7

3. **Figure 1** shows particles of the same substance in three different states of matter.

(a) Give **two** ways in which the model represented by **Figure 1** is limited. **[2 marks]**

....

....

(b) Describe how the boiling points of different substances depend on the strength of the forces between their particles. **[2 marks]**

gas

liquid

solid

cold

Figure 1

....

....

(c) Use **Figure 1** to explain how the strength of the forces between particles affects the arrangement of the particles. Refer to each state of matter in your answer. **[6 marks]**

....

....

....

....

Continue your answer on your own paper.

 Made a start | Feeling confident | Exam ready

Pure substances

② Quick quiz

Which diagrams represent pure substances? ....

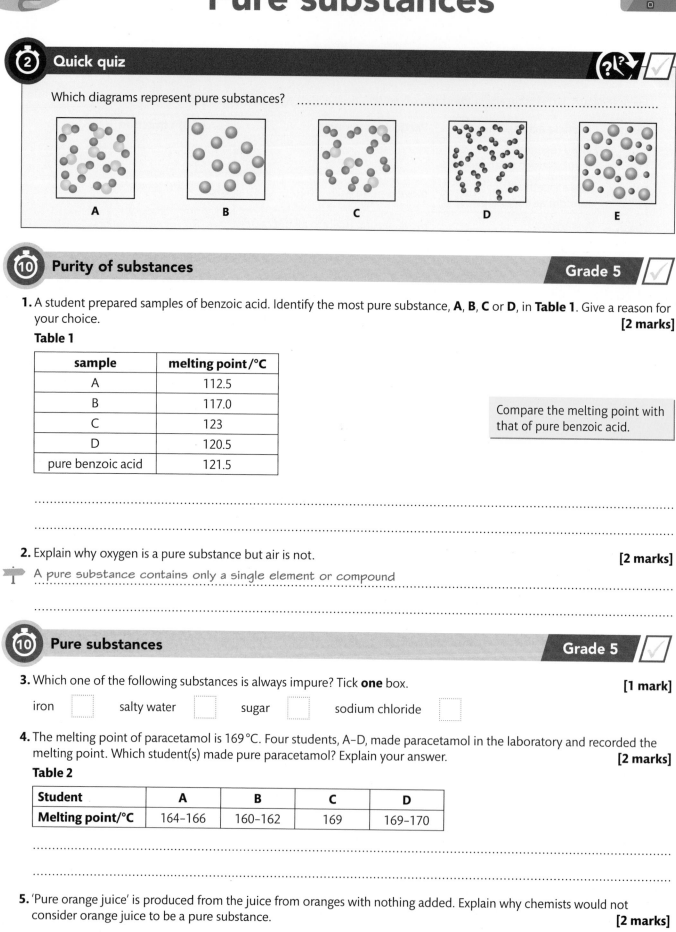

A   B   C   D   E

⑩ Purity of substances   Grade 5

1. A student prepared samples of benzoic acid. Identify the most pure substance, **A**, **B**, **C** or **D**, in **Table 1**. Give a reason for your choice.   **[2 marks]**

Table 1

sample	melting point /°C
A	112.5
B	117.0
C	123
D	120.5
pure benzoic acid	121.5

> Compare the melting point with that of pure benzoic acid.

....

....

2. Explain why oxygen is a pure substance but air is not.   **[2 marks]**

🪧 A pure substance contains only a single element or compound
....

....

⑩ Pure substances   Grade 5

3. Which one of the following substances is always impure? Tick **one** box.   **[1 mark]**

iron ☐   salty water ☐   sugar ☐   sodium chloride ☐

4. The melting point of paracetamol is 169 °C. Four students, A–D, made paracetamol in the laboratory and recorded the melting point. Which student(s) made pure paracetamol? Explain your answer.   **[2 marks]**

Table 2

Student	A	B	C	D
Melting point/°C	164–166	160–162	169	169–170

....

....

5. 'Pure orange juice' is produced from the juice from oranges with nothing added. Explain why chemists would not consider orange juice to be a pure substance.   **[2 marks]**

....

....

☑ Made a start   ☑ Feeling confident   ☑ Exam ready

BBC

Mixtures

② Quick quiz

Draw **one** line from each component in the mixture to match it to the best technique used to separate it out.

coal from slurry (a mixture of solid coal dust and water)	simple distillation
ethanol from a mixture of alcohols	paper chromatography
water from coal slurry	filtration and drying
salts from seawater (a solution of salts)	filtration
pure water from seawater	fractional distillation
coloured substances from leaves, dissolved in ethanol	crystallisation

⑩ Crystallisation   Grade 7

1. (a) State what is meant by the term 'mixture'.   **[1 mark]**

👉 A mixture consists of two or more
....

(b) Figure 1 shows common laboratory apparatus. Copper sulfate is a soluble salt. Describe the laboratory method, using this apparatus, a student could use to safely crystallise copper sulfate from its solution.   **[6 marks]**

👉 Pour the copper sulfate solution into the
....
          Then
....
....
....
....

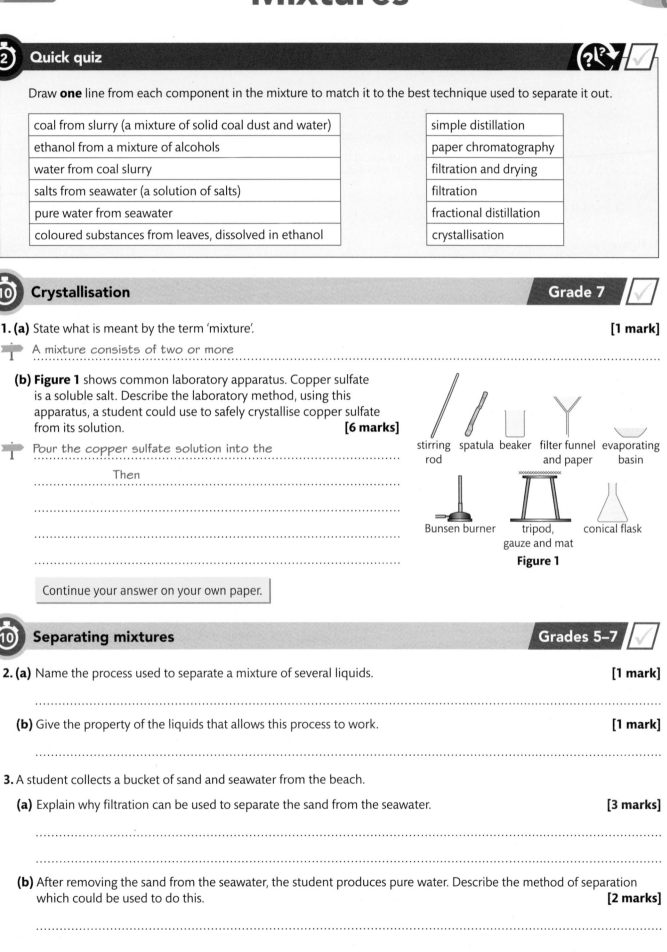

stirring rod   spatula   beaker   filter funnel and paper   evaporating basin

Bunsen burner   tripod, gauze and mat   conical flask

Figure 1

> Continue your answer on your own paper.

⑩ Separating mixtures   Grades 5–7

2. (a) Name the process used to separate a mixture of several liquids.   **[1 mark]**

....

(b) Give the property of the liquids that allows this process to work.   **[1 mark]**

....

3. A student collects a bucket of sand and seawater from the beach.

(a) Explain why filtration can be used to separate the sand from the seawater.   **[3 marks]**

....
....

(b) After removing the sand from the seawater, the student produces pure water. Describe the method of separation which could be used to do this.   **[2 marks]**

....
....

Chromatography

 Quick quiz

True or false?

Under the same conditions, the R_f value of a particular substance is always the same.	**True / False**
The paper used in chromatography is called the mobile phase.	**True / False**
The smaller the R_f value, the more soluble the ink in the solvent.	**True / False**

 Chromatograms **Grade 5**

1. **Figure 1** shows a chromatogram of different inks. Black ink is a mixture of blue, red and yellow substances. Complete **Figure 1** to show what the chromatogram of black ink will look like. **[2 marks]**

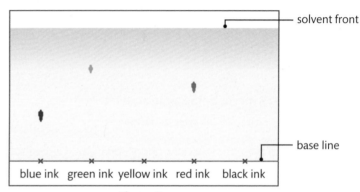

solvent front

base line

blue ink   green ink   yellow ink   red ink   black ink

Figure 1

 Calculating R_f values **Grade 6**

2. A student carried out chromatography on food colouring. The solvent front travelled 7.3 cm and the yellow food colouring travelled 3.7 cm. Calculate the R_f value for the food colouring. Give your answer to 2 significant figures.

[2 marks]

$$R_f = \frac{\text{distance moved by substance}}{\text{distance moved by solvent}}$$

$$R_f = \frac{3.7}{7.3}$$

$$=$$

$R_f = $ ....

R_f values have no units. This is because both values used are distances and so their units cancel out.

Maths skills

You need to know how to give answers to a stated number of significant figures (usually 1, 2 or 3 significant figures). To work out the number of significant figures, start at the first non-zero number, then count the number of figures you need to the right (including zeros). If the number after that is 5 or more, round up. If it is 4 or less, do not round up.

Chromatography **Grade 7**

3. Explain how chromatography works. Use paper chromatography as your example. **[5 marks]**

Remember that all types of chromatography rely upon two difference phases.

....
....
....
....
....
....

 Made a start **Feeling confident** **Exam ready**

Practical: Investigating inks

② Quick quiz

Draw **one** line from each term to match it with its definition.

distillation	the level reached by the solvent
R_f value	the chromatography paper
mobile phase	the distance a substance travels relative to the solvent
solvent front	the liquid solvent
stationary phase	the separation of a solution by evaporation and condensation

⑤ Preparing and analysing chromatograms   Grade 5

1. Give the steps a student would follow to prepare a chromatogram to separate the dyes in ink.
Use the terms: 'base line', 'mobile phase' and 'stationary phase'.   **[4 marks]**

Step 1: Draw the base line using a ruler and ....

Step 2: Put small spots of ink ....

Step 3: ....

Step 4: ....

⑤ Using chromatograms   Grade 7

2. Explain whether the suspected forgery was written in the same green ink.   **[3 marks]**

The original green ink and the ink from the suspected forgery have a different number of

....

One of the spots ....

....

....

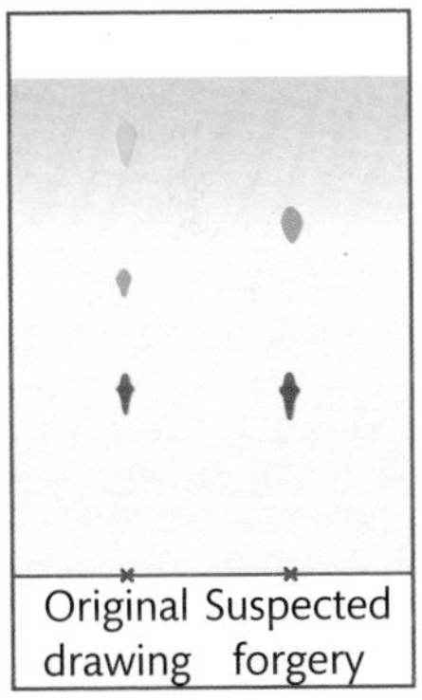

Original Suspected
drawing   forgery

Figure 1

⑩ Analysis of chromatograms   Grade 7

3. A student carried out an investigation on a sample of red food colouring by first placing a spot of the colouring on a pencil base line on a piece of chromatography paper.

(a) Describe how the student would complete the experiment, including what measurements are taken.   **[5 marks]**

....

....

....

(b) Give the formula used to calculate R_f values.   **[1 mark]**

....

....

Potable water

Complete the diagram to show the three main stages of fresh water treatment.

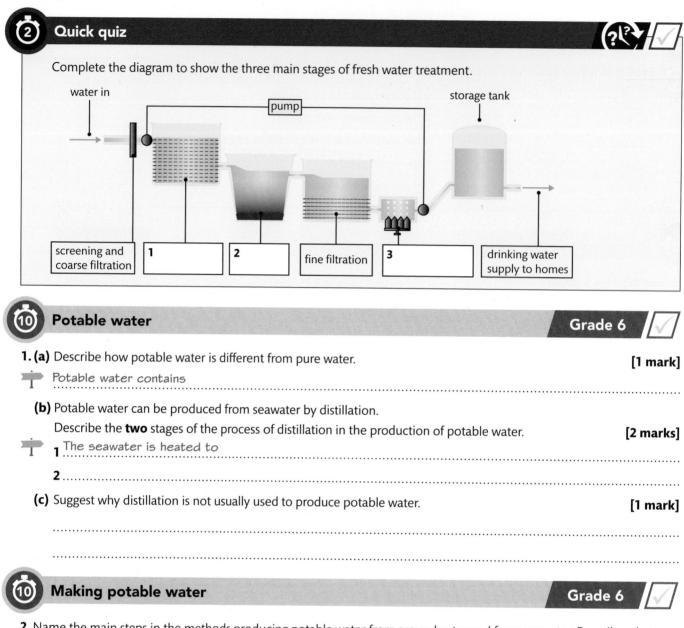

water in | pump | storage tank

screening and coarse filtration | 1 | 2 | fine filtration | 3 | drinking water supply to homes

⑩ Potable water   Grade 6

1. **(a)** Describe how potable water is different from pure water.   **[1 mark]**

   Potable water contains ....

   (b) Potable water can be produced from seawater by distillation.

   Describe the **two** stages of the process of distillation in the production of potable water.   **[2 marks]**

   1 The seawater is heated to ....

   2 ....

   (c) Suggest why distillation is not usually used to produce potable water.   **[1 mark]**

   ....

   ....

⑩ Making potable water   Grade 6

2. Name the main steps in the methods producing potable water from groundwater and from seawater. Describe what happens in each stage of treatment.   **[5 marks]**

   ....

   ....

   ....

   ....

   ....

   ....

3. A student carried out an analysis of a solution of sodium chloride in tap water. Explain why the student should have used deionised water.   **[3 marks]**

   ....

   ....

   ....

Made a start   Feeling confident   Exam ready

The pH scale and neutralisation

---

② **Quick quiz**

Label the pH scale to show the acidic, alkaline and neutral regions.

| 0 | 1 | 2 | 3 | 4 | 5 | 6 | 7 | 8 | 9 | 10 | 11 | 12 | 13 | 14 |

---

⑩ **pH and neutralisation**   **Grade 6**

1. Explain why copper oxide is a base but not an alkali, but sodium hydroxide is a base and an alkali. **[3 marks]**

Bases are substances that react with acids to produce a salt and water. Both
....
....

2. Complete the word equation for the neutralisation reaction between sulfuric acid and magnesium hydroxide. **[2 marks]**

.... + ... → magnesium sulfate + ...

---

⑩ **The pH scale**   **Grade 6**

3. (a) List the order of acidity of the following items, starting with the most acidic and finishing with the most alkaline. **[3 marks]**

☐ baking soda (pH 8.3) ☐ vinegar (pH 2.6) ☐ tomatoes (pH 4.5)

☐ toothpaste (pH 8.8) ☐ drain cleaner (pH 14) ☐ shampoo (pH 7.5)

☐ cola drink (pH 2.4) ☐ bleach (pH 12.3) ☐ battery acid (pH 1.0)

(b) Predict the colour of phenolphthalein when mixed with:

(i) vinegar .... **[1 mark]**

(ii) bleach .... **[1 mark]**

(iii) drain cleaner .... **[1 mark]**

---

⑥ **Neutralisation reactions**   **Grade 8**

4. Which ion is produced by acids when they are in aqueous solution? Tick **one** box. **[1 mark]**

OH^- ☐ OH^+ ☐ H^+ ☐ H^- ☐

5. (a) Write the balanced symbol equation for the neutralisation reaction between hydrochloric acid and sodium hydroxide. Include state symbols. **[3 marks]**

....

(b) Give the pH of the solution which results after the complete neutralisation reaction in **(a)** has occurred. **[1 mark]**

....

(c) Write the ionic equation for neutralisation. Include state symbols. **[2 marks]**

....

 Made a start   ☑ **Feeling confident**   ☑ **Exam ready**

Strong and weak acids

---

② **Quick quiz**

Sort the acids into strong and weak acids.

| citric acid   sulfuric acid   nitric acid |
| carbonic acid   ethanoic acid |
| hydrochloric acid |

Strong acids	Weak acids

---

⑤ **Strength and concentration of acids**   **Grade 7** ✓

1. Acids can be described as concentrated or dilute. They can also be described as strong or weak.
Explain the difference between concentration and strength.   **[4 marks]**

☞ The concentration of an acid is related to the amount of acid dissolved in a given volume. The more acid

dissolved, the more

The strength of an acid

Concentration and strength are two different terms. A weak acid is not necessarily dilute (low concentration).

---

⑤ **pH and hydrogen ions**   **Grade 8** ✓

2. (a) Describe the relationship between pH and hydrogen ion concentration.   **[2 marks]**

☞ As the pH decreases by one unit, the concentration of hydrogen ions in the solution

(b) A solution with a pH of 5 has a hydrogen ion concentration of $0.00001 \, g \, dm^{-3}$. Give the hydrogen ion concentration of a solution with a pH of 9. Give your answer in standard form.   **[2 marks]**

The pH will be the same as the negative number after the 10, so, for example, pH 3 means $1 \times 10^{-3} \, g \, dm^{-3}$.

---

⑩ **Explaining acid strength**   **Grade 8** ✓

3. Describe the difference between a strong acid and a weak acid.   **[2 marks]**

4. A student stated that a solution of dilute hydrochloric acid would be weak. Explain why his statement was incorrect.   **[2 marks]**

5. A solution of hydrochloric acid, a strong acid, has a pH of 4. A solution of citric acid, a weak acid, also has a pH of 4.
Explain what this statement shows about the concentration of hydrogen ions in the two solutions.   **[2 marks]**

   ✓ **Made a start**   ✓ **Feeling confident**   ✓ **Exam ready**

Practical: pH change

② Quick quiz

True or false?

When acid is added to alkali the pH of the solution falls.	**True / False**
Calcium oxide and hydrochloric acid react to produce calcium chloride and hydrogen.	**True / False**
A pH probe determines pH more accurately than universal indicator paper.	**True / False**
Calcium hydroxide and hydrochloric acid react to produce calcium chloride and water.	**True / False**

⑤ Neutralisation   Grade 5

1. Complete the word equations for the following neutralisation reactions.   **[2 marks]**

   + water

(a) calcium oxide + hydrochloric acid → ....

(b) calcium hydroxide + hydrochloric acid → .... + ...

2. In a neutralisation reaction, acids and alkalis react with each other.

> Look at the formula of these acids to help you: HCl, H_2SO_4, HNO_3.

(a) Name the ion which is present in all acids. .... **[1 mark]**

(b) Name the ion which is present in all alkalis. .... **[1 mark]**

⑮ Practical method   Grades 7–8

3. Which one of the following could be used to determine the pH of vinegar? Tick **one** box.   **[1 mark]**

methyl orange ☐   pipette ☐   thermometer ☐   universal indicator ☐

4. In an experiment, a student measured out 25.0 cm³ of hydrochloric acid solution into a beaker and determined the pH of the solution using indicator paper. The student then added 0.2 g of calcium hydroxide powder to the beaker. She stirred the solution and recorded the pH. The student continued to add calcium hydroxide powder in 0.2 g portions, stirring and recording the pH after each addition, until a total of 2.4 g was added.

(a) Name a suitable piece of apparatus used to measure out 25.0 cm³ of hydrochloric acid.   **[1 mark]**

....

(b) Describe how the pH of the solution was determined.   **[2 marks]**

....

....

(c) Give a reason why the mixture was stirred after each addition of calcium hydroxide powder.   **[1 mark]**

....

(d) State how the student could measure the pH in this experiment more accurately.   **[1 mark]**

....

(e) Explain why adding hydroxide ions to an acid solution leads to an increase in pH.   **[2 marks]**

> **Exam focus**
> Make sure you are familiar with different measuring instruments which can be used to measure volumes. Pipettes and burettes are more accurate than measuring cylinders.

....

....

Salt production

② Quick quiz

Name the type of salt produced from each of these acids.

sulfuric acid .... nitric acid ....

hydrochloric acid ....

⑤ Salt equations   Grade 5

1. Complete the word equations for the following neutralisation reactions.

(a) magnesium oxide + sulfuric acid → magnesium sulfate + ... **[1 mark]**

(b) magnesium hydroxide + sulfuric acid → .... + ... **[1 mark]**

(c) copper carbonate + nitric acid → .... + ... + carbon dioxide .... **[1 mark]**

(d) iron oxide + hydrochloric acid→.. **[1 mark]**

(e) zinc carbonate + hydrochloric acid → .... **[1 mark]**

2. When acids react with carbonates, carbon dioxide is formed. Describe the chemical test for carbon dioxide.   **[2 marks]**

....

....

⑮ Ions and neutralisation equations   Grades 7–8

3. Give the formulae of the ions in the following salts.

(a) magnesium chloride .... **[1 mark]**

(b) silver nitrate .... **[1 mark]**

(c) sodium sulfate .... **[1 mark]**

4. Deduce the formula of the salt formed from the ions given below.
Name the salts.

(a) Ca^{2+} and Cl^- .... **[1 mark]**

(b) Li^+ and SO_4^{2-} .... **[1 mark]**

(c) NH_4^+ and SO_4^{2-} .... **[1 mark]**

5. Write balanced equations for the following neutralisation reactions. Give state symbols.

(a) hydrochloric acid and magnesium oxide .... **[3 marks]**

(b) calcium carbonate and sulfuric acid .... **[3 marks]**

(c) copper oxide (CuO) and nitric acid .... **[3 marks]**

(d) sulfuric acid and potassium hydroxide .... **[3 marks]**

The formulae for the acids are: hydrochloric acid HCl, nitric acid HNO_3, sulfuric acid H_2SO_4.

✓ **Made a start**   ✓ **Feeling confident**   ✓ **Exam ready**

Reactions of acids with metals

② Quick quiz

Complete these equations:

metal + acid → .... + ...

magnesium + hydrochloric acid → .... + ...

magnesium + sulfuric acid → .... + ...

zinc + nitric acid → .... + ...

⑩ Redox reactions   Grade 8

1. The following reaction is an example of a redox reaction:

$$Mg(s) + 2HCl(aq) \rightarrow MgCl_2(aq) + H_2(g)$$

(a) Name the salt which is produced in this reaction.   **[1 mark]**

> The products are on the right-hand side. The acid is hydrochloric so the salt will be a chloride.

....

(b) Explain, in terms of electrons, why magnesium is oxidised in this reaction.   **[2 marks]**

Magnesium has lost .... electrons. It has been oxidised from

....

> Remember, metals lose electrons in reactions, and the number of electrons they lose is equal to their group number.

(c) Explain, in terms of electrons, why the acid is reduced.   **[1 mark]**

The hydrogen ions in the acid have ....

⑩ Reactants and products   Grade 8

2. Zinc reacts with sulfuric acid to form hydrogen gas.

(a) Write the balanced symbol equation for the reaction between zinc and sulfuric acid.   **[2 marks]**

....

(b) Explain which species has been oxidised in this reaction.   **[2 marks]**

....

....

(c) Explain which species has been reduced in this reaction.   **[2 marks]**

....

....

(d) Describe the test to show that the gas produced is hydrogen.   **[2 marks]**

....

....

(e) Give a reason why the reaction between zinc and sulfuric acid is an example of a redox reaction.   **[1 mark]**

....

 Made a start   Feeling confident   ✓ Exam ready   **115**

Soluble salts

② Quick quiz

True or false?

Soluble substances can dissolve in water.	**True / False**
Salts can be made by reacting an acid and a carbonate.	**True / False**
Copper reacts with dilute sulfuric acid.	**True / False**
Sodium hydroxide is a soluble base.	**True / False**

⑮ Soluble salts — Grade 8

1. Zinc carbonate reacts with dilute hydrochloric acid to produce a solution of a soluble salt.

(a) Name the salt produced. [1 mark]

zinc ....

(b) Write the balanced symbol equation for the reaction. Include state symbols. [3 marks]

....

> The salt contains Zn^{2+} and Cl^- ions.

(c) Name the process used to obtain the solid salt from the salt solution produced. [1 mark]

....

(d) Describe how the process named in **(c)** is carried out experimentally. Name the apparatus used. [3 marks]

Heat the salt solution in .... using ....

....

Then leave ....

2. Describe how to ensure the reaction is complete when producing a soluble salt from an acid and an insoluble metal oxide. [2 marks]

Add an excess of ....

until no more ....

⑤ Making soluble salts — Grade 6

3. (a) A student produced the salt sodium nitrate by adding solid sodium carbonate to a dilute acid.
Which acid did the student use? Tick **one** box. [1 mark]

hydrochloric acid ☐   sulfuric acid ☐   nitric acid ☐   citric acid ☐

(b) Name the type of reaction taking place. [1 mark]

....

(c) Explain why excess sodium carbonate is added to dilute acid to prepare the sodium nitrate. [1 mark]

....

(d) Name the method used to remove the excess sodium carbonate from the salt solution. [1 mark]

....

 Made a start   **Feeling confident**   **Exam ready**

Practical: Making salts

② Quick quiz

The diagram shows apparatus for making salts. Label it with the words in the box.

| tripod | Bunsen burner | beaker | evaporating dish | filter funnel |

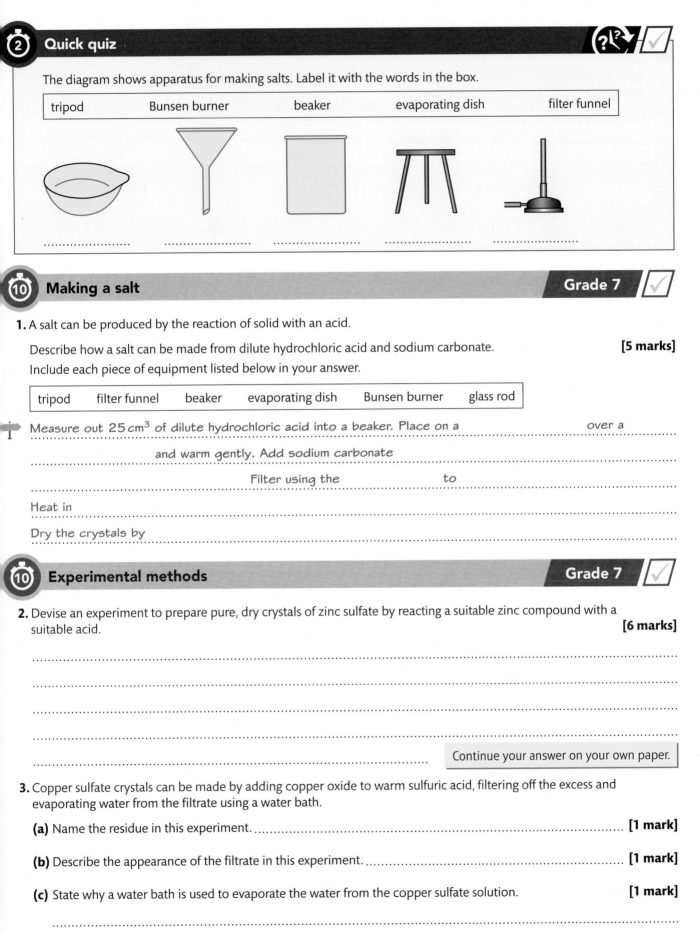

....

⑩ Making a salt   Grade 7

1. A salt can be produced by the reaction of solid with an acid.

Describe how a salt can be made from dilute hydrochloric acid and sodium carbonate.   **[5 marks]**
Include each piece of equipment listed below in your answer.

| tripod | filter funnel | beaker | evaporating dish | Bunsen burner | glass rod |

Measure out 25 cm³ of dilute hydrochloric acid into a beaker. Place on a .... over a ....

.... and warm gently. Add sodium carbonate ....

.... Filter using the .... to ....

Heat in ....

Dry the crystals by ....

⑩ Experimental methods   Grade 7

2. Devise an experiment to prepare pure, dry crystals of zinc sulfate by reacting a suitable zinc compound with a suitable acid.   **[6 marks]**

....

....

....

....

.... | Continue your answer on your own paper. |

3. Copper sulfate crystals can be made by adding copper oxide to warm sulfuric acid, filtering off the excess and evaporating water from the filtrate using a water bath.

(a) Name the residue in this experiment. .... **[1 mark]**

(b) Describe the appearance of the filtrate in this experiment. .... **[1 mark]**

(c) State why a water bath is used to evaporate the water from the copper sulfate solution.   **[1 mark]**

....

✓ **Made a start**   ✓ **Feeling confident**   ✓ **Exam ready**   117

Titration

---

② Quick quiz

What is the colour change when sodium hydroxide solution is added from a burette to hydrochloric acid and methyl orange in a conical flask? Tick **one** box.

orange to yellow ☐   orange to red ☐   red to yellow ☐   yellow to red ☐

---

⑩ Titration method — **Grade 6**

1. A titration was carried out as part of an experiment to prepare sodium chloride crystals. A few drops of phenolphthalein indicator were added to 25.0 cm^3 of sodium hydroxide solution. Dilute hydrochloric acid was added until the indicator first changed colour permanently. The volume of acid added was recorded.

   (a) **Figure 1** shows the apparatus used to measure out 25.0 cm^3 of sodium hydroxide solution. Label the diagram. **[3 marks]**

   (b) Suggest an explanation for why the conical flask is placed on a white tile during the titration. **[1 mark]**

   ....

   (c) Name **one** other piece of measuring apparatus that must be used in a titration. **[1 mark]**

   ....

   (d) State the colour change at the end point. **[2 marks]**

   From .... to ....

   (e) Describe how this experiment could be adapted and used to prepare crystals of sodium chloride. **[3 marks]**

   👉 Repeat the titration using the same volume of acid but no ....

   ....

   ....

   (f) Write a balanced symbol equation for the reaction. **[1 mark]**

   ....

Figure 1

> Think about what type of substance is in the conical flask. Phenolphthalein is colourless in acid and pink in alkali.

---

⑩ Using a titration to prepare a salt — **Grade 8**

2. Potassium sulfate solution is formed by neutralising potassium hydroxide solution with dilute sulfuric acid. Pure crystals of potassium sulfate can be obtained from this solution. The volumes of potassium hydroxide solution and dilute sulfuric acid required to form the potassium sulfate solution must be found by titration.

   Devise a method to prepare a solution of potassium sulfate from potassium hydroxide solution and dilute sulfuric acid. Describe how you would obtain pure, dry potassium sulfate crystals from this solution. **[6 marks]**

   ....

   ....

   ....

   ....

   > Continue your answer on your own paper.

 Made a start   **Feeling confident**   **Exam ready**

Solubility rules

② Quick quiz

Complete the table by tick the correct box, to show if the solid is soluble or insoluble.

solid	Sodium sulfate	Copper hydroxide	Silver nitrate	Calcium carbonate	Barium sulfate	Potassium chloride
soluble						
insoluble						

⑮ Solubility rules Grade 7

1. A student mixed a sodium sulfate solution with a barium chloride solution. A precipitate was formed. Another product was formed in solution.

(a) Write the balanced symbol equation for the reaction. **[1 mark]**

.... $+ BaCl_2 \rightarrow$ .... + ...

(b) Name the precipitate formed. **[1 mark]**

....

(c) The mixture was filtered. Name the residue and the filtrate. **[2 marks]**

> A precipitate is an insoluble solid.

residue = ...

filtrate = ...

> A residue is a solid left in the filter paper.

2. Write balanced equations for the reaction between the following solutions. Include state symbols.

(a) potassium carbonate and magnesium nitrate **[3 marks]**

....

(b) potassium chloride and lead nitrate **[3 marks]**

....

(c) sodium chloride and silver nitrate **[3 marks]**

....

⑤ Precipitation reactions Grade 6

3. Which of these salts is insoluble in water? Tick **one** box. **[1 mark]**

calcium chloride ☐   lead chloride ☐   potassium sulfate ☐   sodium carbonate ☐

4. Solutions of potassium carbonate and zinc chloride are mixed. A precipitate of zinc carbonate forms.

(a) Write a balanced equation for this reaction. Include state symbols. **[3 marks]**

....

(b) Describe how pure, dry zinc carbonate can be obtained from the mixture. **[3 marks]**

....

....

....

 Made a start   **Feeling confident**   **Exam ready**   119

Oxidation and reduction

② Quick quiz

Name the species which has been oxidised in each of the following reactions.

(a) $Mg + 2HCl \rightarrow MgCl_2 + H_2$ ....

(b) $2AgBr + Cl_2 \rightarrow 2AgCl + Br_2$ ....

(c) $Zn + CuCl_2 \rightarrow ZnCl_2 + Cu$ ....

(d) $C + 2O_2 \rightarrow CO_2$ ....

⑩ Redox equations — Grade 8

1. Oxidation and reduction occur during the displacement reaction:

$$Mg + CuSO_4 \rightarrow MgSO_4 + Cu$$

> Remember oxidation is loss of electrons.

Which one of the following species is oxidised? Tick **one** box. **[1 mark]**

magnesium atom ☐   magnesium ion ☐   copper atom ☐   copper ion ☐

2. Chlorine reacts with aqueous iron(III) iodide to form iodine and aqueous iron(III) chloride:

$$3Cl_2(g) + 2FeI_3(aq) \rightarrow 3I_2(aq) + 2FeCl_3(aq)$$

(a) In this reaction, chlorine is reduced to chloride ions. State what is meant by the term 'reduction' in terms of electrons. **[1 mark]**

> Remember OILRIG.

....

(b) Name the species that is oxidised in this reaction. .... **[1 mark]**

(c) Iron(III) ions, Fe^{3+}, are spectator ions in this reaction. They are unchanged in the reaction.

Write a balanced ionic equation for the reaction without the spectator ions. **[2 marks]**

> Look at the two substances in the reaction that contain iron. Work out the other ion in each of these substances. Write the equation so that it only shows these ions and their corresponding elements. Simplify the balancing numbers if possible.

$Cl_2 +$ .... $\rightarrow$ .... $+ 2Cl^-$

(d) Write balanced half equations for the reduction and oxidation taking place in the reaction. **[4 marks]**

Reduction ....

Oxidation $2I^- \rightarrow$ .... $+ 2e^-$ ....

⑩ Redox reactions — Grade 8

3. Lead can be extracted by heating lead oxide, PbO, with carbon. Carbon dioxide is formed in the reaction.

(a) Write a word equation for this reaction. **[1 mark]**

....

(b) Write a half equation to show the reduction of lead in the reaction. **[2 marks]**

....

4. Zinc reacts with lead(II) oxide, PbO, to form zinc oxide, ZnO, and lead.

(a) Write the ionic equation for the reaction between lead(II) oxide and zinc. **[2 marks]**

....

(b) Identify the species that is oxidised in the reaction, and the species that is reduced. **[2 marks]**

Oxidised ....   Reduced ....

 Made a start   Feeling confident   Exam ready

Electrolysis

② Quick quiz

True or false?

In electrolysis, the anode has a negative charge.	**True / False**
The compound being electrolysed must be molten or in solution.	**True / False**
The rods used in the electrolysis cell are the electrolyte.	**True / False**
Electrolysis is used to extract unreactive metals from their ore.	**True / False**

⑩ The process of electrolysis   Grade 7

1. Copper can be produced from copper sulfate solution by electrolysis. To produce copper by electrolysis a student is provided with the following equipment: dc power supply, electrical wires, graphite electrodes.

   (a) Complete the diagram and label the apparatus set up for the electrolysis of copper sulfate to produce copper metal. **[3 marks]**

   (b) Suggest an explanation for why graphite is a good substance to use for the electrodes. **[1 mark]**

   ....

   (c) Name the electrode at which the copper metal will be deposited. **[1 mark]**

   ....

Think about the charge of the copper ion.

   > Ensure you show the correct electrode attached to the correct end of the dc power supply.
   > Don't forget to label your diagram and use the terms 'anode' and 'cathode'.

2. Electrolysis can be used to extract a reactive metal, such as aluminium, from its oxide. During the process, aluminium ions are discharged at one electrode and oxide ions at the other electrode.

   (a) Name the electrode (positive electrode or negative electrode) at which the oxide ions are discharged. **[1 mark]**

   ....

   (b) Suggest the name of the substance formed when oxide ions are discharged. **[1 mark]**

   ....

⑩ Applications of electrolysis   Grade 6

3. State what is meant by the term 'electrolysis'. **[2 marks]**

   ....

   ....

4. Electroplating uses electrolysis to coat a cheap metal with a thin layer of expensive metal.

   A nickel ring may be coated with silver using aqueous silver nitrate as the electrolyte **(Figure 1)**. Explain the movement of silver ions in the process of electroplating the ring. **[2 marks]**

   ....

   ....

battery

positive silver electrode

ring

silver nitrate solution

Figure 1

Electrolysis of molten ionic compounds

② Quick quiz

Circle the correct word in **bold** to make each sentence correct.

Ionic compounds cannot conduct electricity when **solid / liquid / molten.**

When an ionic compound conducts electricity it is called **a metal / an ion / an electrolyte.**

In electrolysis, positive metal ions always travel to the **anode / cathode / electrolyte.**

At the anode the process which occurs is **reduction / oxidation / redox.**

⑩ Electrolysis of molten salts   Grades 7–8

1. Molten magnesium chloride can be electrolysed as shown in **Figure 1**.

(a) Explain why magnesium metal forms at the cathode.   **[3 marks]**

Magnesium ions have ....

....

....

....

....

....

....

graphite electrodes   anode

cathode

molten magnesium chloride

steel case

magnesium

Figure 1

(b) Name the product at the anode. .... **[1 mark]**

(c) Explain why solid magnesium chloride cannot be electrolysed.   **[2 marks]**

The ions in solid magnesium chloride ....

....

⑩ Electrolysis and half equations   Grades 8–9

2. Lead can be obtained by the electrolysis of molten lead bromide. The electrolyte contains the ions Pb^{2+} and Br^-.

(a) Name the electrode at which lead will form.   **[1 mark]**

....

(b) Name the substance formed at the other electrode.   **[1 mark]**

....

(c) Write the half equations for the reactions that take place at each electrode and state if each reaction is reduction or oxidation.

At the negative electrode .... **[3 marks]**

At the positive electrode .... **[3 marks]**

(d) Suggest a reason why molten lead bromide electrolysis must be carried out in a fume cupboard.   **[1 mark]**

....

✓ **Made a start**   ✓ **Feeling confident**   ✓ **Exam ready**

Electrolysis of aqueous solutions

② Quick quiz

Name the positive electrode. ....

Name the negative electrode. ....

What is an ion? ....

....

What is an electrolyte? ....

What is electrolysis? ....

⑩ Products of electrolysis   Grade 6

1. A student carried out the electrolysis of an aqueous sodium sulfate solution.

> The solution will contain Na_2SO_4 dissolved in water H_2O. Each compound contains 2 ions.

(a) Give the formula of each ion present in the aqueous solution.   **[4 marks]**

➡ Na^+, OH^-,   and ....

(b) Name the substance produced at each electrode.   **[2 marks]**

Cathode. ....

➡ **Anode** .oxygen gas ....

(c) Describe how the student could identify **each** of these products.   **[4 marks]**

➡ Place a lighted splint in the gas. If the gas is
....

....

....

....

⑩ Electrolysis of copper chloride solution   Grade 8

2. When a solution of copper chloride, $CuCl_2$, is electrolysed, different products are formed at both electrodes. Explain the formation of the products at the electrodes. Give the name of the product formed at each electrode.

At the anode: .... **[3 marks]**

....

....

....

At the cathode: .... **[3 marks]**

....

....

....

....

Half equations

② Quick quiz

Tick the correct half equations. Rewrite any incorrect equations so they are correct.

$Cl_2^- \rightarrow 2e^- + Cl_2$ ☐ ....

$H_2 + 2e^- \rightarrow 2H^+$ ☐ ....

$Na \rightarrow Na^+ + e^-$ ☐ ....

$Br^- \rightarrow Br + 2e^-$ ☐ ....

$Al^{3+} + 3e^- \rightarrow Al$ ☐ ....

⑩ Writing half equations   Grade 7

1. Write the half equation for the formation of a zinc atom from a zinc ion.   **[2 marks]**

$Zn^{2+} + 2$ .... $\rightarrow$ ....

2. Write balanced half equations for each of the following reactions.

(a) $Cl_2 + 2KBr \rightarrow 2KCl + Br_2$ **[4 marks]**

$2Br^- \rightarrow Br_2 + 2$ .... $Cl_2 +$ .... $\rightarrow$ ....

(b) $Zn + 2HCl \rightarrow ZnCl_2 + H_2$ **[4 marks]**

$Zn \rightarrow$ .... $2H^+ +$ .... $\rightarrow$ ....

(c) $Mg + CuSO_4 \rightarrow Cu + MgSO_4$ **[4 marks]**

....

⑩ Half equations and electrolysis   Grade 8

3. A teacher carries out the electrolysis of molten zinc chloride, $ZnCl_2$. Zinc ions move to the negative electrode where they produce zinc metal. Chloride ions move to the positive electrode where they produce chlorine gas. Write a half equation for the reaction at each electrode.   **[4 marks]**

Negative electrode ....

Positive electrode ....

4. Figure 1 shows the electrolysis of magnesium sulfate solution.

(a) Give the formulae of the **four** ions present in solution.   **[4 marks]**

1 ....

2 ....

3 ....

4 ....

(b) Oxygen gas is produced at the anode. Hydrogen gas is produced at the cathode.

Give the half equation for the reaction at each electrode.   **[4 marks]**

> Hydroxide ions lose electrons at the anode. Four hydroxide ions are needed to produce one oxygen molecule and two water molecules.

Anode ....

Cathode ....

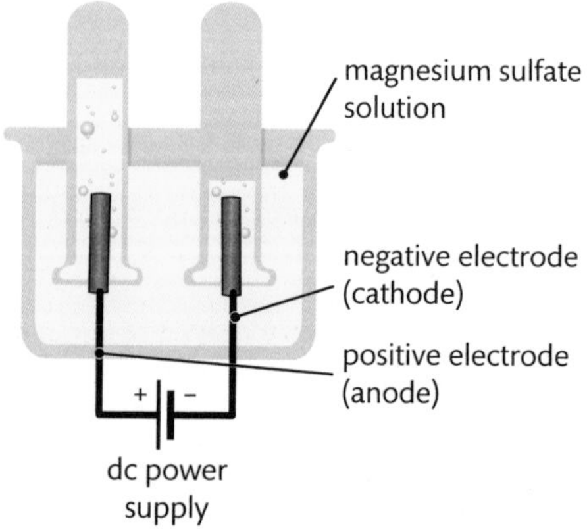

magnesium sulfate solution

negative electrode (cathode)

positive electrode (anode)

dc power supply

Figure 1

 Made a start   Feeling confident   Exam ready

Practical: Electrolysis of copper sulfate

(2) Quick quiz

Label the diagram for the electrolysis of copper sulfate solution using the words in the box.

anode
cathode
electrolyte
cell

A

C   B

D

(15) Electrolysis of copper sulfate   Grade 6

1. The diagram above shows how the electrolysis of copper sulfate solution can be carried out.

(a) Name the substance produced at the positive electrode.   **[1 mark]**

....

(b) Describe a method for the electrolysis of copper sulfate solution.   **[4 marks]**

👉 Graphite electrodes are placed in the electrolyte, which is ....

....

....

....

(c) Explain how copper can be produced by the electrolysis of copper chloride solution. Use information in the diagram to help you.   **[4 marks]**

👉 The solution contains copper ions. Copper ions have a ....

When electricity is passed through the solution the copper ions are attracted to ....

....

(d) Explain why inert electrodes are used in this investigation.   **[2 marks]**

.... | An electrode provides a surface for a reaction to happen on and does not have to react with the substances involved.

....

....

(5) Purifying copper   Grade 6

2. Copper can be purified by the electrolysis of copper sulfate solution, using copper electrodes. Explain how this electrolysis can be used to purify copper.   **[6 marks]**

....

....

....

.... | Continue your answer on your own paper.

 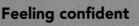

The reactivity series

② Quick quiz

Fill in the missing metals in each reactivity series using words in the box.

potassium ...... *Sodium* .... magnesium

| copper | magnesium | sodium | iron |

calcium ... *Magnesium* .... zinc

zinc .... *Iron* .... copper

⑩ Reactivity experiment   Grade 7

1. A student investigated the reactivity of four unknown metals, **A**, **B**, **C** and **D**. (The letters are not the symbols of the elements.) She mixed solutions of copper chloride, magnesium nitrate or zinc sulfate with the same mass of each powdered metal. She measured the maximum temperature change after they were mixed. The student's results are shown in **Table 1**.

(a) Give a reason why some of the mixtures did not produce a change in temperature.   **[1 mark]**

...... *There was no reaction* ....

(b) Deduce the order of reactivity of the metals using the results provided. Explain your answer.
[5 marks]

Table 1

Solution	Temperature increase (°C)			
	Metal A	Metal B	Metal C	Metal D
copper chloride	57	13	35	0
magnesium nitrate	0	0	0	0
zinc sulfate	10	0	0	0

☞ Metal A reacts with two out of the three salt solutions and so
....

Metal D *did not react at all*
....

Metals B and C *react with 1 out of 3 of the salt solutions*
....

....

Order of reactivity is *D,B,C,A*
....

⑩ Metal reactions   Grade 6

2. Calcium reacts with water and with dilute hydrochloric acid.

(a) Compare and contrast the reaction of calcium with water with the reaction of calcium with dilute hydrochloric acid.
[3 marks]

....

....

....

(b) Write a word equation for the reaction between calcium and water.   **[1 mark]**

....

(c) Write the balanced equation for the reaction between calcium and dilute hydrochloric acid.   **[2 marks]**

Ca +

3. Explain, using ideas about electrons, what determines the reactivity of a metal.   **[2 marks]**

....

....

 Made a start   Feeling confident   Exam ready

Extraction of metals and reduction

② Quick quiz

Circle which, if any, species is being reduced in each reaction.

$Fe_2O_3(s) + 2Al(s) \rightarrow Al_2O_3(s) + 2Fe(s)$

$Mg(s) + H_2SO_4(aq) \rightarrow MgSO_4(aq) + H_2(g)$

$MgO + 2Na \rightarrow Mg + Na_2O$

$2PbO + C \rightarrow Pb + CO_2$

⑩ Extracting copper   Grade 6

1. Copper is extracted from an ore containing copper oxide by the removal of oxygen.

(a) Name this type of reaction. .... **[1 mark]**

(b) Explain, using the reactivity series, how oxygen can be removed from copper oxide to make copper.   **[3 marks]**

☞ Heat the copper oxide with carbon because ....

....

....

(c) Name **one** metal which is found uncombined in the Earth's crust. ....**[1 mark]**

2. Aluminium was first isolated in the early nineteenth century by heating aluminium chloride with potassium:

aluminium chloride + potassium → aluminium + potassium chloride

Today, aluminium is extracted from aluminium oxide using electrolysis.

(a) Explain why aluminium cannot be extracted by heating its oxide with carbon.   **[2 marks]**

....

....

> Think about the reactivity series.

(b) Suggest an explanation for why aluminium can be produced by heating a mixture of aluminium chloride and potassium.   **[2 marks]**

....

....

(c) In the reaction between aluminium chloride and potassium, aluminium ions become aluminium atoms. Identify whether these ions are oxidised or reduced. Give a reason for your answer.   **[2 marks]**

....

> Remember OILRIG.

⑩ Metal extraction   Grade 6

3. Nails can be made from iron. Iron is extracted from iron oxide (Fe_2O_3) by heating it in a blast furnace with other substances.

(a) What element is used to extract the iron from iron oxide? Tick **one** box.   **[1 mark]**

carbon ☐   oxygen ☐   silicon ☐   copper ☐

(b) Suggest an explanation for why a similar process is **not** used to extract magnesium from magnesium oxide.   **[2 marks]**

....

....

Electrolysis to extract metals

② Quick quiz

Label the diagram of the electrolysis of aluminium oxide using the words in the box.

> steel case   graphite electrodes   anode   cathode   aluminium   aluminium oxide dissolved in molten cryolite

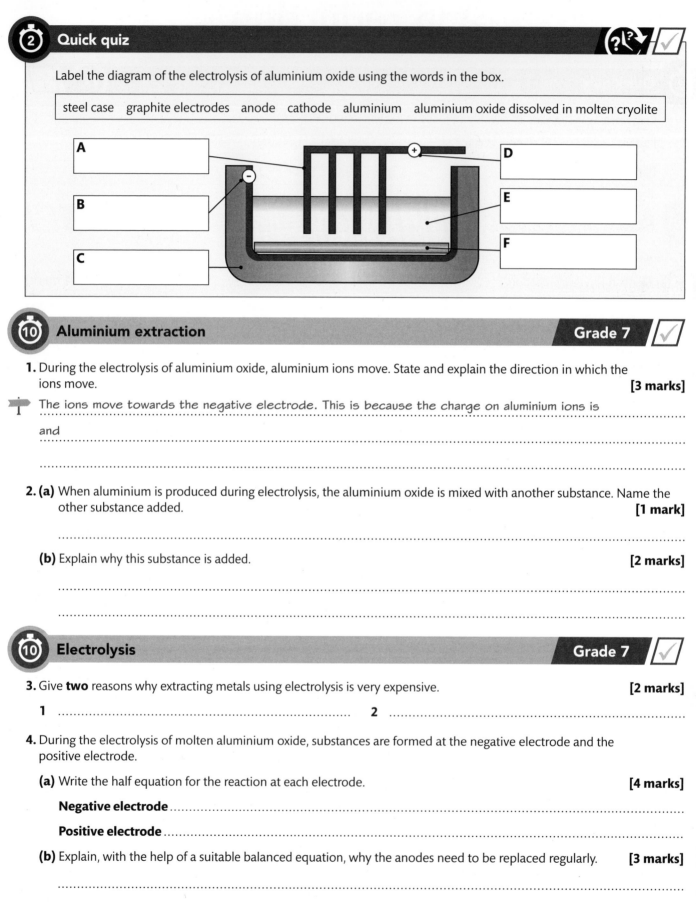

A

B

C

D

E

F

⑩ Aluminium extraction   Grade 7

1. During the electrolysis of aluminium oxide, aluminium ions move. State and explain the direction in which the ions move. **[3 marks]**

The ions move towards the negative electrode. This is because the charge on aluminium ions is

and

2. (a) When aluminium is produced during electrolysis, the aluminium oxide is mixed with another substance. Name the other substance added. **[1 mark]**

(b) Explain why this substance is added. **[2 marks]**

⑩ Electrolysis   Grade 7

3. Give **two** reasons why extracting metals using electrolysis is very expensive. **[2 marks]**

1 .... 2 ....

4. During the electrolysis of molten aluminium oxide, substances are formed at the negative electrode and the positive electrode.

(a) Write the half equation for the reaction at each electrode. **[4 marks]**

Negative electrode ....

Positive electrode ....

(b) Explain, with the help of a suitable balanced equation, why the anodes need to be replaced regularly. **[3 marks]**

Alternative methods of extracting metals

② Quick quiz

Number the statements 1–4 to describe how copper can be extracted by electrolysis.

Electricity is passed through the solution of copper compounds. ☐

Pure copper forms at the electrode. ☐

A solution of copper compounds in sulfuric acid is made. ☐

The copper ions are attracted to the cathode. ☐

🕙 Phytoextraction   Grade 7 ☑

1. Copper ore is a limited resource. Phytoextraction is a relatively new method which is used to extract copper from low-grade copper ore.

(a) Describe the process of extracting copper compounds by phytoextraction.   **[4 marks]**

Plants grow on the soil containing copper. As they grow they absorb ....

.... The plants are ....

The ash produced ....

> The question asks about copper compounds, so you do not need to explain how copper metal is obtained.

(b) Give a reason why phytoextraction, rather than traditional methods, is used to extract copper from low-grade ores.   **[1 mark]**

There is very little copper in ....

(c) Scrap iron displacement can be used to extract the copper from the copper compounds produced in phytoextraction. Name the other method.   **[1 mark]**

....

(d) Explain the process of using scrap iron displacement to extract copper.   **[2 marks]**

Iron is more reactive than copper so ....

....

🕙 Extracting copper   Grade 7 ☑

2. Name **two** methods which can be used to extract copper from its ore.   **[2 marks]**

1 ....   2 ....

3. Explain how bacteria can be used to extract copper ions from copper compounds.   **[2 marks]**

....

....

4. Suggest **two** reasons why copper should not be disposed of in a landfill site.   **[2 marks]**

1 ....

2 ....

Metal oxides

BBC

② Quick quiz

True or false?

Metal oxides have a high boiling point.	**True / False**
Metal oxides have a random arrangement of particles.	**True / False**
Metal oxides have ionic bonding.	**True / False**
Metal oxides have a low melting point.	**True / False**
Metal oxides are usually liquids at room temperature.	**True / False**

⑩ Oxidation and reduction   Grade 7

1. Name the oxides produced in the following reactions.

(a) calcium reacting with oxygen ....calcium... **[1 mark]**

(b) iron wool burning in air .... **[1 mark]**

(c) magnesium burning in air .... **[1 mark]**

2. (a) Explain the terms 'reduction' and 'oxidation'. Relate your answer to the gain or loss of electrons.   **[2 marks]**

Oxidation is loss of
....

....

(b) When a metal reacts with oxygen to form a metal oxide, both oxidation and reduction take place. Give the species that is oxidised and the species that is reduced.   **[2 marks]**

....

3. (a) Name the type of bonding in a metal oxide. .... **[1 mark]**

(b) Give **two** properties metal oxides have due to this type of bonding.   **[2 marks]**

1 .... 2 ....

⑩ Metal oxide reactions   Grade 7

4. Oxidation of metals can be damaging or useful. When iron is oxidised in the presence of water, it corrodes as rust is formed. However, the oxidation of aluminium leads to the production of a natural oxide coating that protects the metal beneath from further reactions.

(a) Identify whether iron is oxidised or reduced in rusting. Give a reason for your answer.   **[1 mark]**

....

(b) During rusting, iron atoms become iron(III) ions, Fe^{3+}. Write a half equation for this reaction.   **[2 marks]**

....

(c) Write the word equation for the reaction between aluminium and oxygen.   **[1 mark]**

....

(d) Write the balanced symbol equation for the reaction between aluminium and oxygen.   **[2 marks]**

....

5. Describe the structure of a metal oxide.   **[2 marks]**

....

....

 Made a start   **Feeling confident**   **Exam ready**

Recycling and life-cycle assessment

② Quick quiz

What are the four main stages to be considered for a life-cycle assessment (LCA) of a product?

....

....

⑩ Considerations for LCAs   Grade 7

1. Explain why companies carry out LCAs before they begin manufacture of a new product.   **[2 marks]**

LCAs assess the impact of ....

....

2. Suggest **three** factors a company would consider for an LCA when producing shopping bags.   **[3 marks]**

1 Energy used to extract ....

2 ....

3 ....

3. Suggest **three** ways in which the environmental impact of plastic bag production can be reduced.
Describe each process.   **[6 marks]**

Recycle ....

....

Burn ....

....

....

⑩ Analysing LCA data   Grade 8

4. Table 1 compares the LCAs for the manufacture of two types of drinking cup.

Identify which cup is less damaging to the environment. Justify your answer using your knowledge and the data in **Figure 1**.   **[6 marks]**

Table 1

Type of cup	plastic	paper
Raw materials	crude oil	wood
Energy used (J)	12 000	21 000
Mass of solid waste (g)	13	67
Mass of CO_2 produced (g)	270	603
Volume of fresh water used (dm³)	367	7245

....

....

....

....

....

Continue your answer on your own paper.

Reversible reactions

Draw **one** line from each key word to match it to its description.

reversible	rate of forward reaction is equal to rate of backward reaction
reactants	substances found to the left of the arrow in an equation
equilibrium	substances found to the right of the arrow in an equation
products	a reaction that can proceed in either direction

⑩ Reversible reactions

Grade 6

1. Cobalt chloride paper can be used to test for water. When cobalt chloride paper is dry, it is blue in colour. If the paper is dipped into water it turns pink. However, if left to dry the paper will turn blue again.

> The statement is saying that a reaction turns the paper from blue to pink, but a reverse reaction can turn the paper from pink to blue.

(a) Chemical reactions involve reactants forming products. In some reactions, like the cobalt chloride paper test for water, the products can react to form the original reactants. Name this type of reaction. **[1 mark]**

....

(b) Give the name for the type of substance which contains water in its crystal structure. **[1 mark]**

....

(c) Complete the word equation to describe the test for water. Include colours of the cobalt chloride. **[3 marks]**

🚏 blue anhydrous cobalt chloride + water ⇌

....

(d) Give **three** changes in conditions that can change the direction of a reversible reaction. **[3 marks]**

🚏 Change in pressure ....

....

⑩ Equilibrium

Grade 6

2. Give the meaning of the symbol ⇌. **[1 mark]**

....

3. Ammonia (NH_3) reacts with hydrogen chloride (HCl) gas at room temperature to produce solid ammonium chloride (NH_4Cl). When heated, ammonium chloride (NH_4Cl) breaks down to form ammonia and hydrogen chloride.

Write a balanced equation to represent this reversible reaction. Include state symbols. **[3 marks]**

....

4. The reaction between iron ions and thiocyanate ions is:

iron(III) ions   thiocyanate ions

$Fe^{3+}(aq)$ + $SCN^-(aq)$ ⇌ $FeSCN^{2+}(aq)$

pale brown   colourless   red

Predict what would be seen if a solution containing Fe^{3+} ions was added to a solution containing SCN^- ions. **[1 mark]**

....

 Made a start   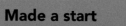 Feeling confident    Exam ready

Dynamic equilibrium and the Haber process

② Quick quiz

Tick the correct statements about reversible reactions at equilibrium.

The reaction goes to completion. ☐

The reaction mixture must be in a closed system. ☐

The rate of the forward and reverse reaction is equal. ☐

There are always more product particles than reactant particles. ☐

⑮ Dynamic equilibrium   Grade 6 ✓

1. The reaction between nitrogen and hydrogen in the Haber process is reversible and can reach a dynamic equilibrium.

(a) Describe what is meant by dynamic equilibrium.   **[2 marks]**

⌐ Dynamic equilibrium occurs in a closed system when the rates of the forward

.... and the amounts of reactants and

....

(b) Explain the effect of increasing the pressure in the Haber process on the yield of ammonia.   **[3 marks]**

⌐ On the left-hand side of the equation there are 4 moles

....

....

Hence increasing the pressure causes the equilibrium position to move to

....

This .... the yield of ammonia.

(c) Suggest an explanation for why the low pressure used in the Haber process is a compromise.   **[2 marks]**

....

....

⑩ The Haber process   Grade 6 ✓

2. Nitrogen and hydrogen react in the Haber process to form ammonia.

(a) Name the two raw materials from which nitrogen and hydrogen are obtained.   **[2 marks]**

....

(b) State the balanced equation for the Haber process.   **[3 marks]**

....

....

(c) Give the conditions used in the Haber process.   **[3 marks]**

....

....

....

Temperature and equilibrium

② Quick quiz

Circle the correct word in **bold** to make each sentence correct.

Increasing the temperature of an exothermic reaction means that **more / fewer** products are formed.

Decreasing the temperature of an endothermic reaction means that **more / fewer** products are formed.

Increasing the temperature of the Haber process means that **more / less** ammonia is formed.

⑩ The effect of temperature on equilibrium · Grade 6

1. Ammonia, NH_3, is produced by reacting hydrogen, H_2, and nitrogen, N_2, in the Haber process, as shown in **Figure 1**. This is an example of a reversible reaction.

> The forward reaction is exothermic, so energy must be transferred from the system to move the equilibrium position in the forwards direction.

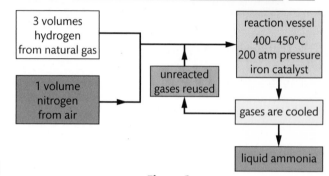

Figure 1

(a) Write a balanced equation with state symbols for the reaction to produce ammonia. **[3 marks]**

.... + ... ⇌ .... $NH_3(g)$

(b) The forward reaction is exothermic. Suggest how the temperature should be altered to produce a maximum yield of ammonia. **[1 mark]**

....

⑩ Predicting changes in equilibrium position on temperature change · Grade 6

2. Sulfur dioxide reacts with oxygen to form sulfur trioxide in an exothermic reaction.

$2SO_2(g) + O_2(g) \rightleftharpoons 2SO_3(g)$

Explain the effects of changing the temperature on the equilibrium yield of SO_3. All other conditions are unchanged. **[4 marks]**

....

....

....

....

....

> **Exam focus**
> You should say how the amounts of reactants and product will change, and give reasons that explain why this happens.

3. The reaction of ammonia gas with hydrogen chloride gas to give solid ammonium chloride is reversible.

(a) When ammonium chloride is heated continually, it decomposes into gases. Identify whether the decomposition is exothermic or endothermic. **[1 mark]**

....

(b) Ammonium chloride can be made by mixing ammonia and hydrogen chloride in a flask and surrounding the flask with an ice bath. Explain the effect of the ice bath on the equilibrium yield of ammonium chloride. **[3 marks]**

....

....

....

✓ **Made a start** ✓ **Feeling confident** ✓ **Exam ready**

Pressure and equilibrium

Will an increase in pressure shift the position of equilibrium left or right in these reactions?

$2SO_2(g) + O_2(g) \rightleftharpoons 2SO_3(g)$ ....

$N_2(g) + 3H_2(g) \rightleftharpoons 2NH_3(g)$ ....

$2CO_2(g) \rightleftharpoons 2CO(g) + O_2(g)$ ....

$N_2(g) + O_2(g) \rightleftharpoons 2NO(g)$ ....

⑩ The Haber process and pressure · Grade 6

1. Ammonia is manufactured using the Haber process. In the reaction, nitrogen reacts with hydrogen.

$N_2(g) + 3H_2(g) \rightleftharpoons 2NH_3(g)$

Figure 1 shows the effect of pressure on the percentage yield of ammonia in the Haber process.

(a) Describe the trend shown in the graph. **[1 mark]**

As pressure increases, the percentage yield of ammonia
....
....

| To describe a trend mention both variables. |

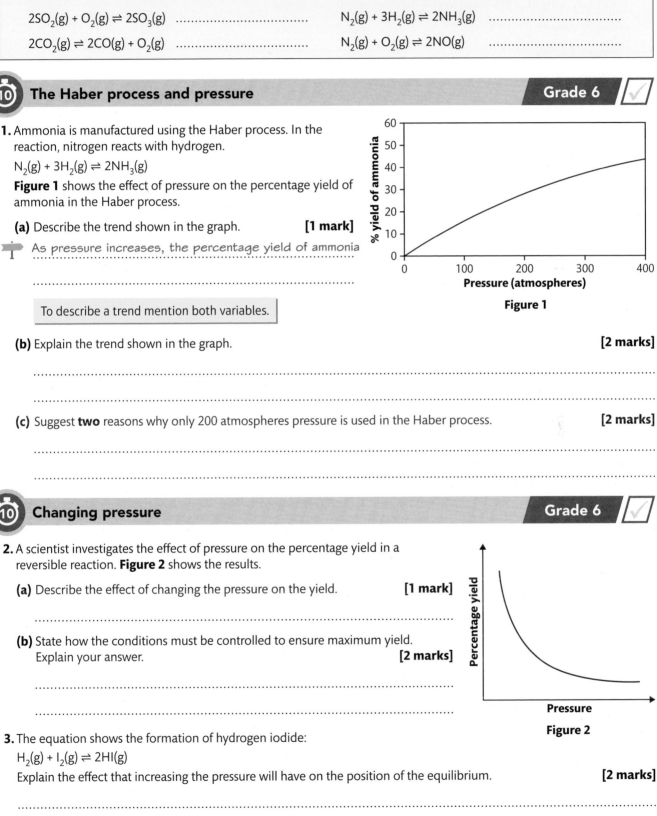

Figure 1

(b) Explain the trend shown in the graph. **[2 marks]**

....
....

(c) Suggest **two** reasons why only 200 atmospheres pressure is used in the Haber process. **[2 marks]**

....
....

⑩ Changing pressure · Grade 6

2. A scientist investigates the effect of pressure on the percentage yield in a reversible reaction. **Figure 2** shows the results.

(a) Describe the effect of changing the pressure on the yield. **[1 mark]**

....

(b) State how the conditions must be controlled to ensure maximum yield. Explain your answer. **[2 marks]**

....
....

Figure 2

3. The equation shows the formation of hydrogen iodide:

$H_2(g) + I_2(g) \rightleftharpoons 2HI(g)$

Explain the effect that increasing the pressure will have on the position of the equilibrium. **[2 marks]**

....
....

Concentration and equilibrium

② Quick quiz

How will each change in concentration affect the position of equilibrium for this reaction?
Write **left** or **right** in the space to give the direction of the change.

$W(aq) + X(aq) \rightleftharpoons Y(aq) + Z(aq)$

increase in concentration of W ....

increase in concentration of Y ....

decrease in concentration of Z ....

decrease in concentration of W ....

⑩ Concentration and equilibrium   Grade 6

1. The reaction between ammonia gas (NH_3) and hydrogen chloride (HCl) gas produces ammonium chloride (NH_4Cl), a white solid. This is an example of a reversible reaction.

ammonia + hydrogen chloride → ammonium chloride

(a) Identify the mistake made in the equation above.   **[1 mark]**

The arrow ....

(b) Write the balanced equation for the reaction. Include state symbols.   **[3 marks]**

.... + ... → NH_4Cl ....

(c) Suggest **two** ways of increasing the yield of ammonium chloride product by changing the concentration of the substances in the system.   **[2 marks]**

1 ....

2 ....

⑩ Changing concentration   Grade 6

2. Ethyl ethanoate is a sweet-smelling liquid used as a solvent in some paints and nail varnish removers. It is made in the laboratory using this reaction:

ethanoic acid + ethanol $\rightleftharpoons$ ethyl ethanoate + water

$CH_3COOH(aq) + C_2H_5OH(aq) \rightleftharpoons CH_3COOC_2H_5(aq) + H_2O(l)$

The reaction reaches equilibrium in a stoppered flask.

(a) State **one** piece of evidence to show that this reaction occurs in a closed system.   **[1 mark]**

....

(b) Calcium chloride absorbs water. Predict the effect on the position of equilibrium of adding calcium chloride powder to the reaction mixture. Explain your answer.   **[2 marks]**

....

....

(c) Explain what will happen to the equilibrium position if the concentration of ethanoic acid is increased.   **[2 marks]**

....

....

Group 1

② Quick quiz

Which statements about the reactions of lithium, sodium and potassium with water are correct?

They float on the surface of the water.

They all produce an orange flame.

They fizz in water.

They all explode at the end of the reaction.

Universal indicator turns red when added to the solution after the reaction.

⑮ Reactions with water   Grade 6

1. Explain, in terms of electronic configurations, why lithium is more reactive than potassium.   **[3 marks]**

Lithium has electronic configuration 2.1 and potassium has electronic configuration

....

The outer electron is

....

....

2. Potassium is an alkali metal. It reacts with water to produce a gas and an alkali solution, as shown in **Figure 1**.

bubbles of gas   potassium

water

Figure 1

(a) Write the word equation for the reaction of potassium and water.   **[1 mark]**

potassium + water → potassium hydroxide +

....

(b) Lithium, Li, has a similar reaction with water, H_2O, to form lithium hydroxide, LiOH. Write the balanced equation for the reaction. Include state symbols.   **[3 marks]**

.... + ... → 2LiOH(aq) + H_2(   )

(c) Give **two** differences you would see between the reactions of potassium and lithium with water.   **[2 marks]**

1 ....

2 ....

⑩ Pattern in reactivity of alkali metals   Grade 6

3. Alkali metals react with water.

(a) Give a reason why the Group 1 elements are called **alkali** metals.   **[1 mark]**

....

(b) Write the balanced equation for the reaction of potassium with water to produce potassium hydroxide and hydrogen.   **[2 marks]**

....

(c) Describe what would be seen when a piece of potassium is dropped into a container of water.   **[3 marks]**

....

....

....

Group 7

② Quick quiz

Complete the sentences by circling the correct word in **bold** of each pair.

Group 7 elements have **low / high** melting and boiling points.

Group 7 elements are **metals / non-metals**.

The halogens are **good / poor** conductors of electricity and heat.

The halogens form **coloured / colourless** vapours and gases.

Group 7 elements exist as **single atoms / molecules**.

⑩ Properties and reactivity of the halogens

Grade 7

1. Which row of the table shows the correct appearance and state of a halogen? **[1 mark]**

Table 1

	Halogen	Colour	State at room temperature
A	bromine	red-brown	gas
B	chlorine	colourless	gas
C	iodine	grey	solid
D	iodine	brown	liquid

Exam focus

The colours of substances are not usually something you can work out. Spend time learning the colours of the halogens.

2. Fluorine is more reactive than chlorine. Halide ions form when halogen molecules react.

(a) Give the electronic configuration of fluorine and chlorine. **[2 marks]**

....

The atomic numbers of fluorine (9) and chlorine (17) give the number of electrons.

(b) Explain, in terms of electronic configurations, why fluorine is more reactive than chlorine. **[3 marks]**

....

When halogens react they gain electrons to form ions.

....

....

....

(c) Write a half equation for a chlorine molecule, Cl_2, forming chloride ions, Cl^-. **[2 marks]**

Cl_2 + ... → ....

(d) Write a balanced equation for the reaction of sodium with chlorine to form sodium chloride. **[2 marks]**

....

⑩ Properties of Group 7

Grade 8

3. Explain why boiling points increase down Group 7. **[3 marks]**

....

....

....

4. Describe a test which could be used to show that a sample of gas is chlorine. **[2 marks]**

....

....

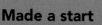 Made a start 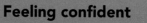 Feeling confident Exam ready

Group 7 reactivity

② **Quick quiz**

Tick the reactions which will occur.

chlorine + sodium bromide ☐   potassium iodide + bromine ☐

iodine + potassium chloride ☐   sodium iodide + chlorine ☐

⑩ **Displacement reactions** **Grade 7**

1. A student investigated the reactions between halogens and aqueous solutions of their salts. The student placed a tick in **Table 1** if a reaction occurred, and a cross if no reaction took place.

Table 1

	potassium chloride	potassium bromide	potassium iodide
chlorine	not done	✓	✓
bromine	x	not done	
iodine	x		not done

(a) Two boxes are blank in **Table 1**. Complete the table by placing a tick if the reaction took place or a cross if the reaction did not take place.
[2 marks]

> Remember, in a displacement reaction a more reactive halogen will displace a less reactive halogen from solution – think about the halogens in each reaction.

(b) Explain how the results show the order of reactivity of the halogens. **[4 marks]**

➡ The more reactive the halogen the more reactions will take place. Chlorine has two ticks in the table and

so is the most reactive, as it can displace bromine and iodine.

Bromine has

Iodine has

2. The reaction shown below is a displacement reaction.

$Cl_2(g) + 2KBr(aq) \rightarrow Br_2(aq) + 2KCl(aq)$

(a) Explain why this is a redox reaction. **[5 marks]**

(b) Describe the colour change in the solution which occurs in this reaction. **[1 mark]**

> Explain in terms of loss or gain of electrons.

⑩ **Properties of Group 7** **Grade 8**

3. Devise an experiment using displacement reactions to determine the order of reactivity of bromine and iodine. **[6 marks]**

Continue your answer on your own paper.

 Made a start   **Feeling confident**   ☑ **Exam ready**

Group 0

② Quick quiz

Which statements are correct? Rewrite the incorrect statements so that they are correct.

The noble gases are inert, or unreactive. ☐ ....

Helium is placed at the bottom of Group 0. ☐ ....

Neon exists as single atoms. ☐ ....

The size of the atoms increases down the group. ☐ ....

The noble gases all have 8 electrons in their outer shell. ☐ ....

⑩ Properties of group 0 — Grade 6

1. Give the electronic structures of helium and argon. **[2 marks]**

He .... **Ar** .2...

2. Draw the electronic configuration for neon. **[2 marks]**

3. Give a reason why the noble gases are unreactive. **[1 mark]**

....

> Look at the electronic configurations above to help.

4. Explain why the noble gases exist as separate atoms rather than as molecules. Give your answer in terms of electrons. **[2 marks]**

....

....

> A covalent bond is a shared pair of electrons. The atoms in a molecule are joined together by covalent bonds.

⑩ Melting and boiling points — Grade 5

5. Table 1 gives the melting and boiling points of some of the noble gases.

(a) Deduce approximate values for the melting and boiling point of argon. **[2 marks]**

(b) State the trend in boiling point down the group. **[1 mark]**

Table 1

Noble gas	Melting point (°C)	Boiling point (°C)
helium	−272	−269
neon	−248	−246
argon		
krypton	−157	−153

....

(c) Explain the trend in boiling point down the group. **[2 marks]**

....

....

(d) Give **two** reasons why helium is used in balloons. **[2 marks]**

....

....

✓ **Made a start** ✓ **Feeling confident** ✓ **Exam ready**

Calculating rate of reaction

② Quick quiz

Which of these are correct units for rate of reaction? Rewrite any incorrect units to give the correct units.

mol/s ☐ ....

mol³/s ☐ ....

cm³/s³ ☐ ....

cm³/s ☐ ....

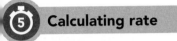 **Calculating rate** — Grade 8

1. Figure 1 shows the volume of gas released during a reaction.

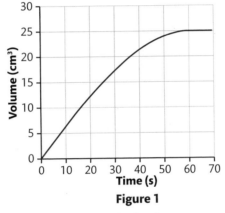

Figure 1

Calculate the rate of reaction at 10 s. Include appropriate units for the rate. **[3 marks]**

$$\text{rate of reaction} = \frac{\text{change in volume (cm}^3)}{\text{change in time (s)}}$$

> You need to draw a tangent so that it touches the curve at 10 s, but the tangent **must not** cross the curve.

rate of reaction at 10 s = ...

 Interpreting rate graphs — Grade 8

2. (a) Calculate the rate of reaction at 40 s in **Figure 1**. **[4 marks]**

rate of reaction at 40 s = ...

(b) Describe what happens to the rate of reaction as the reaction proceeds. **[2 marks]**

....

....

(c) Draw a curve on **Figure 1** to represent the same reaction but with a catalyst. **[2 marks]**

 Made a start   **Feeling confident**   **Exam ready**

Factors affecting rate of reaction

② Quick quiz

Write 'increase' or 'decrease' to complete these sentences.

An increase in the concentration of reactants will .... the rate of reaction.

Decreasing the pressure of reacting gases will .... the rate of reaction.

A catalyst will .... the rate of reaction.

Decreasing the surface area of reactants will .... the rate of reaction.

⑩ Factors affecting rate of reaction   Grade 6

1. A student planned to investigate the effect of temperature on the rate of reaction. He predicted that the rate of reaction would increase as the temperature was increased. Explain why the student's prediction was correct.   **[4 marks]**

As temperature is increased the particles will have more

....

.... and so will move

....

leading to

....

> Remember, for a reaction to happen the reactant particles need to collide with enough energy to react.

2. Explain how a catalyst speeds up the rate of reaction.   **[2 marks]**

They provide a pathway

....

This increases the frequency of

....

⑩ Surface area and rate   Grade 6

3. **(a)** A student investigated the reaction between acid and marble chips. The results of the investigation are given in **Table 1**.

Table 1

Time (s)	Mass lost (g)
0	0
20	0.8
40	1.4
60	1.8
80	2.1
100	2.1

Plot these results.   **[3 marks]**

(b) The student then repeated the experiment using the same mass of smaller marble chips. Describe how the graph would differ for the second investigation.   **[2 marks]**

....

....

(c) Identify the factor that was changed when the student repeated the experiment.   **[1 mark]**

....

 Made a start   Feeling confident   ✓ Exam ready

Practical: Monitoring rate of reaction – colour change

② Quick quiz

Write down **three** methods that can be used to measure the rate of a reaction.

....

....

⑤ Sodium thiosulfate and acid   Grade 7

1. Sodium thiosulfate solution reacts with dilute hydrochloric acid to produce a pale yellow precipitate.

   sodium thiosulfate + hydrochloric acid → sodium chloride + water + sulfur dioxide + sulfur

   (a) Name the precipitate which is formed.   **[1 mark]**

   | The products on the right of the arrow are formed. Which one is a yellow solid? |

   ....

   (b) Complete the equation for the reaction. Include state symbols.   **[3 marks]**

   🚩 $Na_2S_2O_3$ ( ) +   ( ) →   ( ) +   ( ) + SO_2( ) +   ( )

   (c) Suggest **one** precaution needed to reduce the risk of harm in this experiment, other than wearing eye protection. Give a reason for your answer.   **[2 marks]**

   | Look carefully at the equation and determine if there are any hazardous substances present in it. |

   ....

   ....

⑮ Changing the temperature   Grade 7

2. A student investigated the effect of changing the temperature on the rate of the reaction between sodium thiosulfate solution and hydrochloric acid. The time for a fixed amount of sulfur to be formed was measured and the experiment repeated using hydrochloric acid at different temperatures.

   (a) Draw a labelled diagram to show how the student could carry out this experiment at room temperature.   **[4 marks]**

   (b) Describe how the acid could be safely heated.   **[1 mark]**

   ....

   (c) Predict the effect of increasing the temperature on the rate of reaction. Explain your answer in terms of particles.   **[4 marks]**

   > **Exam focus**
   > The rate of reaction means how many successful collisions occur in a unit of time, e.g. per second. You could describe whether a collision is successful, and the frequency or rate of collisions.

   ....

   ....

   ....

   (d) Give **two** variables which must be controlled to make the student's results valid.   **[2 marks]**

   ....

Practical: Monitoring rate of reaction – gas production

② Quick quiz

Which of the following reactions can be monitored by collecting gas in a gas syringe? Tick the correct answers.

magnesium and hydrochloric acid ☐

sodium hydroxide and hydrochloric acid ☐

calcium carbonate and hydrochloric acid ☐

copper sulfate and sodium hydroxide ☐

sodium thiosulfate and hydrochloric acid ☐

zinc and sulfuric acid ☐

⑩ Calcium carbonate and hydrochloric acid — Grade 7

1. A student investigated the rate of reaction between calcium carbonate, $CaCO_3$, and dilute hydrochloric acid, HCl, by adding calcium carbonate to $25\,cm^3$ of hydrochloric acid in a conical flask and recording the volume of gas produced every 30 seconds in a gas syringe.

(a) Write a balanced equation for the reaction. Include state symbols **[3 marks]**

$CaCO_3(\ ) +$ _____ $(\ )$ $\rightarrow$ _____ $(\ ) + H_2O(\ ) + CO_2(g)$ ....

(b) Complete the labelled diagram of the apparatus set up to carry out this experiment. **[3 marks]**

(c) Explain why the bung must be inserted immediately once the calcium carbonate is added to the acid. **[1 mark]**

....

(d) Another student carried out the same experiment. Instead of collecting the gas in a syringe, she collected it in an upturned measuring cylinder over water. State one disadvantage to using this method. **[1 mark]**

....

⑮ Measuring the rate of reaction — Grade 6

2. A student investigated the effect of concentration on the rate of reaction between excess dilute hydrochloric acid and marble chips. The volume of gas was collected every 30 seconds in a gas syringe.

(a) Give the chemical name for the main compound in marble chips. **[1 mark]**

....

(b) State **two** observations which would be seen in the conical flask. **[2 marks]**

....

....

(c) State **two** variables which must be controlled to make this a fair test. **[2 marks]**

....

....

(d) State how the student would know when the reaction was over. **[1 mark]**

....

> **Exam focus** 📌
> In a fair test, only one variable is changed by the experimenter, in this case the concentration.

 Made a start   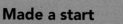 Feeling confident   Exam ready

Collision theory and activation energy

② **Quick quiz**

Draw a line to match an increase in each factor to the explanation of how it affects the rate of a reaction.

temperature	There are more particles present in the same volume and so a higher chance of collisions.
concentration	The volume in which the particles are located is reduced, therefore the particles are more likely to collide.
pressure	Particles have more energy and move faster, colliding more frequently.

⑩ **Activation energy** | **Grade 7**

1. Explain what is meant by the term 'activation energy'. **[1 mark]**

It is the minimum amount ....

....

2. Figure 1 shows the results from an experiment in which an excess of marble chips is added to dilute hydrochloric acid.

(a) Draw a second line on the graph to show the reaction at a higher temperature, but with all the other conditions unchanged. **[2 marks]**

(b) Explain your answer to **(a)** in terms of particles. **[4 marks]**

The higher temperature provides the particles with ....

....

....

....

....

Key words to include are: energy, collision, frequent, activation energy

The reaction will be faster but the final volume of gas produced when the reaction ends will be the same as the same amounts of reactants is used.

Figure 1: graph of Volume of gas produced (cm³) against Time (s)

⑩ **Factors affecting rate** | **Grade 7**

3. Suggest an explanation in terms of particles, why the rate of the reaction shown in **Figure 1** decreases during the reaction. **[2 marks]**

....

....

4. Explain how increasing the pressure of reacting gas particles has the same effect as increasing the concentration of reacting particles in a solution. **[3 marks]**

....

....

....

Chemistry | Rates of reaction and energy changes | Rates of reaction

Reaction profiles

② Quick quiz

This reaction profile shows an exothermic reaction. Label it to show reactants, products, activation energy and the overall energy change.

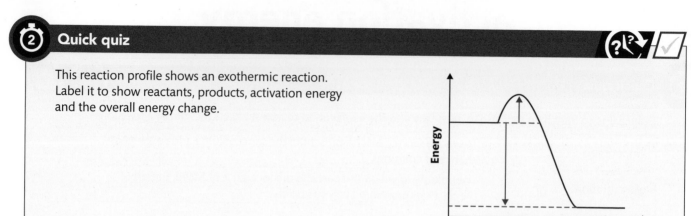

⑮ Reaction profiles — Grade 6

1. The reaction profile in **Figure 1** shows an exothermic reaction.

(a) Give a reason why the diagram shows that the reaction is exothermic. **[1 mark]**

The products have less energy than

(b) Identify what is shown by X. **[1 mark]**

X is the overall energy

(c) The reactants need a minimum amount of energy to react. State the name given to this minimum amount of energy. **[1 mark]**

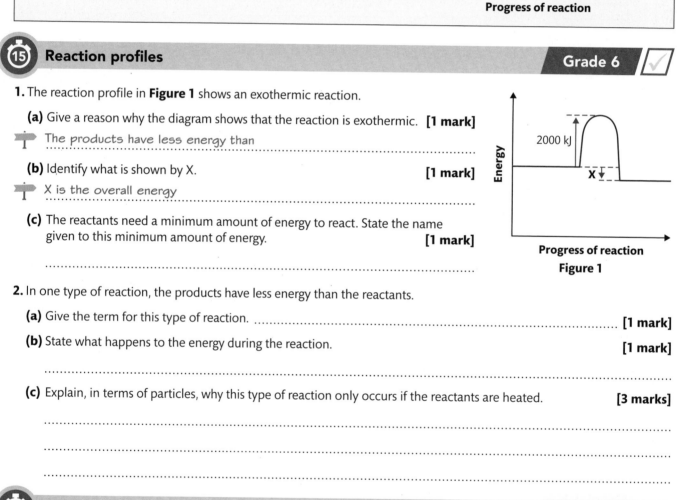

2000 kJ

Figure 1

2. In one type of reaction, the products have less energy than the reactants.

(a) Give the term for this type of reaction. **[1 mark]**

(b) State what happens to the energy during the reaction. **[1 mark]**

(c) Explain, in terms of particles, why this type of reaction only occurs if the reactants are heated. **[3 marks]**

⑤ Endothermic reaction profile — Grade 8

3. Draw and label a reaction profile diagram for an endothermic reaction, identifying the activation energy and the overall energy change. **[3 marks]**

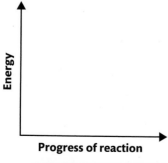

Exam focus
The number of marks indicates how much information is required. Remember to label the axes.

 Made a start   Feeling confident   Exam ready

Catalysts

② Quick quiz

True or false?

A catalyst speeds up a reaction.	**True / False**
A catalyst permanently changes into a different chemical in the reaction.	**True / False**
The catalyst in the Haber process is iron.	**True / False**
The mass of the catalyst present at the end of the experiment is less than at the start.	**True / False**
Biological catalysts are called enzymes.	**True / False**

⑩ Properties of catalysts   Grade 6

1. Catalysts are used to speed up many chemical reactions in industry.

(a) Explain how a catalyst increases the rate of reaction.   **[4 marks]**

🚩 Catalysts provide a different pathway for the reaction which has ....

....

This means there are more ....

....

....

(b) Name the catalyst used in the Haber process.   **[1 mark]**

....

2. Which of these describes the change in mass of a catalyst against time in a catalysed reaction? Tick **one** box.   **[1 mark]**

The mass of catalyst decreases slowly. ☐

The mass of catalyst increases slowly. ☐

The mass of catalyst remains unchanged. ☐

The mass of catalyst remains steady and then decreases at the end of the reaction. ☐

> Make sure you learn the full definition of a catalyst.

⑩ Reaction profiles and catalysts   Grade 6

3. (a) Complete the reaction profile in **Figure 1** to show an exothermic reaction.   **[3 marks]**

> **Exam focus**
> In this type of question, remember to include the relative energies of the reactants and products, activation energy and overall energy change.

(b) Draw the curve for the catalysed reaction on the reaction profile in **Figure 1** and label it 'catalysed reaction'.   **[1 mark]**

(c) Explain how you would change the reaction profile in **Figure 1** for an endothermic reaction.   **[2 marks]**

....

....

....

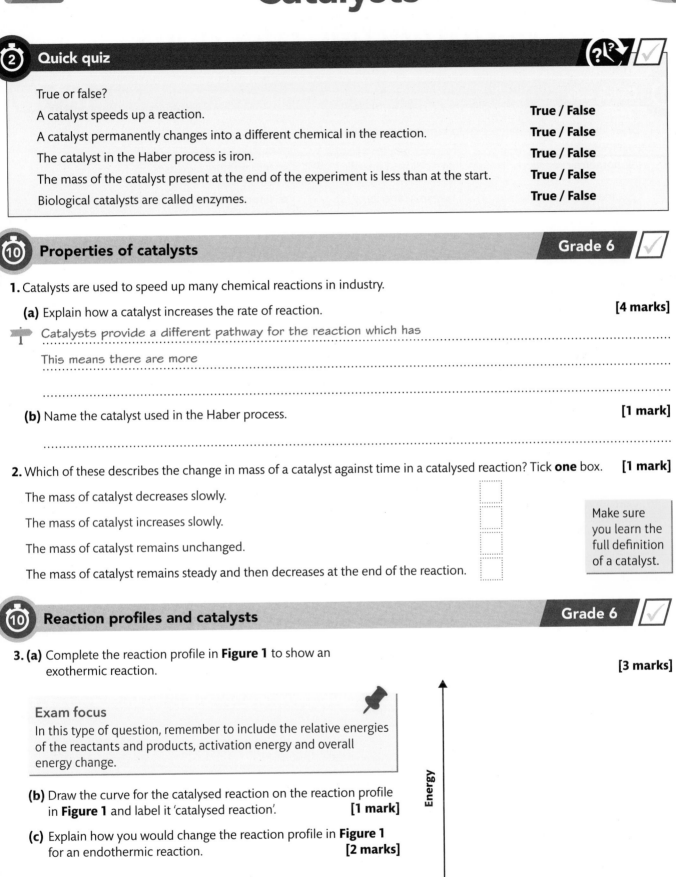

Energy

Progress of reaction

Figure 1

Exothermic and endothermic reactions

1 Quick quiz

Draw lines to link the statements to form two correct sentences.

| Endothermic reactions | give out heat energy | so temperature increases. |
| Exothermic reactions | take in heat energy | so temperature decreases. |

5 Reactions involving energy changes   Grade 6

1. Table 1 shows the experimental results for the temperature at the start and end of a reaction.

Table 1

Trial	Start temperature (°C)	End temperature (°C)
1	25	57
2	23	55
3	23	54

(a) Name the type of reaction that took place. Explain your answer.   **[2 marks]**

....

....

> Decide if the temperature has increased or decreased.

(b) Name three types of reaction that are exothermic.   **[3 marks]**

 Combustion,

....

15 Temperature change and data analysis   Grades 6–7

2. The reaction between citric acid solution and solid sodium hydrogencarbonate is an example of an endothermic reaction.

(a) State what is meant by the term 'endothermic'.   **[1 mark]**

....

(b) Describe how you could show experimentally that this reaction is endothermic.   **[3 marks]**

....

....

....

3. A student mixed four different metal samples of the same mass and particle size with 25 cm³ of dilute acid. The maximum temperatures reached were recorded. The results are shown in **Table 2**.

Table 2

Metal sample	A	B	C	D
Initial temperature (°C)	21	21	22	22
Maximum temperature (°C)	38	26	59	34
Temperature increase (°C)				

(a) Complete the table to show the temperature increase for each experiment.   **[1 mark]**

(b) Explain how these results can be used to determine the order of reactivity of the metals. Give the metals in order of reactivity, starting with the most reactive metal.   **[2 marks]**

....

....

Temperature changes

② Quick quiz

Is each change exothermic or endothermic? Circle the correct answer.

neutralisation **exothermic / endothermic**   metal displacement **exothermic / endothermic**

combustion **exothermic / endothermic**   photosynthesis **exothermic / endothermic**

HCl + NaOH **exothermic / endothermic**   dissolving sodium hydroxide **exothermic / endothermic**

⑩ Neutralisation data analysis `Grade 8`

1. The reaction between dilute hydrochloric acid, HCl, and sodium hydroxide, NaOH, solution is exothermic. A student investigated the temperature change when the reaction takes place. The apparatus used is shown in **Figure 1**.

The student added $5\,cm^3$ of sodium hydroxide solution to $20\,cm^3$ of dilute hydrochloric acid, stirred, then recorded the temperature. The process was repeated until a total of $30\,cm^3$ of sodium hydroxide was added. The results are shown in **Table 1**.

Plot a graph of temperature against volume of sodium hydroxide solution added. **[3 marks]**

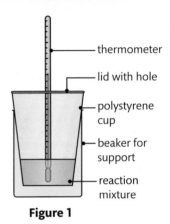

Figure 1

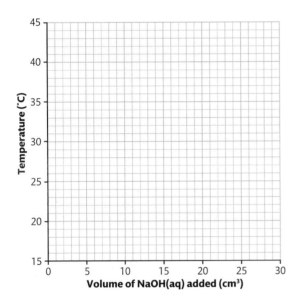

Table 1

Volume of NaOH(aq) added (cm^3)	0	5	10	15	20	25	30
Temperature (°C)	18	27	35	40	42	41	37

> Remember to plot a line or curve of best fit, ignoring any anomalous points.

⑩ Experimental procedure `Grade 7`

2. When powdered zinc is added to hydrochloric acid, a temperature change takes place. Devise a plan to determine if the reaction is an endothermic or exothermic reaction. Include the following apparatus in your answer: thermometer, measuring cylinder, polystyrene cup. **[6 marks]**

....

....

....

....

....

....

....

....

✓ **Made a start**   ✓ **Feeling confident**   ✓ **Exam ready**   149

Energy changes in reactions

② Quick quiz

Fill in the gaps using the words in the box.

negative positive exothermic endothermic

A reaction which gives out heat energy is .... This type of reaction always has

.... values for the energy change. A reaction which takes in heat energy is

.... This type of reaction always has .... values for the energy change.

⑩ Calculating energy changes — Grade 8

1. Figure 1 shows the reaction of ethene with bromine.
Table 1 shows the bond energies.

Table 1

Bond	C–H	Br–Br	C=C	C–Br	C–C
Bond energy (kJ mol⁻¹)	413	193	614	276	348

Figure 1

Calculate the energy change for the reaction of ethene with bromine. **[3 marks]**

Bond breaking: (1 × C=C) + (4 × C–H) + Br–Br

= (1 × 614) + (4 × 413) + ... = ...

Bond making: (1 × C–C) + ...

= ....

Energy change =
energy used in bond breaking − energy released in bond making

= ....

energy change = ... kJ mol⁻¹

> Work out the number of each type of bond being broken. Look at the diagram to see which bonds are broken.

> Work out the number of each type of bond being made. Look at the diagram to see which bonds are made.

> Calculate the overall energy change.

⑮ Explaining energy changes — Grade 8

2. Explain, in terms of the energy involved in bond breaking and bond making, why the combustion of a fuel is exothermic.
[2 marks]

....

....

3. Figure 2 shows the reaction of propene with bromine.
Calculate the overall energy change for the reaction.
Use the bond energies given in **Table 1**. **[3 marks]**

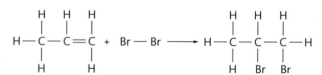

Figure 2

energy change = ... kJmol⁻¹

Exam focus

Consider whether energy is taken in or given out when bonds break or form, and how the difference in energy involved determines the type of reaction.

 Made a start **Feeling confident** 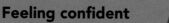 **Exam ready**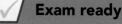

Crude oil and hydrocarbons

① Quick quiz

Draw **one** line from each word to match it with its definition.

alkane	family of molecules with the same general formula
homologous series	the simplest hydrocarbon molecule
methane	a series of molecules with general formula C_nH_{2n+2}

⑩ Crude oil   Grade 6

1. (a) Explain why crude oil is a **finite** resource.   **[1 mark]**

➤ It is a resource made slowly over millions of years and supplies will
....

(b) Crude oil is a source of useful chemicals. Name one industry which uses crude oil as a feedstock.   **[1 mark]**

....

(c) Which statement about crude oil is correct? Tick **one** box.   **[1 mark]**

crude oil is a single substance ☐   crude oil contains only straight chain compounds ☐

crude oil is a mixture of hydrocarbons ☐   crude oil is made only of hydrocarbon rings ☐

2. The alkanes are a homologous series. Alkane molecules contain carbon atoms and hydrogen atoms.

(a) Name the type of chemical bond present in an alkane molecule.   **[1 mark]**

....

> Carbon and hydrogen are non-metals.

(b) Give **four** reasons why the alkanes are a homologous series.   **[4 marks]**

➤ They have the same general formula
....
....
....
....

⑩ General formula of alkanes   Grade 6

3. (a) What is the general formula for the alkanes? Tick **one** box.   **[1 mark]**

C_nH_n ☐ C_nH_{n+2} ☐ C_nH_{2n} ☐ C_nH_{2n+2} ☐

(b) Deduce the number of hydrogen atoms in an alkane containing 22 carbon atoms.   **[1 mark]**

....

number of hydrogen atoms = ...

(c) Write the molecular formulae for:

(i) an alkane with two carbon atoms. ....   **[1 mark]**

(ii) an alkane with six carbon atoms. ....   **[1 mark]**

(d) Explain why C_2H_5OH is not a hydrocarbon.   **[2 marks]**

....
....

Fractional distillation

② Quick quiz

True or false?

Fractional distillation separates the components of crude oil by their melting points.	**True / False**
During fractional distillation the hydrocarbon compounds are evaporated.	**True / False**
The hydrocarbon compounds must be solidified before they can be collected from the column.	**True / False**
A hydrocarbon molecule contains carbon, hydrogen and other elements.	**True / False**

⑩ Separating crude oil   Grade 6

1. Crude oil is a mixture of hydrocarbons which can be separated by fractional distillation.

(a) Describe how the size of the hydrocarbon molecules changes from the fraction at the top of the column to the fraction at the bottom. **[1 mark]**

....

....

(b) Describe how crude oil is separated into simpler more useful mixtures by fractional distillation. **[4 marks]**

☞ The crude oil is heated in order to ....

The gaseous hydrocarbons travel up a fractionating column from hot to cooler ....

....

....

The fractions with higher boiling points ....

....

⑩ The fractions   Grade 6

2. Complete **Table 1** to give the names and uses of some of the fractions obtained in fractional distillation of crude oil. **[4 marks]**

3. The boiling points of three fractions are given in **Table 2**.

(a) Explain how you can tell that these fractions are mixtures and not pure substances. **[2 marks]**

....

....

....

(b) Explain which fraction will be produced towards the top of the fractionating column. **[2 marks]**

....

(c) Name **two** changes of state which occur in a fractionating column. **[2 marks]**

....

Table 1

petrol	
	fuel for aircraft
	fuel for large ships
bitumen	

Table 2

Fraction	Boiling point (°C)
petrol	30–205
kerosene	150–300
diesel oil	200–350

 Made a start   **Feeling confident**   **Exam ready**

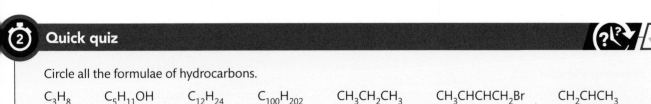

Properties of hydrocarbons

Chemistry / Fuels and Earth science / Fuels

② Quick quiz

Circle all the formulae of hydrocarbons.

C_3H_8 $C_5H_{11}OH$ $C_{12}H_{24}$ $C_{100}H_{202}$ $CH_3CH_2CH_3$ $CH_3CHCHCH_2Br$ CH_2CHCH_3

⑩ Combustion of hydrocarbons   Grade 6

1. **Figure 1** shows the apparatus used to investigate the products of complete combustion of hydrocarbons.

   (a) Name the products of complete combustion of a hydrocarbon. **[2 marks]**

   ....

   (b) Describe any changes that would be observed in the U-tube, A.   **[1 mark]**

   ....

   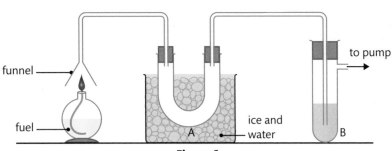

   Figure 1

   > Part **(a)** will help. Which product will condense? What will it look like?

   ### Exam focus

   Learning the two products of combustion will enable you to write equations for combustion of any fuel.

   (c) Name the solution in the side-arm tube, tube B. Describe any changes that would be observed in the tube.   **[2 marks]**

   Solution ....

    The solution would change from colourless to ....

   (d) Name **two** products of incomplete combustion of a hydrocarbon which are different from those of complete combustion.   **[2 marks]**

   ....

   (e) Explain why combustion of a hydrocarbon in limited oxygen is dangerous.   **[2 marks]**

   ....

⑩ Properties of hydrocarbons   Grade 6

2. Propane, C_3H_8, and nonane, C_9H_{20}, are two hydrocarbons.

   (a) State which is more viscous. .... **[1 mark]**

   (b) State which has the higher boiling point. .... **[1 mark]**

   (c) State which is easier to ignite. .... **[1 mark]**

   (d) Camping gas contains the alkane propane, C_3H_8. Write a balanced equation for the complete combustion of propane.   **[3 marks]**

   ....

3. A fuel used in car engines needs to have low viscosity and high flammability. Suggest an explanation for why these **two** properties are important for the fuels in a car engine.   **[2 marks]**

   ....

   ....

✓ **Made a start**   ✓ **Feeling confident**   ✓ **Exam ready**   **153**

Atmospheric pollutants

① Quick quiz

Draw **one** line from each pollutant to match it to its impact.

carbon dioxide	toxic gas
sulfur dioxide	acid rain
carbon monoxide	greenhouse effect

⑩ Pollution from combustion of fuels   Grade 7

1. A student investigated the products formed when a hydrocarbon fuel is burned. As the fuel burned, the student noticed that soot had formed on the equipment above the flame.

(a) Name the element found in soot. .... **[1 mark]**

(b) Explain why the soot forms. **[2 marks]**

There was a limited supply of ....

....

2. (a) Write a word equation for the incomplete combustion of natural gas. **[1 mark]**

natural gas + oxygen → .... + ... + carbon

(b) Describe the problems caused by two products of the incomplete combustion of natural gas. **[2 marks]**

....

....

> Which two of the products in the word equation in **(a)** could cause problems?

⑩ Pollutants and environmental impact   Grade 6

3. (a) Explain how impurities in some hydrocarbon fuels result in the production of acid rain. **[3 marks]**

....

....

....

(b) Explain **two** environmental problems caused by acid rain. **[2 marks]**

....

....

4. (a) Explain how oxides of nitrogen can form in a car engine. **[2 marks]**

....

....

(b) Nitrogen dioxide is a pollutant which is changed in a catalytic converter, forming nitrogen and oxygen. Write a symbol equation for this reaction. **[2 marks]**

....

5. Write a word equation for the incomplete combustion of diesel oil to produce three different products. **[1 mark]**

....

 Made a start   **Feeling confident**   **Exam ready**

Comparing fuels

(2) Quick quiz

Are the following resources renewable or non-renewable?

Coal ....   Natural gas ....

Vegetable oil ....   Petrol ....

Diesel oil ....   Wood ....

(10) Hydrogen as a fuel   Grade 6

1. Natural gas is mainly methane. Hydrogen is produced by reacting natural gas with steam. Hydrogen can also be obtained by electrolysis of water.

   (a) Write a balanced equation for the reaction of methane with steam to produce carbon monoxide and hydrogen. Include state symbols. **[3 marks]**

   $CH_4(g)$ + _____ ( ) → _____ (g) + $3H_2(g)$
   _____

   (b) Explain if this reaction is a renewable source of hydrogen. **[2 marks]**

   ....
   ....

   > Think about the source of natural gas.

   (c) Name the electrode at which hydrogen is obtained in the electrolysis of water. **[1 mark]**

   > What charge does a hydrogen ion have?

   ....

   (d) Explain if the electrolysis of water is a renewable source of hydrogen. **[2 marks]**

   ....
   ....

   (e) State a disadvantage of using hydrogen as a fuel in cars. **[2 marks]**

   Hydrogen is flammable and so ....
   ....

(10) Renewable fuels   Grade 6

2. What is the term for energy resources that can be replaced? Tick **one** box. **[1 mark]**

   finite ☐   non-renewable ☐   saturated ☐   renewable ☐

3. When burned, 1 litre of ethanol releases 20 MJ of energy and 1 litre of petrol releases 35 MJ of energy. Ethanol can be produced from sugar beet. Evaluate the use of ethanol in car engines. **[2 marks]**

   ....
   ....
   ....
   ....

Cracking and alkenes

BBC

② Quick quiz

Complete the equations to show the cracking of hydrocarbons.

$C_{74}H_{150} \rightarrow C_{56}H_{114} + \dots\dots\dots\dots\dots\dots\dots\dots$

$C_{40}H_{82} \rightarrow C_{18}H_{38} + \dots\dots\dots\dots\dots\dots\dots\dots$

$\dots\dots\dots\dots\dots\dots\dots \rightarrow C_{12}H_{24} + C_{16}H_{34}$

$C_{28}H_{58} \rightarrow C_2H_4 + C_{12}H_{26} + \dots\dots\dots\dots\dots\dots$

⑩ Cracking   Grade 6

1. Hydrocarbons can be cracked.

(a) Explain what is meant by the term 'cracking'.   **[2 marks]**

Cracking involves breaking down larger saturated
....

....

(b) Explain why cracking is necessary.   **[2 marks]**

Some fractions obtained from crude oil contain larger hydrocarbon molecules, so they have limited
....

....

2. Hydrocarbons can be cracked to form a mixture of saturated and unsaturated hydrocarbons.

(a) Explain the term 'saturated hydrocarbon'.   **[2 marks]**

....

....

> **Exam focus**
> You need to explain the meaning of each word.

(b) Name the type of unsaturated hydrocarbon which is produced in cracking.   **[1 mark]**

....

⑩ Cracking   Grade 7

3. What type of reaction is cracking? Tick **one** box.   **[1 mark]**

displacement ☐   exothermic ☐   neutralisation ☐   thermal decomposition ☐

4. (a) Complete the balanced equation for the cracking of C_8H_{18} to form two molecules of ethene (C_2H_4) and one alkane.   **[2 marks]**

$C_8H_{18} \rightarrow \dots\dots\dots\dots\dots\dots\dots + \dots\dots\dots\dots\dots\dots\dots$

(b) Give a reason why there is a greater demand for the products of cracking than for C_8H_{18}. **[1 mark]**

....

....

5. Fractions such as fuel oil have limited uses and so are often cracked. Describe this process. **[3 marks]**

....

....

....

 Made a start   **Feeling confident**   **Exam ready**

Earth's early atmosphere

② Quick quiz

Complete the table to show whether the percentage of each gas in the Earth's atmosphere has **increased** or **decreased** over time.

Gas	% in early atmosphere	% in atmosphere today	Change
nitrogen	3.50	80	
oxygen	0.50	20	
carbon dioxide	95	0.04	

⑩ Changes in Earth's atmosphere   Grade 6

1. Give reasons for the change in the amount of different gases in the early atmosphere compared to the gases in the atmosphere today. **[3 marks]**

Nitrogen.volcanic activity...

Oxygen ....

Carbon dioxide...

2. (a) The percentage of argon in the atmosphere of Mars is very similar to the percentage of argon in Earth's atmosphere today. Give a reason why. **[1 mark]**

Argon is an inert gas, so...

(b) Give a reason why levels of oxygen are very low on Mars. **[1 mark]**

....

(c) Carbon dioxide is the main gas in the atmosphere of Mars today. Explain the difference between the levels of this gas in the atmospheres of Earth and Mars. **[2 marks]**

....

....

Exam focus

The gases in our early atmosphere are thought to have been similar to the atmosphere of Mars today. If an exam question refers to the atmosphere of Mars you are expected to apply your knowledge of Earth's early atmosphere.

⑩ Changes over time   Grades 6–7

3. Billions of years ago, the Earth's surface was covered in volcanoes and the atmosphere was mainly carbon dioxide and water vapour. Today, the surface is mainly covered with oceans and the atmosphere is composed of mostly nitrogen and oxygen with small amounts of other gases. Explain how the early Earth's surface and its atmosphere have changed to form the atmosphere of the Earth today. **[6 marks]**

....

....

....

....

.... | Continue your answer on your own paper. |

 Made a start   **Feeling confident**   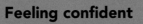 **Exam ready**

Oxygen and carbon dioxide levels

① Quick quiz

True or false?

Carbon dioxide is produced during photosynthesis.	**True / False**
Carbon dioxide is a greenhouse gas.	**True / False**
Oxygen causes climate change.	**True / False**

⑩ Changes in oxygen levels   Grade 5

1. Figure 1 shows how the level of oxygen in the Earth's atmosphere has changed over time.

(a) Determine the maximum percentage of oxygen in the Earth's atmosphere over the last billion years.   **[1 mark]**

....%

(b) Explain the overall change in the level of oxygen shown in **Figure 1**.   **[2 marks]**

Algae and plants carried out ....

....

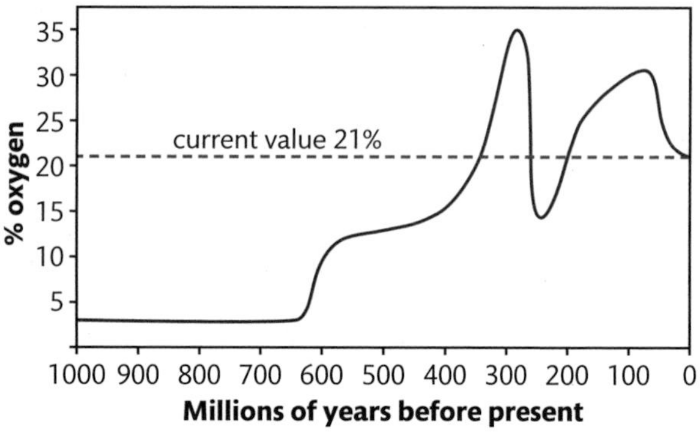

Figure 1: Graph showing % oxygen on the y-axis (ranging from 5 to 35) against Millions of years before present on the x-axis (1000 to 0). A dashed line indicates "current value 21%".

Millions of years before present

Figure 1

2. Write a word equation for photosynthesis.   **[1 mark]**

carbon dioxide + ... → glucose + ...

⑩ Changes in carbon dioxide levels   Grades 5–7

3. The percentage of carbon dioxide in the atmosphere has changed over time.

(a) The formation of limestone and fossil fuels affected the percentage of carbon dioxide.

(i) Limestone is mostly calcium carbonate. Give the chemical formula of calcium carbonate.   **[1 mark]**

....

(ii) Name **two** fossil fuels.   **[2 marks]**

....

(b) Describe **one** way in which the formation of the Earth's oceans affected the amount of carbon dioxide in the atmosphere.   **[2 marks]**

....

....

(c) Describe the composition of the Earth's early atmosphere.   **[4 marks]**

....

....

....

....

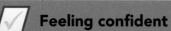

Gases in the atmosphere

(2) Quick quiz

(a) Name a relatively unreactive atmospheric gas that is not a noble gas.................................

(b) What gas in the atmosphere is needed for combustion? ....

(c) What gas in the atmosphere contributes to global warming? ....

(5) Percentages of gases Grade 6

1. **Table 1** shows the approximate percentage of gases in today's atmosphere.

Table 1

Gas	oxygen	nitrogen	other gases
% in atmosphere	20	80	<1

(a) Calculate the fraction of the Earth's atmosphere that is nitrogen. Give your answer as the simplest fraction possible. **[1 mark]**

 $\frac{80}{100} =$

(b) Draw a bar chart to show the information given in **Table 1**. **[3 marks]**

> Draw this on your own paper.

(15) Gas proportions Grade 6

2. The gases in the Earth's atmosphere, other than nitrogen and oxygen, are mostly noble gases (such as argon), carbon dioxide and water vapour. Approximately 0.04% of the atmosphere is carbon dioxide and 0.96% is argon. The water vapour content of air varies but can be 0.5%.

(a) Calculate the ratio of carbon dioxide to argon in the atmosphere. **[2 marks]**

ratio of carbon dioxide to argon = ...

(b) Calculate the ratio of water to carbon dioxide in the atmosphere. **[2 marks]**

ratio of water to carbon dioxide = ...

3. It is thought that the percentage of carbon dioxide in the Earth's early atmosphere was approximately 95%. It is 0.04% today. Calculate the difference between these two values. Determine, using your answer, the percentage change from the original carbon dioxide content. **[3 marks]**

difference between early atmosphere and today = ... %

percentage change = ...

4. Scientists can measure the exact proportions of each gas in the Earth's atmosphere.

Give **one** reason why their results may change over time. **[1 mark]**

....

 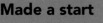

Greenhouse gases

⑤ **Quick quiz**

Fill in the gaps using the words in the box.

| greenhouse gases | infrared radiation | warming | re-emitted | carbon dioxide |

.... is one of several ...., so called because they trap

.... as it is emitted by the Earth's surface. The trapped radiation

is .... back to the Earth's surface causing ....

⑫ **Greenhouse gases** | **Grade 7**

1. Carbon dioxide is a greenhouse gas. Give the name and formula of two other greenhouse gases. **[2 marks]**

CH_4 and water vapour

2. Describe how greenhouse gases help maintain temperatures on Earth. **[4 marks]**

....

....

....

....

....

| Use the words below in your answer: |
| gases   radiated   absorb   warming   long wavelength |

....

⑤ **Interpreting data on carbon dioxide levels** | **Grades 5–7**

3. Figure 1 shows how levels of carbon dioxide in the Earth's atmosphere have changed since 1700.

(a) Give a reason why there is such a large increase in carbon dioxide level between 1900 and 2000. **[1 mark]**

....

....

(b) Scientists are concerned about the rise in carbon dioxide level. Explain the effect this increase may have on the environment. **[4 marks]**

....

....

....

....

....

....

....

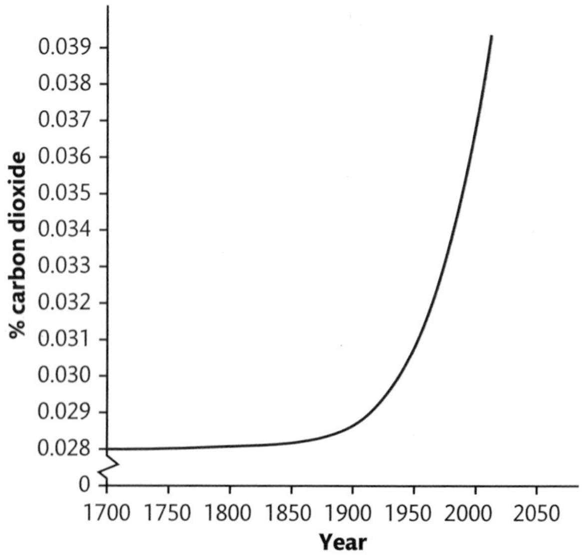

% carbon dioxide (y-axis: 0.028 to 0.039)
Year (x-axis: 1700 1750 1800 1850 1900 1950 2000 2050)

Figure 1

 Made a start   **Feeling confident**   ☑ **Exam ready**

Human contribution to greenhouse gases

② Quick quiz

Butane is a hydrocarbon obtained from fossil fuels. Complete the word equation and balanced equation to show the complete combustion of butane. Circle any products that contribute to global warming.

butane + ... → .... + ...

.....C_4H_{10} + ... → .... + ...

⑮ Human effect on greenhouse gases   Grade 5

1. (a) Suggest an explanation for **two** human activities that are causing an increase in the levels of methane in the atmosphere.   **[4 marks]**

1 The increasing number of farm animals leads to ....

....

2 Burning fossil fuels and dumping waste in landfills ....

....

(b) Lots of human activities contribute to the production of the greenhouse gas carbon dioxide. Explain how each activity contributes to the production of carbon dioxide.   **[4 marks]**

1 **Deforestation** ....

2 **Combustion of fossil fuels** ....

3 **Population increase** ....

4 **Increased use of landfill** ....

⑩ Scientific methods   Grade 6

2. Scientists agree that carbon dioxide causes global warming, as scientific findings are subjected to peer review. Explain the term 'peer review'.   **[3 marks]**

....

....

....

3. The concentration of carbon dioxide in the atmosphere increased from 308 parts per million in 1930 to 405 parts per million in 2018. Calculate the percentage increase in carbon dioxide during this time. Give your answer to 3 significant figures.   **[2 marks]**

percentage increase in carbon dioxide = ... %

4. Biofuels are derived from plants rather than fossil fuels. Many people believe they are better for the environment. Give a reason why biofuels still contribute to global warming.   **[1 mark]**

....

Global climate change

② Quick quiz

True or false?

Global warming is causing sea levels to rise.	**True / False**
Global warming alters the types of crop plants that farmers can grow.	**True / False**
Global warming has no effect on habitats.	**True / False**
Global warming does not cause coastal erosion.	**True / False**

⑩ Global climate change issues — Grade 7

1. Global climate change is affecting sea levels. Describe the environmental, social and economic issues caused by changing sea levels.

(a) Environmental – as sea levels rise, habitats will be lost, causing .... **[2 marks]**

....

(b) Social – rising sea levels will cause erosion of .... **[2 marks]**

....

(c) Economic – .... **[2 marks]**

....

⑩ Data processing — Grade 7

2. Figure 1 shows how average global temperature has changed over the last 150 years.

(a) Identify the average global temperature in 1960.

.... **[1 mark]**

(b) Determine how much the average global temperature rose:

(i) from 1880 to 1920 **[1 mark]**

....

(ii) from 1980–2000 **[1 mark]**

....

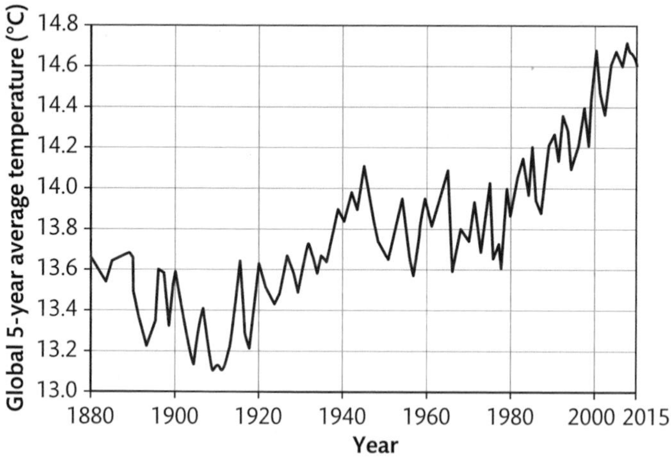

(c) Calculate, using your answers to question **(b)** parts **(i)** and **(ii)**, how many times the recent temperature rise is greater than the earlier rise.

[1 mark]

ratio of the recent temperature rise = ...

Figure 1

(d) Describe the trend shown in the graph. **[2 marks]**

....

....

(e) The change in average global temperature is driving global climate change and altering weather patterns. Give **two** ways in which weather patterns are changing around the world. **[2 marks]**

1 .... 2 ....

✓ **Made a start** ✓ **Feeling confident** ✓ **Exam ready**

Reducing the use of resources

② Quick quiz

True or false? Rewrite the false statements to make them true.

All renewable and non-renewable resources need to be recycled or reused to sustain them.　　**True / False**

Recycling is better for the environment than producing from raw materials.　　**True / False**

Carbon dioxide can be removed from the atmosphere by carbon capture and storage.　　**True / False**

Metals are a finite resource in the Earth's crust.　　**True / False**

....

....

⑤ Why reduce use of resources? 　　Grade 7

1. Explain why it is important that we try to reduce our use of raw materials.　　**[2 marks]**

We need to save our resources for

....

....

2. Give **two** reasons why we should recycle metals.　　**[2 marks]**

1 To conserve our supply of ....

2 ....

⑩ Environmental effects of reducing waste 　　Grade 7

3. Explain why reducing the amount of waste is beneficial for the environment.　　**[2 marks]**

....

....

4. (a) Describe **two** ways in which carbon dioxide is released into the atmosphere.　　**[2 marks]**

....

....

(b) Carbon dioxide can cause global warming. State **two** ways in which carbon dioxide can be removed from the Earth's atmosphere.　　**[2 marks]**

....

....

⑤ Climate change mitigation 　　Grade 6

5. Increased levels of carbon dioxide and methane in the atmosphere can cause climate change. The effects of climate change can be mitigated.

(a) State what is meant by 'climate change mitigation'.　　**[1 mark]**

....

(b) State **two** methods of climate change mitigation.　　**[2 marks]**

....

....

Key concepts in Physics

② Quantities and their units

Draw **one** line from each unit to match it to its quantity.

metre	kilogram	second	ampere	metre cubed	volt	coulomb

mass	charge	volume	potential difference	time	current	distance

② Prefixes

Draw lines to match each prefix to its conversion factor and its abbreviation.

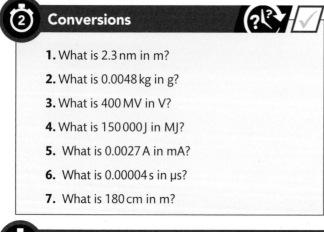

milli		$\times 10^6$		k
mega		$\times 10^{-2}$		n
nano		$\times 10^9$		μ
micro		$\times 10^{-3}$		m
giga		$\times 10^3$		G
kilo		$\times 10^{-6}$		M
centi		$\times 10^{-9}$		c

② Conversions

1. What is 2.3 nm in m?
2. What is 0.0048 kg in g?
3. What is 400 MV in V?
4. What is 150 000 J in MJ?
5. What is 0.0027 A in mA?
6. What is 0.00004 s in μs?
7. What is 180 cm in m?

② Time

True or false?

30 minutes is 180 seconds	**True / False**
2 hours is 180 minutes	**True / False**
24 hours is 86 400 seconds	**True / False**
32 400 seconds is 9 hours	**True / False**

② Calculations

Show your working for each question.

1. A woman has a mass of 160 pounds. 1 kg = 2.205 pounds. Calculate her mass in kilograms. Give your answer to 2 significant figures.

   ....

2. The radius of the Earth is 6370 km. Calculate the diameter of the Earth in metres. Give your answer in standard form.

   ....

3. Light travels through space at 300 000 km/s. Calculate the speed of light in m/s. Give your answer in standard form.

   ....

4. The circumference of the Sun is 4 400 000 km. Calculate the radius of the Sun in metres. Give your answer to 1 significant figure.

   ....

✓ **Made a start**　　✓ **Feeling confident**　　✓ **Exam ready**

Scalar and vector quantities

 Quick quiz

Is each quantity scalar or vector? Circle the correct answer for each.

distance	**scalar / vector**	acceleration	**scalar / vector**
momentum	**scalar / vector**	weight	**scalar / vector**
efficiency	**scalar / vector**	force	**scalar / vector**
speed	**scalar / vector**	temperature	**scalar / vector**

 Adding vectors   **Grade 5**

1. **Figure 1** shows two people pushing a car to move it. One person is exerting a force of 300 N and the other is exerting a force of 150 N. Both people are pushing the car in the same direction.

    (a) The arrow in **Figure 1** represents the 150 N force.

    Draw an arrow next to it to represent the 300 N force. **[1 mark]**

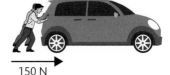

150 N

Figure 1

    (b) Calculate the resultant force on the car. **[1 mark]**

    Both forces are acting in the same direction so the resultant force is the sum of the individual forces.

    resultant force = ... N + ... N = ...

    resultant force = ... N

2. A boat is being rowed east at 5 m/s. The wind blows it north at 1.5 m/s.

    Use a scale drawing to calculate the boat's resultant velocity and direction of travel. **[3 marks]**

    Use a protractor to measure the angle of the final velocity vector. The angle should be measured from north.

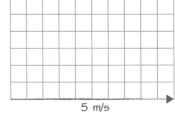

5 m/s

Figure 2

    resultant velocity = ... m/s at ....°

 Using scale diagrams   **Grade 5**

3. An aeroplane's engine propels it west at 70 m/s. There is a northerly wind of 10 m/s. The speed and velocity of the plane are different.

    (a) Describe the difference between speed and velocity. **[1 mark]**

    ....

    (b) Draw a scale diagram to calculate the resultant velocity of the plane and its direction of travel. **[3 marks]**

    resultant velocity = ... m/s at ....°

Distance and speed

② Quick quiz

True or false?

Distance is a scalar quantity.	**True / False**
Displacement has no direction.	**True / False**
Distance has a magnitude and a direction.	**True / False**
Distance measures how far an object has moved in total.	**True / False**

⑩ Final displacement   Grade 5

1. Julie's work place is 10 miles away from her home. She drives to work in the morning and home again in the evening.

(a) Give the total distance travelled each day.   **[1 mark]**

....

(b) Give Julie's displacement when she gets home from work.   **[1 mark]**

....

2. A car travels 3.5 km due north and then 5.0 km due east. Draw a scale diagram to calculate the magnitude and direction of the car's final displacement from its starting position.   **[3 marks]**

> **Exam focus**
> Choose a suitable scale to ensure your diagram is accurate. Check that your answer makes sense – the displacement should never be greater than the distance.

magnitude of displacement = ... km   direction = ...°

⑩ Direction and magnitude of displacement   Grade 5

3. A car starts at point A and travels 300 m north. It then turns and travels 250 m east, before arriving at point B.

(a) Draw a scale diagram to show the movement of the car.   **[1 mark]**

(b) Calculate the total distance travelled by the car.   **[1 mark]**

total distance = ...m

(c) Calculate the direction and resultant displacement of the car when travelling from A to B.   **[2 marks]**

resultant displacement = ...m   direction = ...°

 Made a start   **Feeling confident**   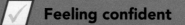 **Exam ready**

Speed and velocity

② Quick quiz

Fill in the gaps using the words in the box.

| direction | distance | speed | time |

Velocity is the .... of an object travelling in a particular ....

Speed is a measure of the .... an object has moved in a specific amount of ....

⑩ Speed and velocity
Grade 6

1. A bus travels 100 km in 2 hours. Calculate its average speed in m/s. **[2 marks]**

100 km = ... m; 2 hours = ... s

> 1 hour = 3600 seconds

$$\text{average speed} = \frac{\text{distance}}{\text{time}} = \text{...........................}$$

average speed = ... m/s

2. A cyclist travels 3 km north. It takes him 30 minutes. Calculate the cyclist's average velocity in m/s. **[3 marks]**

distance = ... m; time = ... s

$$\text{average velocity} = \frac{\text{distance}}{\text{time}} = \text{...........................}$$

Maths skills
To convert km to m, multiply by 1000.
To convert minutes to seconds, multiply by 60.

average velocity = ... m/s ....

> Remember, you must give the direction as well as the speed.

⑩ Average velocity
Grade 7

3. Give typical speeds for these objects:

(a) a person running .... **[1 mark]**

(b) a person cycling .... **[1 mark]**

4. A bus is travelling due west and covers 50 km in 1.5 hours.

(a) Calculate the average velocity of the bus in m/s. **[2 marks]**

velocity = ... m/s ....

(b) Explain why the velocity you calculated in **(a)** is an average velocity. **[1 mark]**

....

(c) A second bus travels in the same direction, covering twice the distance in the same amount of time.

Calculate the average velocity of the second bus. **[1 mark]**

average velocity = ... m/s ....

Distance–time graphs

 ② Quick quiz

Draw **one** line from each description of the distance–time graph to match it to the motion of the object.

the gradient of the line increases	this means the object is stationary
the gradient of the line decreases	this means the object is accelerating
the gradient of the line is zero	this means the object is decelerating

 ⑤ Using distance–time graphs **Grade 7**

1. Figure 1 shows the journey of a cyclist. Describe the journey. **[3 marks]**

A–B: The cyclist travels .... km in .... hours.

The speed of the cyclist is .... km/h.

B–C: The cyclist is .... for .... hours.

C–D The cyclist travels a further .... km in .... hours.

The speed is .... km/h.

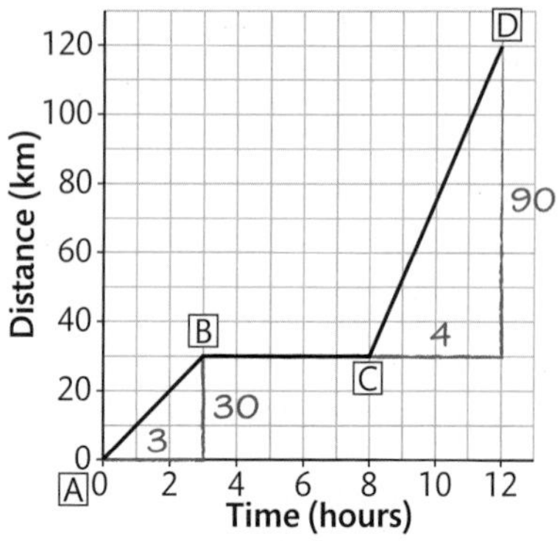

Figure 1

⑮ Distance–time graphs **Grade 7**

2. Figure 2 shows the distance–time graph for part of a bus journey.

(a) Give the total distance travelled by the bus in the first minute of the journey.
[1 mark]

....

(b) Describe the motion of the bus in the first 20 seconds of the journey. **[1 mark]**

....

(c) Determine the speed of the bus at 50 seconds. Show on **Figure 2** how you obtained your answer. **[3 marks]**

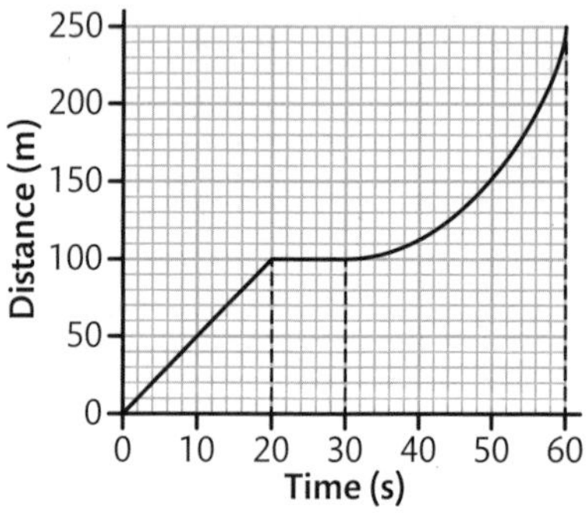

Figure 2

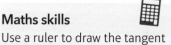

Maths skills

Use a ruler to draw the tangent to the curve at 50 seconds.

speed = ... m/s

3. A cyclist is stationary at a set of traffic lights. When the traffic lights turn green, the cyclist accelerates.

Sketch a distance-time graph to show the cyclist's acceleration. **[2 marks]**

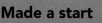 **Made a start** **Feeling confident** 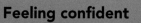 **Exam ready**

Uniform acceleration

BBC

 Quick quiz

Draw lines to match the symbol, quantity and unit.

x	time	m/s²
u	acceleration	m/s
v	initial velocity	m
a	displacement	s
t	final velocity	m/s

 **Using equations of motion** | Grade 8

1. A leopard is resting and then accelerates in a straight line to chase a deer. It accelerates at 3 m/s² for 6 seconds.

(a) Calculate the final velocity of the leopard. **[3 marks]**

> Direction is not mentioned, so you don't need to consider it here.

$$a = \frac{(v - u)}{t} \qquad v = u + at$$

$v = \underset{\cdots\cdots}{\quad} + (\underset{\cdots\cdots\cdots}{\quad} \times \underset{\cdots\cdots}{\quad}) = \underset{\cdots\cdots\cdots\cdots\cdots}{\quad}$

final velocity = ... m/s

(b) Calculate the distance travelled by the leopard. **[3 marks]**

$$v^2 - u^2 = 2ax \text{ so } x = \frac{v^2 - u^2}{2a} =$$

distance = ... m

> **Exam focus** 📌
> In an exam, you will be asked to choose the correct equation from the Physics equation sheet.

 Acceleration | Grade 7

2. A tennis ball is thrown vertically upwards at 10 m/s. Assume that air resistance can be ignored and that freefall acceleration is 9.8 m/s².

(a) Calculate the maximum height reached by the ball. **[3 marks]**

maximum height = ... m

(b) Calculate the time it takes the ball to reach the maximum height. **[3 marks]**

time = ... s

3. A Formula One racing car accelerates in a straight line from rest at 15 m/s² for 5 seconds.

(a) Calculate the final velocity of the car. **[2 marks]**

final velocity = ... m/s

(b) Calculate the distance travelled by the car in this time. **[3 marks]**

distance = ... m

4. A skater accelerates at 2 m/s² in a straight line. This causes the velocity of the skater to increase from 8 m/s to 10 m/s. Calculate the distance the skater travels during the acceleration. **[3 marks]**

distance = ... m

 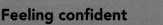

Velocity–time graphs

② Quick quiz

Draw **one** line to match each feature of a velocity–time graph to the information it gives you.

gradient of the line		constant speed
area under the line		acceleration
a horizontal line		distance travelled

⑤ Velocity–time graphs | Grade 8

1. Distance–time graphs and velocity–time graphs give different information about the motion of an object.

(a) Give what can be found from the gradient of a distance–time graph. **[1 mark]**

The gradient $= \dfrac{\text{distance}}{\text{time}}$ so tells us the

....

(b) Give what can be found from the gradient of a velocity–time graph. **[1 mark]**

The gradient $= \dfrac{\text{speed}}{\text{time}}$ so tells us the

....

(c) Give what can be found from the area under a velocity–time graph. **[1 mark]**

The area under the line $=$ speed $\times$ time so tells us the

....

⑮ Acceleration | Grade 7

2. A bus travels the following journey. For the first 10 seconds, it accelerates from rest to a speed of 8 m/s. It then travels at a constant velocity of 8 m/s for a further 60 seconds. Over the last 20 seconds of the journey, the bus decelerates until it is stationary.

(a) Plot a velocity–time graph of this journey. **[4 marks]**

(b) Calculate the distance the bus travels when it has a constant velocity. **[2 marks]**

distance = ... m

3. A cyclist travels the following journey. For the first 20 seconds of the journey, she accelerates from rest to a speed of 10 m/s. She continues travelling at 10 m/s for a further 30 seconds. Over the next 10 seconds, she decelerates to stop at some traffic lights.

(a) Plot a velocity–time graph of this journey. **[4 marks]**

(b) Calculate the cyclist's acceleration during the first 20 seconds of the journey. **[2 marks]**

acceleration = ... m/s^2

(c) Calculate the total distance travelled by the cyclist. **[3 marks]**

distance = ... m

✓ **Made a start** ✓ **Feeling confident** ✓ **Exam ready**

Gravity

---

② **Quick quiz**

Draw lines to match each quantity with its meaning and its unit.

mass	the force acting on an object due to gravity	N/kg
weight	the strength of gravity at any one point	kg
gravitational field strength	the amount of matter in an object	N

---

⑤ **Gravitational field strength** | **Grade 7** |

1. A rock has a weight of 25 N on Earth. The gravitational field strength on Earth (g) is 9.8 N/kg.

(a) Calculate the mass of the rock. **[2 marks]**

➡ weight = mass × gravitational field strength

mass = ——————————— =

mass = ... kg

(b) The rock is taken to the Moon where it weighs 4.1 N.

Calculate the gravitational field strength (g) on the Moon. Give your answer to 2 significant figures. **[2 marks]**

➡ gravitational field strength = ——————————— =

gravitational field strength = ... N/kg

---

⑮ **Mass and weight** | **Grade 7** |

2. A moon lander weighs 1.6×10^5 N on Earth. The gravitational field strength on Earth is 9.8 N/kg.

(a) Calculate the mass of the moon lander. **[3 marks]**

mass = ... kg

(b) The gravitational field strength on the Moon is 1.6 N/kg.

(i) Give the mass of the moon lander on the Moon. .... **[1 mark]**

(ii) Calculate the weight of the moon lander on the Moon. **[2 marks]**

weight = ... N

3. The gravitational field strength on Earth is 9.8 N/kg. On the Moon it is 1.6 N/kg. An astronaut has a mass of 55 kg.

(a) Calculate the weight of the astronaut on Earth. **[2 marks]**

weight = ... N

(b) Calculate the difference in weight when the astronaut stands on the Moon when compared to standing on the Earth. **[3 marks]**

difference in weight = ... N

Newton's laws of motion

---

(2) Quick quiz

Draw **one** line from each law to match it to the correct statement.

Newton's first law	The acceleration of an object is proportional to the resultant force and inversely proportional to the mass of the object.
Newton's second law	When two objects interact, they exert an equal and opposite force on each other.
Newton's third law	An object will continue to move in the same direction at the same speed unless acted upon by a resultant force.

---

(5) Newton's laws **Grade 7**

1. Figure 1 shows a racing bike.

Explain why engineers develop racing bikes to have as low a mass as possible.
Use Newton's second law in your answer. **[2 marks]**

The racing bikes have low mass because the lower the mass, the

....

.... the acceleration for the same

....

> Remember, Newton's second law states that resultant force is proportional to acceleration.
> $a \propto \frac{1}{m}$ so if mass decreases, acceleration increases for a given force.

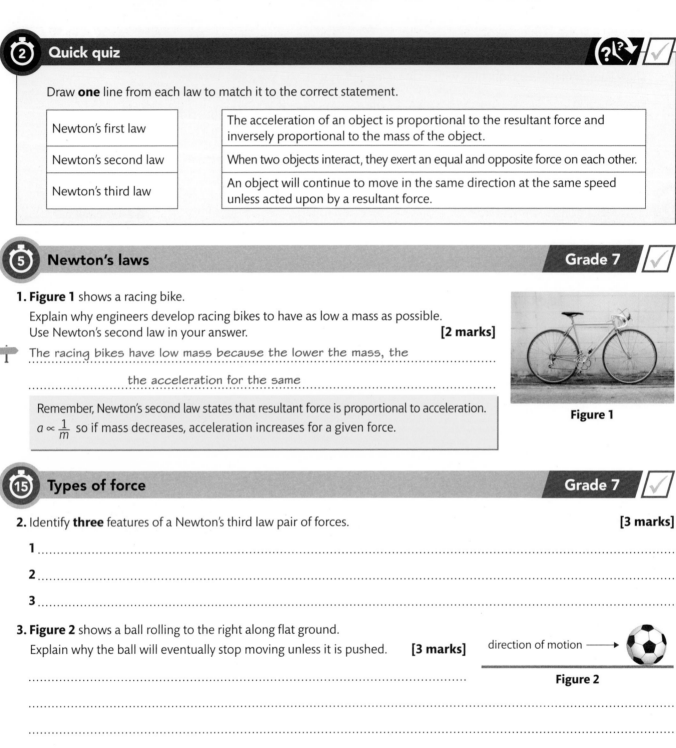

Figure 1

---

(15) Types of force **Grade 7**

2. Identify **three** features of a Newton's third law pair of forces. **[3 marks]**

1 ....

2 ....

3 ....

3. Figure 2 shows a ball rolling to the right along flat ground.

Explain why the ball will eventually stop moving unless it is pushed. **[3 marks]**

direction of motion ⟶

....

Figure 2

....

....

4. Figure 3 shows a racing car. The resultant force on the car is zero.

(a) It is possible that the car is stationary.

Describe the other possible motion of the car. **[2 marks]**

....

(b) Racing cars are designed to have the maximum acceleration possible.

Explain how a racing car could be modified to increase the
maximum acceleration. **[3 marks]**

Figure 3

....

....

 Made a start **Feeling confident** **Exam ready**

Newton's second law

② Quick quiz

True or false?

The resultant force needed to accelerate the car is proportional to its mass. **True / False**

force = mass × acceleration **True / False**

$$acceleration = \frac{force}{mass}$$ **True / False**

The resultant force needed to accelerate the car is inversely proportional to its acceleration. **True / False**

⑤ $F = m \times a$ — Grade 7

1. Figure 1 shows a car. The horizontal forces on the car have been labelled.

1200 N → ← 600 N

Figure 1

The mass of the car is 1500 kg.

Calculate the acceleration of the car. **[3 marks]**

resultant force = ... − .... = ... N in the .... direction

$F = m \times a$ so $a =$ _____ =

acceleration = ... m/s²

> Work out the resultant force first. Remember that acceleration is a vector quantity and so your answer should give a direction as well as a magnitude.

⑩ Newton's second law — Grade 6

2. Figure 2 shows a boy on a skateboard. The boy and the skateboard accelerate at 2 m/s². The forward force is 150 N and the force of air resistance is 30 N. Calculate the total mass of the boy and the skateboard. **[3 marks]**

total mass = ... kg

Figure 2

3. A resultant force of 12 kN acts on a lorry. The mass of the lorry is 15 000 kg. Calculate the acceleration of the lorry. **[2 marks]**

> **Maths skills**
> Rearrange the equation carefully.

acceleration = ... m/s²

4. Inertial mass is a measure of how difficult it is to change the velocity of an object. It is calculated using the equation:

$$inertial\ mass = \frac{mass}{acceleration}$$

Suggest, using the equation, why more massive objects take a greater force to stop them than less massive objects travelling at the same velocity. **[2 marks]**

....

....

Centripetal force

---

② Quick quiz

True or false?

Any object moving in a circle is accelerating.	**True / False**
Any object moving in a circle has a centripetal force acting on it.	**True / False**
The unit of centripetal force is the newton.	**True / False**
The centripetal force acting on an object is always provided by friction.	**True / False**

---

⑤ Centripetal force   **Grade 6**

1. Explain why an object travelling along a circular path has a resultant force acting on it. **[3 marks]**

🚩 An object travelling in a circular path is changing direction so it must be changing
....
....
....   The object must be accelerating.

---

⑩ Centripetal force   **Grade 6**

2. Figure 1 shows a student whirling a conker around on the end of a piece of string in a horizontal circle.

(a) State what provides the centripetal force to keep the conker moving in a circle.   **[1 mark]**
....

(b) Explain what will happen to the motion of the conker if the string breaks.   **[2 marks]**
....
....
....

Figure 1

3. Figure 2 shows the Earth in orbit around the Sun.

(a) Draw an arrow on **Figure 2** to show the direction in which the Earth is accelerating. Label the arrow A.   **[1 mark]**

(b) Draw an arrow on **Figure 2** to show the direction of the resultant force on the Earth. Label the arrow R.   **[1 mark]**

(c) Explain what would happen to the radius of the Earth's orbit if the gravitational force of the Sun on the Earth increased.   **[3 marks]**
....
....
....

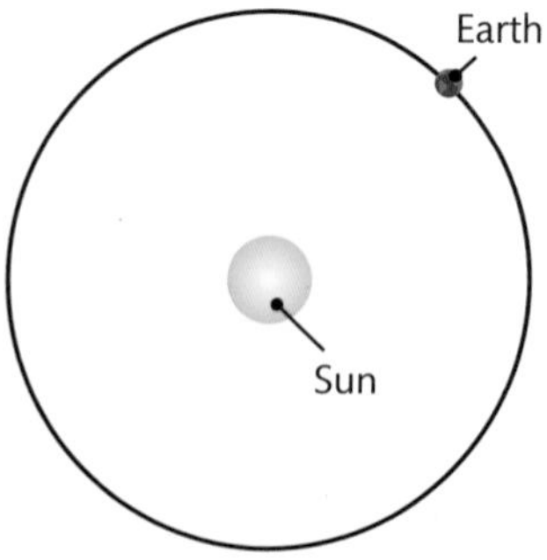

Earth

Sun

Figure 2

 Made a start   ✓ **Feeling confident**   ✓ **Exam ready**

Practical: Investigating acceleration

Quick quiz

Draw **one** line from each quantity to match it to its unit.

speed	m/s^2
mass	N
acceleration	m/s
force	kg

Investigating acceleration

Grade 8

1. A student carried out an investigation into the effect of force on the acceleration of an object. She used the equipment shown in **Figure 1**.

   The student changed the force by adding more mass to the holder at the end of the bench. The light gate measured the acceleration.

   (a) She plotted a graph of the results, with the independent variable on the x-axis and the dependent variable on the y-axis.

   Figure 1

   (i) Explain which quantity is plotted on the x-axis. [2 marks]

   The independent variable is the one that is changed deliberately in the experiment and so is

   ....

   ....

   (ii) Explain which quantity is plotted on the y-axis. [2 marks]

   The dependent variable is the one that is measured in the experiment and so is

   ....

   ....

   (b) State what the gradient of the graph shows. [1 mark]

   $F = ma$ so the gradient of the graph is $\dfrac{acceleration}{force}$, which is equal to $\dfrac{1}{\text{\_\_\_\_}}$

   ....

Investigating $F = ma$

Grade 8

2. A student investigates the relationship between the mass and the acceleration of an object. The following equipment is available: light gate, trolleys of different masses, mass holder and masses.

   (a) Give **one** factor that must be kept constant to ensure the investigation is valid. [1 mark]

   ....

   (b) Describe an experiment the student could carry out in order to investigate how mass affects acceleration. [4 marks]

   ....

   ....

   ....

   ....

 Made a start   Feeling confident   Exam ready

Momentum

BBC

② Quick quiz

True or false?

An object's momentum depends on its velocity and displacement.	**True / False**
The units for momentum are kg/m/s.	**True / False**
Momentum is a vector quantity.	**True / False**
momentum = mass × velocity	**True / False**

⑮ Momentum equation

Grade 6

1. (a) Calculate the momentum of a car of mass 1000 kg that is moving at 25 m/s.

Give the unit of momentum. **[3 marks]**

momentum = mass × velocity = ... × .... = ...

momentum = ... unit ....

(b) The velocity of the car halves. State the effect this has on the momentum of the car. **[1 mark]**

As momentum = mass × velocity, if the velocity halves, momentum will ....

(c) Sketch the shape of the graph produced when momentum (*y*-axis) is plotted against velocity (*x*-axis). **[1 mark]**

(d) Identify the features of the graph that show that momentum is directly proportional to velocity. **[2 marks]**

....

....

> **Maths skills**
> When two quantities are directly proportional, a graph of the quantities will always give a straight line through the origin.

(e) Give the quantity represented by the gradient of a momentum–velocity graph. **[1 mark]**

gradient = $\frac{momentum}{velocity}$ = ...

> **Maths skills**
> Look at the formula for momentum to work out the quantity that is given by $\frac{momentum}{velocity}$.

⑩ Change in momentum

Grade 7

2. A rocket has an initial mass of 15 000 kg. Its initial speed is 200 m/s. After a few seconds, it has burned 1000 kg of fuel and is now travelling at a speed of 210 m/s. Calculate the change in momentum of the rocket. **[4 marks]**

> You can give your final answer as a standard form number or as an ordinary number.

change in momentum = ...kg m/s

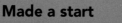 **Made a start** 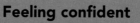 **Feeling confident** **Exam ready**

Conservation of momentum

② Quick quiz

Fill in the gaps using the words in the box.

| after | closed | collide | conserved | external | law | momentum | system |

When two objects ...., the total momentum they have is always ....

This means that it is the same .... the collision as before it. This is always true, as long as there

are no .... forces acting on the .... This is called a .... system.

This is known as the .... of conservation of ....

⑤ Conserving total momentum   Grade 7 ☑

1. **Figure 1** shows two trolleys. The trolleys collide and stick together.
   Calculate the velocity of the trolleys after the collision. Give your answer
   to 2 significant figures.   **[4 marks]**

[5 kg 4 m/s →]   [7 kg 2 m/s →]

Figure 1

momentum before = (........... × ....) + (........... × ....) = ... kg m/s

momentum after = momentum before

velocity = $\frac{momentum}{mass}$ = $\frac{............}{12kg}$ = ...

velocity = ... m/s

⑮ Collisions   Grade 8

2. A bus is travelling at 8 m/s and has a mass of 15 000 kg. It collides with a stationary car of mass 1000 kg.

   (a) Calculate the momentum of the bus prior to the collision.   **[2 marks]**

   momentum = ... kg m/s

   (b) After the collision, the bus and the car move off together.

   Give the combined momentum after the collision.   **[1 mark]**

   combined momentum = ... kg m/s

   (c) Calculate the velocity of the bus and the car after the collision. **[2 marks]**

   velocity = ... m/s

   (d) The bus driver has a mass of 75 kg. Calculate the change in momentum of the driver during the collision. **[3 marks]**

   change in momentum = ... kg m/s

Stopping distance

② Quick quiz

True or false?

Being tired affects your braking distance.	**True / False**
Your stopping distance is the distance travelled while the driver is reacting.	**True / False**
Your thinking distance increases when your reaction time is longer.	**True / False**
Icy roads increase your thinking distance.	**True / False**

⑤ Thinking distance   Grade 6

1. (a) A driver's reaction time is measured as 1.3 s. Calculate her thinking distance when travelling at 13 m/s. **[2 marks]**

$$speed = \frac{distance}{time} \text{ so distance} =$$

thinking distance = ... m

> **Maths skills**
> Show all your working clearly.

(b) The driver takes the same journey the following day, but has had very little sleep. Explain how being tired will affect her thinking distance. **[2 marks]**

....

....

⑮ Reaction times   Grades 6–7

2. Figure 1 shows typical stopping distances for a car travelling at different speeds.

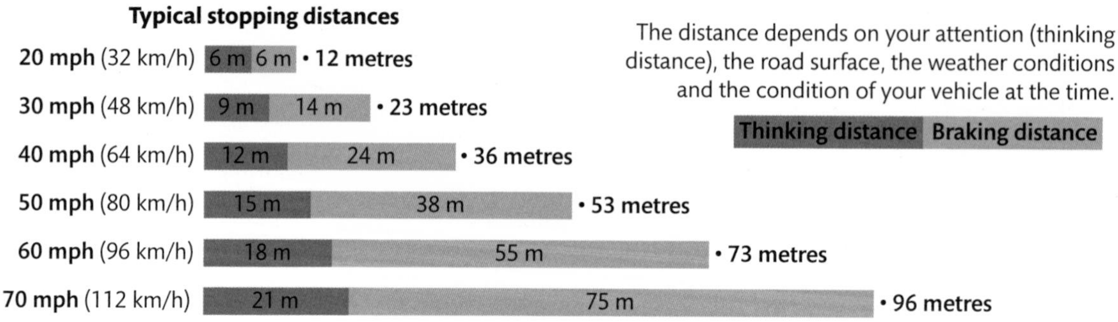

Typical stopping distances

20 mph (32 km/h)	6 m 6 m	• 12 metres
30 mph (48 km/h)	9 m 14 m	• 23 metres
40 mph (64 km/h)	12 m 24 m	• 36 metres
50 mph (80 km/h)	15 m 38 m	• 53 metres
60 mph (96 km/h)	18 m 55 m	• 73 metres
70 mph (112 km/h)	21 m 75 m	• 96 metres

The distance depends on your attention (thinking distance), the road surface, the weather conditions and the condition of your vehicle at the time.

Thinking distance   Braking distance

Figure 1

(a) Describe the patterns shown by the data in **Figure 1**. **[3 marks]**

....

....

....

> **Exam focus**
> Remember to make three distinct points for a question worth three marks.

....

....

(b) The data in **Figure 1** is for average conditions.
State the effect, if any, of a wet road on:

(i) the thinking distance .... **[1 mark]**

(ii) the braking distance .... **[1 mark]**

✓ **Made a start**	✓ **Feeling confident**	✓ **Exam ready**

Factors affecting braking distance

② Quick quiz

Complete the sentences using words from the box.

| braking | stopping | thinking |

Distance travelled under the braking force is the .... distance.

Distance travelled between the driver seeing a hazard and applying the brakes is the .... distance.

Thinking distance plus the braking distance is the .... distance.

⑤ Braking distance   Grade 6

1. Explain how the condition of the road will affect the braking distance of a vehicle. **[3 marks]**

Anything that reduces the frictional force between the tyres and the road will
....

....

....

> There must be a frictional force between the vehicle's tyres and the road surface for braking to take place.

⑩ Braking distance   Grade 9

2. Explain how the speed of a vehicle affects its braking distance. **[3 marks]**

....

....

....

3. A driver applies the brakes of his car over a long period of time while driving down a hill.

Explain how this reduces the efficiency of the brakes. **[2 marks]**

....

....

4. A driver applies the brakes, which brings the car to a stop in 2.4 seconds. The average braking force is 12 kN. The mass of the car is 1000 kg.

Calculate the initial speed of the car. Give your answer to 2 significant figures. **[4 marks]**

initial speed = ... m/s

Gravitational potential energy

 Quick quiz

Which rearrangements of the equation to calculate the change in gravitational potential energy (ΔGPE) are correct? Tick the correct rearrangements.

$\Delta h = \dfrac{\Delta GPE}{m \times g}$ ☐

$\Delta h = \Delta GPE \times m \times g$ ☐

$g = \dfrac{\Delta GPE}{M \times \Delta h}$ ☐

$m = \dfrac{g \times \Delta h}{\Delta GPE}$ ☐

 Calculating energy   **Grade 7**

1. Mount Snowdon is 1.09 km above sea level. A 65 kg climber starts at sea level and climbs to the top of Mount Snowdon.

   Calculate the change in the climber's gravitational potential energy. Assume g = 10 N/kg. **[3 marks]**

 $\Delta GPE = m \times g \times \Delta h$

   1.09 km = ...m

   ΔGPE = ... × .... × .... = ...

> **Maths skills**
> Check the units for each quantity. Height needs to be in metres.

   change in gravitational potential energy = ...J

 Gravitational potential energy stores   **Grade 7**

Assume g = 10 N/kg for all questions.

2. The viewing platform at the top of the Eiffel Tower is 300 m above the ground level.

   (a) A tourist climbs to the viewing platform. The mass of the tourist is 60 kg.

   Calculate the tourist's gain in gravitational potential energy. **[2 marks]**

   gain in gravitational potential energy = ...J

   (b) The same tourist climbs to the top of another building. The increase in her gravitational potential energy is 223 000 J.

   Calculate the height of the other building. Give your answer to 2 significant figures. **[3 marks]**

   height of the building = ... m

3. A passenger rises 98 m from the ground in a lift and gains 63 700 J of gravitational potential energy.

   Calculate the mass of the passenger. **[3 marks]**

   mass of passenger = ... kg

 Made a start   Feeling confident   Exam ready

Kinetic energy

 Quick quiz

The kinetic energy of a moving object can be calculated using: $E_k = \frac{1}{2} \times m \times v^2$

Rearrange the equation to make each of the following the subject of the equation:

mass =   speed =

 Kinetic energy   **Grade 7**

1. A bus with a mass of 10 000 kg is travelling at a speed of 10 m/s.

(a) Calculate the kinetic energy of the bus.   **[2 marks]**

$E_k = \frac{1}{2} \times m \times v^2$

> Remember, in the equation for E_k, v is the speed.

$E_k = \frac{1}{2} \times$ .... $\times$ .... $^2 =$ ....

kinetic energy = ... J

(b) The bus comes to a stop.

Determine the work done by the brakes on the bus.   **[1 mark]**

work done = kinetic energy, so work done = ... J

(c) Ten extra passengers get on the bus. Explain the effect this has on the kinetic energy the bus has when travelling at 10 m/s.   **[2 marks]**

An increase in the number of passengers means an increase in mass. ....

If mass increases, ...

> Use the equation to help you. You could even put numbers into the equation to see the effect.

....

 Kinetic energy calculations   **Grades 6–7**

2. A cyclist's speed increases from 3 m/s to 6 m/s. Explain what happens to the kinetic energy of the cyclist.   **[2 marks]**

....

....

3. A car travels along a straight, flat road. The car has a mass of 1200 kg. Calculate the increase in the car's kinetic energy when it accelerates from 10 m/s to 15 m/s.   **[3 marks]**

increase in kinetic energy = ... J

4. A dog with a mass of 12 kg runs at a constant speed. It has 21 J of kinetic energy.

Calculate the speed of the dog.   **[3 marks]**

speed = ... m/s

 Made a start   **Feeling confident**   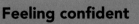 **Exam ready**

Conservation of energy

⏱️② Quick quiz

True or false?

A moving object always has kinetic energy.	**True / False**
Energy is created in electric circuits.	**True / False**
A stretched spring always stores gravitational potential energy.	**True / False**
Friction in the brakes of a car raises the temperature of the brake pads.	**True / False**
A light bulb always wastes energy by heating the surroundings.	**True / False**

⏱️⑩ Conservation of energy   Grade 5

1. **Figure 1** shows a television. Energy is transferred to it by electricity.

   (a) Identify the energy transfers in this device.   [1 mark]

   🪧 Energy transferred by heating,
   ....

   ....

   (b) State the useful energy transfers for the device.   [1 mark]

   ....

   (c) State the wasted energy transfer for the device.   [1 mark]

   ....

Figure 1

⏱️⑩ Energy transfers   Grade 6

2. Machinery wastes energy due to friction in the moving parts.

   (a) State how the wasted energy is transferred.   [1 mark]

   ....

   (b) Give **one** way in which the amount of wasted energy can be reduced.   [1 mark]

   ....

   (c) Describe what will eventually happen to the energy wasted in the system.   [1 mark]

   ....

3. **Figure 2** shows a ball being dropped and then bouncing on the ground. Describe the energy transfers that take place.   [3 marks]

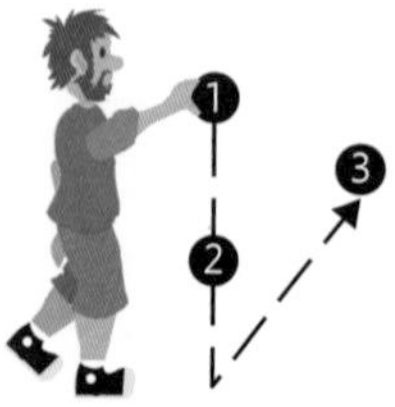

   ....

   ....

   ....

Figure 2

4. Describe the energy transfers when a car driver presses the brake and brings a car to a standstill.   [2 marks]

   ....

   ....

> **Exam focus** 📌
> Always look at the number of marks for each question. This tells you how many points you need to make.

Efficiency

② Quick quiz

Which statements about efficiency are correct? Tick the correct statements.

Efficiency is measured in joules. ☐

The closer to 1 (or 100%), the more efficient the device. ☐

The lower the number for efficiency, the more efficient the device. ☐

A very efficient device will have an efficiency greater than 100%. ☐

If a device is 40% efficient, 40% of the energy is usefully transferred and 60% is wasted. ☐

⑤ Calculating efficiency　　　　　Grade 7

1. Table 1 shows information about two lamps.
Explain which lamp is more efficient. **[3 marks]**

$$\text{efficiency} = \frac{\text{useful power output}}{\text{total power input}}$$

....

If both lamps have the same

....

then the one with the greater power input each second must be

....

Lamp .... is more efficient.

Table 1

Lamp	Energy input each second (J)	Energy output each second (J)
A	60	15
B	30	15

⑮ Efficiency calculations　　　　　Grades 6–7

2. A hairdryer transfers 1800 J of useful energy each second. The hairdryer is supplied with 2 kJ of energy each second.

(a) Calculate the energy wasted each second by the hairdryer. **[1 mark]**

energy wasted each second = ...J

(b) Calculate the efficiency of the hairdryer. **[2 marks]**

efficiency = ...

(c) Describe the useful energy transfers in the hairdryer. **[2 marks]**

....

....

(d) Describe the energy transfers that waste energy in the hairdryer. **[2 marks]**

....

....

3. The efficiency of a car engine is 0.40. The total energy supplied to the engine from the fuel is 30 MJ. Calculate the energy wasted by the car in MJ. **[4 marks]**

energy wasted = ... MJ

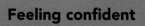

Renewable energy resources

 Quick quiz

Draw lines to match the name of each energy source to a description of its use.

Sun	wind forces turbines to rotate, generating electricity
wind	daily movement of the ocean is used to generate electricity
tides	energy transferred by light is used to generate electricity using solar panels

 Wind power Grade 5

1. Figure 1 shows some wind turbines.

Give **two** advantages and **two** disadvantages of using wind power to generate electricity. **[4 marks]**

Advantages: can be placed in isolated locations
....

Disadvantages: some people think they spoil the landscape
....

Figure 1

Solar power and hydroelectricity Grade 6

2. Figure 2 shows a tidal barrage (left) and a hydroelectric dam (right).

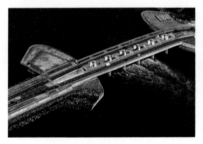 

Figure 2

Give **one** advantage and **one** disadvantage of using each one to generate electricity. **[4 marks]**

Tidal barrage

Advantage..

Disadvantage ....

Hydroelectric dam

Advantage ....

Disadvantage...

3. A medium-sized town in the UK wants to provide electricity to its houses using solar power only. Give **two** reasons why this is not realistic. **[2 marks]**

1 ....

2 ....

 Made a start **Feeling confident** **Exam ready**

Non-renewable energy resources

② Quick quiz

Name **three** fossil fuels.

....

⑤ Nuclear power

Grade 6

1. **Figure 1** shows a nuclear power station. Nuclear power is clean but the nuclear waste has to be disposed of correctly.

Describe **two** further advantages and **two** further disadvantages of using nuclear power. **[4 marks]**

Advantages Steam is the only gas emitted – nuclear power has no effect on

....

Small amounts of fuel produce   amounts of

....

Disadvantages Transport of radioactive fuel and waste is

....

Nuclear power plants are expensive to

....

Figure 1

⑮ Renewable and non-renewable energy resources

Grade 6

2. Research is continually being carried out into renewable energy resources.

Explain why this research is necessary by considering the issues surrounding the use of non-renewable resources. **[3 marks]**

....

....

....

3. Most vehicles on the road are powered by either petrol or diesel despite the environmental problems associated with these fuels.

Suggest **two** reasons why these fuels are still used. **[2 marks]**

1 ....

2 ....

4. Explain **two** disadvantages of using fossil fuel power stations to generate electricity rather than using renewable energy resources. **[4 marks]**

1 ....

....

2 ....

....

Types of wave

② Quick quiz

Circle the type of wave described.

The vibrations are parallel to the direction the wave is travelling.	**longitudinal / transverse**
The vibrations are perpendicular to the direction the wave is travelling.	**longitudinal / transverse**
Ripples on water are an example of this type of wave.	**longitudinal / transverse**
The wave has compressions and rarefactions.	**longitudinal / transverse**
Sound waves are an example of this type of wave.	**longitudinal / transverse**

⑩ Speed of sound in air　　　　　　　　　　　　　Grade 6

1. Two students measured the speed of sound in air. This is the method they used.

1. Student 1 stands 25 m away from a large wall.
2. She claps her hands to make a sound.
3. Student 2 uses a microphone and data logger.
4. He measures the time between the clap and hearing the echo.

> Remember that the wave travels to the wall and back before the echo is heard.

It takes 0.15 seconds for the sound to travel to the wall and back.

Calculate the speed of sound in air from their results. **[3 marks]**

$$speed = \frac{distance\ travelled}{..........................}$$

distance travelled = 25 × .... = ... m

$$speed = \frac{..........................}{0.15} = ...$$

speed = ... m/s

⑩ Speed of sound waves　　　　　　　　　　　　　Grade 6

2. You can often hear sound from train rails before you hear the train through the air.

A train is 495 m from a station. Calculate the difference in the time it takes the sound to travel through the air and through the rails. Give your answer to 3 decimal places.

Speed of sound in air = 330 m/s. Speed of sound in steel rails = 5800 m/s. **[4 marks]**

difference in time = ... s

3. (a) Which equation correctly links wave speed and frequency? Tick **one** box. **[1 mark]**

wave speed = frequency × wavelength ☐

$$frequency = \frac{wavelength}{wave\ speed}$$ ☐

frequency = wavelength × wave speed ☐

$$wave\ speed = \frac{frequency}{wavelength}$$ ☐

(b) The frequency of a sound wave is 11 000 Hz.

Calculate the wavelength of the sound wave when its wave speed is 330 m/s. **[3 marks]**

wavelength = ... m

 Made a start　　 Feeling confident　　 Exam ready

Properties of waves

BBC

② Quick quiz

Draw **one** line from each key word to match it to its definition.

amplitude	the number of waves passing a point each second
crest	the distance from a point on a wave to an identical point on an adjacent wave
frequency	the top of a wave
trough	the time taken to complete one full cycle or wave
wavelength	the maximum displacement of a point on a wave away from its undisturbed position
time period	the bottom of a wave

⑤ Wave equations **Grade 7**

1. The speed of sound in air is 340 m/s.

(a) A sound wave has a wavelength of 1.7 m.
Calculate its frequency. **[3 marks]**

> Remember that λ is the symbol for the wavelength.

$v = f \times \lambda$ so $f = \frac{v}{\lambda} = $ ....

frequency = ... Hz

(b) The frequency of a sound wave is 50 Hz and its wavelength is 6.8 m.
Calculate how far the wave travels in 20 s. **[4 marks]**

$v = f \times \lambda$ and $v = \frac{x}{t}$ so $f \times \lambda = \frac{x}{t}$ and $x = t \times f \times \lambda = $ ....

distance travelled = ... m

⑩ Using wave equations **Grade 7**

2. A stone is thrown into a pond. The stone causes small waves in the water. The waves spread out at a speed of 0.5 m/s. The ripples are 10 cm apart.

(a) Calculate the frequency of the waves. **[3 marks]**

frequency = ... Hz

(b) Some other waves are 20 cm apart and have a frequency of 2 Hz.
Calculate the time the waves take to travel 50 m. **[4 marks]**

time = ... s

3. A student measures the frequency of waves on the sea. He counts how many waves go past him in 30 seconds. He then divides this number by 30. Explain why he counts for 30 seconds. **[2 marks]**

....

....

4. The speed of sound in water is 1500 m/s. A diver makes a sound underwater.
Calculate how long it will take the sound to reach a detector 500 m away in the water. **[3 marks]**

time = ... s

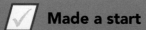 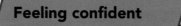

Practical: Investigating waves

② Quick quiz

Number the steps to show a method for determining the wavelength of waves in a ripple tank. The first one has been done for you.

Measure the distance the wave travelled.	
Calculate the wavelength of the wave.	
Measure the time it takes for one wave to travel from the paddle to the edge of the ripple tank.	1
Calculate the wave speed.	
Time 10 rotations of the motor and divide by 10 to get the time period of the wave.	
Calculate the frequency of the wave.	

⑩ Waves on a string

Grade 5 ✓

1. The apparatus in **Figure 1** can be used to investigate the speed of a wave on a string. The frequency of the wave depends on the frequency set on the frequency generator.

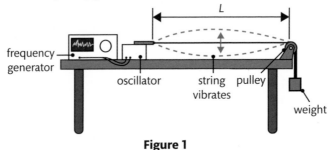

L

frequency generator

oscillator

string vibrates

pulley

weight

Figure 1

(a) Which value does the length L represent? Tick **one** box. **[1 mark]**

the wavelength ☐   half the wavelength ☐   twice the wavelength ☐   four times the wavelength ☐

(b) Explain how to determine the speed of the wave on the string. **[3 marks]**

Determine the wavelength by ....

Use the frequency from the frequency generator. Calculate the speed using the equation ....

....

⑤ Investigating speed of waves

Grade 6 ✓

2. A student investigated the effect of the length of a string on the speed of waves on the string. The student used the apparatus shown in **Figure 1**. The length of the string is changed by moving the oscillator.

> Remember that a fair test is one in which only one variable is changed; all others are kept the same.

(a) Give **two** factors the student must keep the same in order to make the experiment valid. **[2 marks]**

1 ....   2 ....

(b) Describe how the student could measure the length of the string accurately. **[3 marks]**

....

....

....

 Made a start   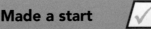 Feeling confident   Exam ready
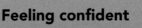

Types of electromagnetic waves

② Quick quiz

Fill in the electromagnetic spectrum by adding the waves in order of increasing frequency.

Lowest frequency ⟶ Highest frequency

radio waves			visible light			

⑩ Ultraviolet radiation   Grade 6

1. **Figure 1** shows a sunbed. People use sunbeds to tan their skin. Sunbeds use ultraviolet radiation.

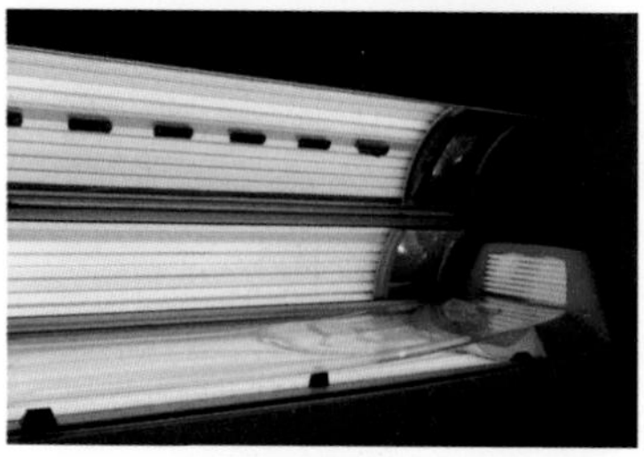

   (a) The wavelength of ultraviolet radiation used in sunbeds is 3.5×10^{-7} m. The speed of light is 3.0×10^8 m/s.

   Calculate the frequency of this radiation.   **[2 marks]**

   $v = f \times \lambda$, so $f = \dfrac{v}{\lambda} = $ ....

   frequency = ... Hz

Figure 1

   (b) Give **two** reasons why large doses of ultraviolet radiation can be harmful.
   [2 marks]

   1 ....

   2 ....

Maths skills

You can use the $(\times 10^x)$ key to enter standard form numbers on your calculator.

⑩ X-ray radiation   Grade 7

2. **Figure 2** shows images of a patient's broken arm made using X-rays.

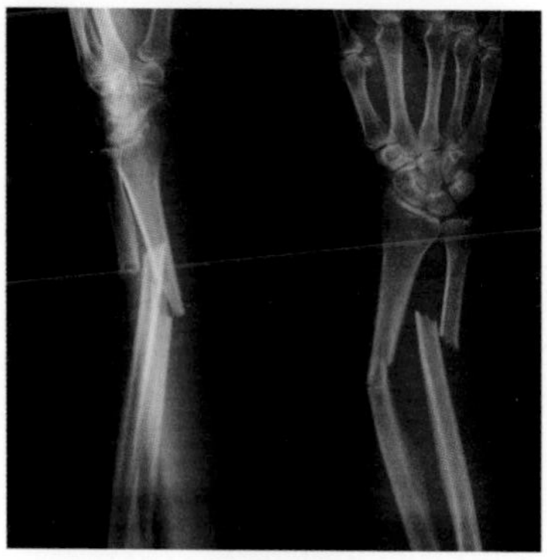

   (a) Explain why X-rays can be used to make this kind of image.   **[2 marks]**

   ....

   ....

   ....

   (b) Explain why X-rays can be dangerous.   **[2 marks]**

   ....

   ....

   ....

Figure 2

   (c) Explain why hospitals use X-rays to diagnose some medical problems in spite of the risk to patients.   **[2 marks]**

   ....

   ....

   ....

Think about the benefits of using X-rays.

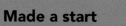 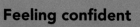

Properties of electromagnetic waves

② Quick quiz

Label the diagram using the words in the box.

angle of incidence	incident ray
angle of refraction	refracted ray
normal	

⑤ Reflection and absorption of light   Grade 7

1. Explain why grass appears to be green. Use ideas about reflection and absorption of light in your answer.   **[2 marks]**

Remember that wavelengths of light that are not reflected are absorbed.

Grass .... all the wavelengths in visible light except .... light.

The grass ....

⑮ Properties of light   Grade 7

2. Figure 1 shows a ray of light entering a glass block.

Draw the ray as it continues to go through the block and leaves at the other side.

[2 marks]

3. An electromagnetic wave travels through the air and into another substance. Part of the electromagnetic wave is reflected back into the air.

(a) State what is meant by reflection.   **[1 mark]**

....

(b) Give **two** other processes that could take place as the electromagnetic wave enters the substance.   **[2 marks]**

Figure 1

1 ....   **2** ....

4. Light waves slow down when they travel from air into glass. Draw a wave front diagram to show light waves travelling from air into glass.   **[2 marks]**

Practical: Investigating refraction

② Quick quiz

True or false?

The normal is a line drawn parallel to a refracting surface.	**True / False**
The angle of incidence is measured between the incident ray and the refracting surface.	**True / False**
When light travels from air into a glass block, the angle of refraction is always less than the angle of incidence.	**True / False**

③ Refraction of light   Grade 4

1. Explain what is meant by refraction.   **[3 marks]**

 Refraction is the change in .... of a ray of light due to a change in ....

as it passes from ....

⑮ Refraction of light   Grades 5–7

2. A device called a refractometer can be used to measure the concentration of sugar in a soft drink. Light travelling from air into the drink is refracted. The more sugar in the drink the greater the refraction.

A technician measured the angle of refraction for light in different concentrations of sugar solution.

Table 1 shows her results.

(a) Explain why the technician was **not** able to use an ordinary protractor to measure the angle of refraction.   **[2 marks]**

....

....

Table 1

Concentration of sugar solution (%)	Angle of refraction (degrees)
10	40.0
30	38.8
50	37.6
70	36.2
90	35.0

(b) Plot a graph of angle of refraction on the y-axis against concentration of sugar solution on the x-axis.   **[4 marks]**

(c) Describe the pattern shown by the graph.   **[2 marks]**

....

....

(d) Estimate the concentration of sugar solution when the angle of refraction is 38.2°.   **[1 mark]**

....

(e) Predict the angle of refraction for light in pure water. Use information from your graph.   **[2 marks]**

....

....

Applications of EM waves

② Quick quiz

Draw **one** line from each type of wave to match it to one of its applications.

radio waves	medical imaging
infrared	tanning
visible	thermal imaging
ultraviolet	TV and communications
X-rays	lasers

⑤ Uses of microwaves   Grade 6

1. **Figure 1** shows potatoes being cooked with microwaves.

   (a) Explain how microwaves cook food.   **[2 marks]**

   🚏 The microwaves are absorbed by ....

   in the food and transfer .... to the food.

   (b) Explain how microwaves cook a potato faster than using infrared radiation.

   [2 marks]

   ....

   ....

Figure 1

⑩ Uses of electromagnetic waves   Grade 7

2. Explain why gamma rays are used to sterilise medical equipment.   **[2 marks]**

....

....

3. Microwaves are used for satellite communication because they are able to pass through the Earth's atmosphere.

   (a) Name another group of electromagnetic waves that are used for communication.   **[1 mark]**

   ....

   (b) Explain why X-rays are suitable for diagnosing broken bones.   **[2 marks]**

   ....

   ....

   (c) Gamma rays are high-energy, short wavelength waves that can cause damage to cells and tissues in the body.

   Explain how this can be beneficial.   **[1 mark]**

   ....

 Made a start   **Feeling confident**   **Exam ready**

The structure of an atom

② Quick quiz

A carbon-12 atom contains 6 protons, 6 neutrons and 6 electrons.
Draw and label the structure of a carbon-12 atom.

⑤ Protons, neutrons and electrons   Grade 5

1. Atoms contain protons, neutrons and electrons.

Give the location of each subatomic particle in the atom and the type of each particle's relative charge.   **[3 marks]**

Electrons .... the nucleus. An electron is .... charged. Protons are found

.... A proton is .... charged.

Neutrons are found .... A neutron is ....

⑩ Subatomic particles   Grade 6

2. The radius of a magnesium atom is approximately 1.45×10^{-10} m. The radius of its nucleus is approximately 1×10^{-15} m.

Calculate how many times larger the radius of the atom is than the radius of the nucleus.

> Divide the radius of the atom by the radius of the nucleus.

[2 marks]

radius of atom is .... times larger

3. Protons and neutrons are both found in the nucleus of atoms.

Compare and contrast the properties of protons and neutrons.   **[3 marks]**

....

....

....

⑤ Electrons and energy   Grade 9

4. Some substances fluoresce. This means that they appear to glow.

Suggest, using ideas about electrons changing energy levels, how fluorescence occurs.   **[3 marks]**

....

....

....

Mass number, atomic number and isotopes

② Quick quiz

True or false?

The mass number of an atom is the total number of protons and electrons.	**True / False**
The atomic number tells you how many electrons an atom has.	**True / False**
mass number – atomic number = number of neutrons	**True / False**
The number of neutrons is always the same as the number of electrons.	**True / False**

⑤ Isotopes   Grade 6

1. Carbon-12 and carbon-14 are different forms of the element carbon. They are isotopes.

(a) Explain what is meant by isotopes of an element.   **[2 marks]**

Isotopes are atoms with the same .... but a different ....

....

(b) (i) Describe the similarities between the isotopes carbon-12 and carbon-14.   **[2 marks]**

Both isotopes of carbon have 6 .... and 6 ....

(ii) Give **one** difference between the isotopes carbon-12 and carbon-14.   **[1 mark]**

Carbon-14 has .... extra ....

⑮ Atomic structure   Grade 6

2. (a) Uranium-238 can be represented by the symbol $^{238}_{92}U$. Give the number of each of these subatomic particles in the uranium atom.   **[3 marks]**

protons: ....

electrons: ....

neutrons: ....

(b) Uranium-238 and uranium-235 are different isotopes of the element uranium. Compare the numbers of protons, neutrons and electrons in the two isotopes.   **[3 marks]**

....

....

....

3. When atoms gain or lose electrons they become charged.

(a) State what a charged atom is called.   **[1 mark]**

....

(b) A magnesium atom loses two electrons to become charged.

Give the charge of a charged magnesium atom.   **[1 mark]**

....

 Made a start   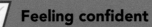 Feeling confident   Exam ready

Development of the atomic model

---

② Quick quiz

In one atomic model, the mass of an atom is distributed throughout the atom. What is the name of this model?

....

Where is most of the mass of the atom in the nuclear model?

....

---

⑩ The Bohr model   **Grade 6**

1. Describe the adaptations, made by Bohr and others, to the development of the model of the atom.   **[3 marks]**

Bohr predicted that .... travel in circular orbits around the nucleus, which contains

positively charged ....

Later, evidence was found for the existence of uncharged particles called .... in the nucleus.

2. Compare the differences between the plum pudding model and the nuclear model of the atom.   **[2 marks]**

The plum pudding model has electrons ....

.... , but the nuclear model has electrons

....

....

....   **Exam focus**

....   You need to compare the models, so make sure you
                                                                    give facts about both models.

---

⑮ The gold foil experiment   **Grade 8**

3. The nuclear model of the atom replaced the plum pudding model.

Explain how the findings of the alpha particle scattering experiment **(Figure 1)** led to the
replacement of the plum pudding model.   **[5 marks]**

....

....

....   **Figure 1** Rutherford's
                                                                                                          scattering experiment
....

....

....

....

Ionising radiation

True or false?

All ionising radiation comes from the outer part of the atom.	**True / False**
Some ionising radiation is charged.	**True / False**
All ionising radiation consists of particles.	**True / False**
Some ionising radiation is a type of electromagnetic wave.	**True / False**

⑤ Radioactive decay — Grade 5

1. Radioactive decay is a random process. Explain what is meant by a 'random process'. **[3 marks]**

A random process means that there is no way to predict which

....

and there is no way to predict when

....

The process is not affected by external conditions such as .... or ....

....

⑮ Ionising radiation — Grade 5

2. State what an alpha particle consists of. **[1 mark]**

....

3. State the nature of a beta particle. **[1 mark]**

....

4. Explain why ionising radiation can be harmful to the human body. **[4 marks]**

....

....

....

....

....

5. Explain why gamma rays have a longer range in air than either alpha or beta particles. **[4 marks]**

....

....

....

....

....

....

....

....

> **Exam focus** 📌
> The question mentions alpha and beta particles and gamma rays, so your answer should refer to all three of these.

 Made a start   **Feeling confident**   **Exam ready**

| Physics | Radioactivity | Radiation |

Background radiation

② Quick quiz

True or false?

Most background radiation comes from nuclear accidents.	**True / False**
Some background radiation comes from our food.	**True / False**
Cosmic rays are radioactive sources in rocks.	**True / False**
Nuclear power stations may be a source of background radiation.	**True / False**

⑤ Detecting and measuring radiation — Grade 6

1. Explain the difference between the activity of a radioactive source and the count rate from the radioactive source.

[2 marks]

The activity from a radioactive source is the rate at which nuclei in the source

The count rate from the source is the number of decays

....

⑮ Detecting and measuring radiation — Grades 5–7

2. Suggest why it is difficult to measure the count rate from a source of alpha particles using a Geiger-Müller tube. **[3 marks]**

> Think about the penetrating power of alpha particles.

....

....

....

....

3. (a) Explain why the level of background radiation a person is exposed to depends on where they are in the country.

[3 marks]

....

....

....

....

(b) Describe other things that can affect the level of background radiation a person is exposed to. **[2 marks]**

....

....

4. A teacher is measuring the count rate from a radioactive source. Describe what the teacher should do to prevent background radiation causing an error in the measurement. **[3 marks]**

....

....

....

 Made a start   Feeling confident   Exam ready

197

Beta decay

② **Quick quiz**

Does each description match a β– particle, a β+ particle or both? Circle the correct answers.

An electron from the nucleus   **β– particle / β+ particle / both**

A positron from the nucleus   **β– particle / β+ particle / both**

Charge of +1   **β– particle / β+ particle / both**

Charge of -1   **β– particle / β+ particle / both**

Negligible mass   **β– particle / β+ particle / both**

⑤ **Beta decay**   **Grades 7–8**

1. Explain why the emission of a β– particle results in the formation of a new element.   **[2 marks]**

When an unstable nucleus decays by β– emission, a neutron changes to a proton and an .... ,

which is immediately emitted from the nucleus. The proton remains in the nucleus, so the ....

number increases by .... , forming a new element.

2. Compare and contrast β+ particles and β– particles.   **[5 marks]**

....

....

....

....

....

3. A source of β– particles is placed close to two charged electric plates. A stream of β– particles from the source passes between the plates as shown in **Figure 1**.

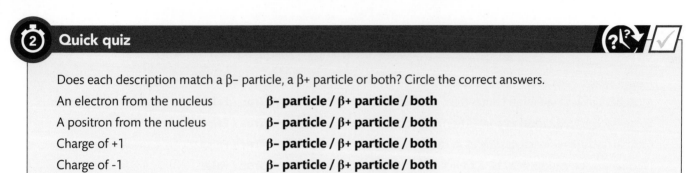

Figure 1

Explain why the stream of β– particles follows the path shown.   **[4 marks]**

....

....

....

....

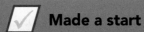 **Made a start**   **Feeling confident**   **Exam ready**

Nuclear decay

⑤ Quick quiz

Fill in the gaps in the nuclear equations.

$$^{226}_{......}Ra \longrightarrow ^{222}_{86}Rn + ^{......}_{2}He$$

$$^{......}_{6}C \longrightarrow ^{14}_{......}N + ^{......}_{......}e$$

$$^{......}_{11}Na \longrightarrow ^{24}_{......}Mg + ^{0}_{-1}e$$

$$^{219}_{......}Rn \longrightarrow ^{......}_{84}Po + ^{......}_{......}He$$

⑤ Alpha decay · Grade 6

1. Explain why the emission of an alpha particle results in the formation of a new element. **[2 marks]**

☞ When an unstable nucleus decays by emitting an alpha particle, it loses two protons and .... ,

so the atomic number ....

2. Explain what happens when a stream of alpha particles passes between two oppositely charged electric plates. **[4 marks]**

....

....

....

....

⑩ Gamma decay · Grade 6

3. (a) Explain what happens in the process of gamma decay. **[2 marks]**

....

....

(b) Explain what happens to the atomic number and the mass number of a nucleus when it emits gamma radiation. **[3 marks]**

....

....

....

⑤ Neutron decay · Grade 6

4. Explain what happens in the process of neutron decay. **[3 marks]**

....

....

....

 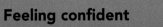

Half-lives

Fill in the gaps.

The .... -life of a radioactive source is the .... it takes for the count ....

to fall to .... its initial value. It is also the .... taken for half of the unstable

.... in a sample to decay.

⑤ **Determining half-life**   **Grade 7**

1. A sample of caesium-137 has a half-life of 30 years and activity of 50 Bq. The sample started with an activity of 1500 Bq. Determine the approximate age of the sample.   **[2 marks]**

Activity (Bq)	1500	750				
Time (years)	O	30				

The sample is approximately .... years old.
....

> Draw a table showing the activity halving every 30 years.

⑮ **Using graphs to determine half-life**   **Grade 7**

2. Table 1 shows how the number of unstable nuclei in a sample changes over time.

Table 1

Time (min)	0	2	4	6	8	10
Number of radioactive nuclei	1000	850	680	540	430	350

(a) Plot a graph to show the data, joining your points with a smooth line.   **[3 marks]**

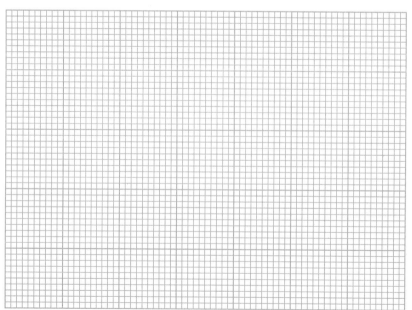

(b) Determine the half-life of the sample. Show clearly on your graph how you worked out your answer.   **[3 marks]**

half-life = ... minutes

 Made a start   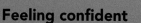 Feeling confident   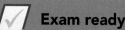 Exam ready

Dangers of radioactivity

② Quick quiz

True or false?

The risk of harm is the same from all radioactive sources.	**True / False**
Alpha radiation is always more dangerous than beta radiation.	**True / False**
Being exposed to gamma radiation always causes cancer.	**True / False**
Alpha emitters are not used as medical tracers.	**True / False**

⑮ Dangers of ionising radiation   Grades 6–7

1. Explain why ionising radiation may be dangerous for humans.   **[3 marks]**

Ionising radiation may cause direct damage to body tissue if the radiation collides with

....

Indirect damage can occur if the radiation causes

....

....

....

2. A woman is given a gamma scan to investigate a spine problem. She is injected with a liquid containing a gamma emitter. The liquid collects in areas of the spine where there is injury. After two hours she is placed in a machine that detects gamma rays.

(a) Give the reason why the woman is not placed in the detector immediately after the injection.   **[1 mark]**

> Think about the injected liquid moving to the woman's spine.

....

(b) Explain why a gamma emitter is used in the investigation, rather than an alpha emitter.   **[3 marks]**

....

....

> Think about the penetrating power of alpha particles and gamma rays.

....

(c) Explain why the medical staff stand behind a lead screen while the woman is in the detector.   **[2 marks]**

....

....

(d) Explain why the medical staff wear film badges.   **[2 marks]**

....

....

(e) During the investigation the detector rotates slowly around the woman's body.

Explain why the detector needs to rotate around the woman.   **[2 marks]**

....

....

Radioactive contamination and irradiation

② Quick quiz

Fill in the gaps using words from the box. | damaging   dose   precautions   radioactive   X-rays |

Although they are less powerful and less penetrating than gamma rays, ... can also have a .... effect on the body.

When handling .... materials, ... can be taken to minimise the radioactive .... the body receives.

⑤ Irradiation   Grade 6

1. (a) Give **two** ways that the dose received by irradiation can be increased.   **[2 marks]**

1 increased exposure time
....

2 ....

(b) State what is meant by the terms 'irradiation' and 'contamination'.   **[2 marks]**

Irradiation is the process of exposing an object to
....

Contamination is the   presence of materials containing
....

....

⑤ Peer review   Grade 5

2. (a) State what peer review is.   **[1 mark]**

....

(b) Explain why peer review is important in science.   **[1 mark]**

....

....

⑩ Precautions against irradiation and contamination   Grade 7

3. A teacher carries out a demonstration using a sample of a beta particle emitter in a school laboratory. She prevents contamination and reduces the dose from irradiation while doing the demonstration.

(a) The teacher wears plastic gloves during the demonstration. Wearing gloves does not reduce the dose from irradiation.

Explain why she wears gloves.   **[1 mark]**

....

(b) Suggest **one** measure the teacher could take to reduce the dose from irradiation.   **[1 mark]**

....

(c) Although the teacher is handling a radioactive source, it is safe for her to carry out the demonstration.

Suggest why it is safe to do this.   **[1 mark]**

....

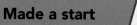 Made a start   Feeling confident   Exam ready

Revising energy transfers

② Quick quiz

True or false?

All energy transfers are useful.	**True / False**
Efficient appliances waste a large fraction of their input energy.	**True / False**
Moving objects always have kinetic energy.	**True / False**
Wasted energy is transferred to the surroundings by heating.	**True / False**
When an object is raised through a height it gains elastic potential energy.	**True / False**

⑤ Energy transfer   Grade 4

1. When a hairdryer is switched on, 50% of the input energy is transferred to thermal energy by the heater and 40% is transferred to kinetic energy to drive the fan.

(a) Calculate the percentage of the energy transferred by sound.   **[1 mark]**

 energy transferred by sound + 50% + 40% = 100%

energy transferred by sound = ...

(b) Draw a Sankey diagram for the hairdryer.   **[2 marks]**

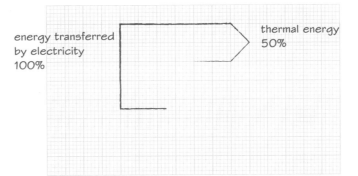

⑩ Energy   Grades 4–5

2. A child in a playground slides down a slide back to the ground.

Draw an energy flow diagram to show how the energy stores change.   **[3 marks]**

3. A car is travelling at 13 m/s and has a kinetic energy of 108 kJ.

Calculate the mass of the car.   **[4 marks]**

mass = ... kg

Work done and energy transfer

② Quick quiz

True or false?

Work done is measured in N.	**True / False**
Work is only done if the force is acting in the same direction as the displacement.	**True / False**
Force is measured in joules.	**True / False**
work done = $\dfrac{\text{force}}{\text{distance}}$	**True / False**
force = $\dfrac{\text{work done}}{\text{distance}}$	**True / False**

⑩ Calculating work done　　　　　　　　　　Grade 6

1. A car has 30 000 J of kinetic energy before the driver applies the brakes.

(a) State how much work will be done by the brakes to stop the car. **[1 mark]**

 work done = kinetic energy transferred =

work done = ... J

(b) The average braking force of the car is 2.5 kN.

Calculate the braking distance. **[3 marks]**

 Work done = ... N

$E = F \times s$ so $s = \dfrac{W}{F}$ = ...

Maths skills
To convert from kN into N multiply by 1000.

braking distance = ...

⑩ Energy transfers　　　　　　　　　　Grade 7

2. (a) Write the equation that links distance, force and work done. **[1 mark]**

....

(b) A lorry has 750 kJ of kinetic energy. The driver applies the brakes. The lorry travels a distance of 75 m as it comes to a stop. Calculate the average braking force of the lorry. **[4 marks]**

braking force = ... N

3. A person of weight 600 N climbs a set of stairs of total height 2.5 m. Calculate the amount of work done against gravity by the person in climbing the stairs. **[2 marks]**

work done = ... J

Made a start　　Feeling confident　　Exam ready

Power

---

② Quick quiz

Which equations have been correctly rearranged?

energy transferred = power × time ☐

power = $\frac{\text{work done}}{\text{time}}$ ☐

energy transferred = $\frac{\text{power}}{\text{time}}$ ☐

work done = power × time ☐

---

⑤ Calculating energy from power   Grade 6 ☑

1. A kettle has a power of 2.5 kW.

Calculate the energy transferred to the water if it takes 2 minutes to boil 1 kg of water in the kettle. **[3 marks]**

> Convert to standard units before using the equation. You need to convert from kW to W and from minutes to seconds.

2.5 kW = ... W, 2 minutes = ... s

$E = P \times t$

$E = $ .... W × .... s = ...

energy transferred = ... J

---

⑮ Calculating power   Grade 6 ☑

2. Figure 1 shows a man climbing a set of steps.

The man has a weight of 800 N. The height of the steps is 7.5 m.

(a) Calculate the amount of work done against gravity when the man climbs the steps. **[2 marks]**

work done = ... J

Figure 1

(b) It takes 15 seconds for the man to climb the steps.

Calculate the man's power. **[2 marks]**

> work done = force × distance

power = ... W

3. A fan heater takes 30 minutes to heat up a room. The power of the heater is 3 kW.

Calculate the amount of energy required to heat the room. Give your answer in standard form. **[4 marks]**

energy = ... J

4. A microwave has a power rating of 800 W. It transfers 240 000 J of energy.

Calculate how many minutes the microwave was used for. **[3 marks]**

time = ... minutes

☑ **Made a start**   ☑ **Feeling confident**   ☑ **Exam ready**

Forces

② Quick quiz

Sort the forces into contact and non-contact forces.

- weight
- tension
- magnetic force
- friction
- electrostatic force
- gravitational force

Contact forces	Non-contact forces

⑤ Labelling forces   Grade 5

1. **Figure 1** shows a block sliding down a slope.

   (a) Draw labelled arrows on the diagram to show the forces acting on the block. **[3 marks]**

   (b) Draw the diagram as a free body force diagram. **[3 marks]**

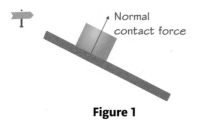

Normal
contact force

Figure 1

Represent the forces on the block as arrows passing through the centre of the dot.

⑩ Types of force   Grade 6

2. **Figure 2** shows an aeroplane in flight.

Figure 2

Draw labelled arrows to show the forces acting on the plane. **[4 marks]**

3. A student is going to carry out an investigation using a trolley on a runway.
   Before starting the investigation, the student must compensate for the effects of frictional forces acting on the trolley.

   Explain how the student could do this. **[3 marks]**

....

....

....

✓ **Made a start**   ✓ **Feeling confident**   ✓ **Exam ready**

Resultant forces

② Quick quiz

Order these statements to explain how a skydiver reaches terminal velocity.

As speed increases, air resistance increases. This cancels part of the weight. The resultant force, which causes acceleration, is a lot smaller. The speed is still increasing, but at a reduced acceleration.	
When weight and air resistance are equal, the resultant force and acceleration are zero. The skydiver has reached maximum speed.	
As the skydiver jumps, initially there is no air resistance. The resultant force is just due to the weight of the skydiver and closed parachute.	

⑩ Resultant forces　　　　　　　　　　　　　Grade 7

1. A car of mass 1000 kg is accelerating at 1.5 m/s². The total resistive force acting on the car is 500 N.

   Calculate the force from the engine. **[3 marks]**

   resultant force = $m \times a$ = ... × .... = ...

   force from engine = 500 + ... = ...

   force = ... N

   > Use $F = ma$ to find the resultant force. The force from the engine must be the sum of the resultant force and the drag force.

2. Draw a scale diagram to work out the resultant of a 500 N force and a 150 N force acting at right angles to each other. **[4 marks]**

   Maths skills 🖩
   Choose a suitable scale for your diagram.

   resultant force .... N

⑩ Terminal velocity　　　　　　　　　　　　Grade 8

3. A skydiver jumps out of a plane. She accelerates at 9.8 m/s² just as she leaves the plane. After about 10 seconds in flight, she reaches her terminal velocity.

   (a) State what is meant by 'terminal velocity'. **[1 mark]**

   ....

   (b) Explain how the skydiver reaches terminal velocity. **[4 marks]**

   ....

   ....

   ....

   ....

   (c) After about 15 seconds in flight, the skydiver opens her parachute.
   Explain why this causes her to reach a second, lower, terminal velocity. **[4 marks]**

   ....

   ....

   ....

   ....

Circuit diagrams

⑤ Quick quiz

Draw the circuit symbol for each component.

thermistor	lamp	ammeter

⑩ Series and parallel circuits   Grade 5

1. (a) Draw a circuit diagram to show three lamps connected **in series** with a battery.   **[2 marks]**

> Remember: when components are connected in series they form one single route for charge to flow.

(b) Draw a circuit diagram to show three lamps connected **in parallel** with a battery.   **[2 marks]**

> In a parallel circuit, each parallel loop is connected to the power supply.

(c) State in which circuit, series or parallel, the lamps would be brighter.   **[1 mark]**

The lamps in the .... circuit would be brighter.
....

⑤ Test circuits   Grade 5

2. A student wanted to measure the current through a lamp and the potential difference across it.
Draw the circuit the student should use to do this.   **[3 marks]**

> The test circuit is the same for measuring the current and potential difference of any component.

⑤ Circuits   Grade 6

3. Lamps and LEDs can be used in a circuit to transfer energy by light (radiation).

(a) Describe what an LED does.   **[1 mark]**

....

(b) Draw a circuit diagram of a cell in series with a resistor, a switch and an LED. The LED should light up when the switch is closed.   **[2 marks]**

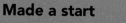 **Made a start**   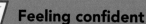 **Feeling confident**   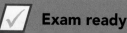 **Exam ready**

Current, resistance and potential difference

BBC

② **Quick quiz**

Draw **one** line from each key word to match it with its definition.

current	opposition to the flow of charge, measured in ohms (Ω)
potential difference	the flow of charge, measured in amps (A)
resistance	the energy given to each unit of charge, measured in volts (V)

⑩ **Linking current, pd and resistance**   **Grade 6**

1. Each resistor in the circuit in **Figure 1** has a resistance of 10 Ω. The battery has a potential difference of 6 V.

(a) Explain what the reading on the voltmeter will be.   **[2 marks]**

   The reading will be .... because ....
   ....

(b) Calculate the current in the circuit.   **[3 marks]**

   total resistance = ...

   $\text{current} = \dfrac{\text{potential difference}}{\text{resistance}} = $ ....

                                                      current = ... A

(c) The potential difference is halved.

   Explain what effect this will have on the current in the circuit.   **[2 marks]**

   ....

   ....

> Remember that pd is proportional to current.

Figure 1

⑮ $V = I \times R$ **Grade 6**

2. A car headlight is switched on. The potential difference from the supply is 12 V and the current is 5 A.

   Calculate the resistance of the lamp in the car headlight.   **[3 marks]**

                                                      resistance = ... Ω

3. Calculate the resistance of a component that draws 10 A of current with a potential difference of 230 V.   **[3 marks]**

                                                      resistance = ... Ω

4. A resistor with a resistance of 30 mΩ is placed in a circuit. The potential difference across the resistor is 4.5 V.

   Calculate the current through the resistor.   **[4 marks]**

                                                      current = ... A

Charge, current and energy

 Quick quiz

True or false?

The unit of potential difference is the joule.	**True / False**
The unit of charge is the volt.	**True / False**
The unit of current is the amp.	**True / False**

 Charge calculations **Grade 6**

1. The current in an appliance is 10 A. The appliance is switched on for 30 minutes.

(a) Calculate the charge flow in the appliance. **[3 marks]**

 30 minutes = 30 × 60 = 1800 seconds

charge = current × time

charge = ... A × .... s = ...

charge flow = ... C

> **Maths skills**
> Convert quantities into standard units before substituting into the equation.

(b) The appliance is connected to the mains supply with a potential difference of 230 V.

Calculate the energy transferred by the appliance in 30 minutes. **[2 marks]**

energy transferred = charge flow × potential difference

energy transferred = ... × 230 = ... energy transferred = ...J

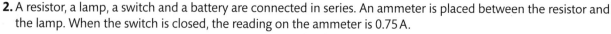 **Electrical charge** **Grade 6**

2. A resistor, a lamp, a switch and a battery are connected in series. An ammeter is placed between the resistor and the lamp. When the switch is closed, the reading on the ammeter is 0.75 A.

(a) The ammeter is moved so it is placed between the lamp and the closed switch. Explain what would happen to the reading on the ammeter. **[2 marks]**

....

(b) Calculate the charge transferred when the switch is closed for 120 seconds. **[2 marks]**

charge = ... C

3. A lamp in a series circuit transfers 50 C of charge. The current in the lamp is 0.5 A.

(a) Calculate how long the lamp was on for. **[3 marks]**

time = ... s

(b) The lamp is connected in series with a 12 V cell. Calculate the energy transferred to the lamp. **[2 marks]**

energy transferred = ...J

 Made a start **Feeling confident** **Exam ready**

Series and parallel circuits

② Quick quiz

Does each statement apply to a **series** or **parallel** circuit?

The current is the same through all components.	series / parallel
The current is the sum of the currents through each component.	series / parallel
The potential difference is the same across each component.	series / parallel
The potential difference is split across the components.	series / parallel
The total resistance is the sum of all the resistances.	series / parallel

⑤ Resistance   Grade 6

1. Two resistors have resistances of 10 Ω and 3 Ω.

> The total resistance in a series circuit is the sum of the individual resistances.

(a) Give the total resistance if the resistors are connected in series.   **[1 mark]**

➤ 10 + ...

(b) Describe the total resistance if the resistors are connected in parallel.   **[1 mark]**

➤ Total resistance will be less than ....

⑮ Combining resistance   Grade 8

2. A buzzer, a lamp and a 12 V battery are connected in series. The resistance of the buzzer is 10 Ω and the resistance of the lamp is 14 Ω. There is a current of 0.5 A flowing through the lamp.

(a) There is a potential difference of 7 V across the lamp. Calculate the potential difference across the buzzer.   **[1 mark]**

potential difference = ...V

(b) Calculate the total resistance of the circuit.   **[2 marks]**

total resistance = ...Ω

(c) Explain how the total resistance of the circuit will change if the buzzer and lamp are connected in parallel.   **[2 marks]**

....

....

3. Three resistors with resistances of 3 Ω, 5 Ω and 2 Ω are connected in series with a 12 V power supply.

(a) Draw a circuit diagram showing this circuit.   **[2 marks]**

(b) Calculate the total resistance in the series circuit.   **[1 mark]**

total resistance = ...Ω

(c) The resistors are now connected in parallel. Describe the total resistance of the resistors in parallel.   **[1 mark]**

....

☑ Made a start   ☑ Feeling confident   ☑ Exam ready

Practical: Resistance

② Quick quiz

Which is the best definition of resistance? Tick **one** box.

The flow of electrical charge in a wire. ☐

The opposition to the flow of electrical charge in a circuit. ☐

The energy given to the charge as it flows. ☐

A measure of the number of electrons flowing in a circuit. ☐

⑤ Reducing errors   Grade 5

1. A student investigated the effect of the length of a wire on its resistance. The circuit is shown in **Figure 1**.

   (a) The student cleaned the ends of the wire with wire wool before carrying out the experiment.

   Explain why the student did this.   **[2 marks]**

   The wire needed to be cleaned to
   ....
   ....

   (b) Give **two** ways to prevent the wire getting too hot in the experiment.
                                                        [2 marks]
   ....
   ....

Figure showing circuit with ammeter A, voltmeter V, ruler, test wire, moveable connector (e.g. crocodile clips).

Figure 1

> Think about wire length and current.

⑮ Thermistor investigation   Grade 8

2. Describe how to carry out an investigation into the effect of temperature on the resistance of a thermistor.   **[6 marks]**

....
....
....
....

> **Exam focus**
> Remember to write your answers to extended response questions in a structured and logical way.

....
....
....
....

3. A cell, a variable resistor and a fixed resistor are connected in series. The resistance of the variable resistor is increased.

   Explain the effect of this on the current in the fixed resistor.   **[4 marks]**

....
....
....
....

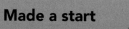 Made a start   Feeling confident   Exam ready

Resistors

② Quick quiz

Draw lines to match the shape of each *I–V* graph to its component.

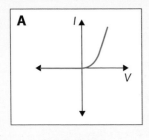 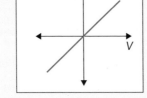 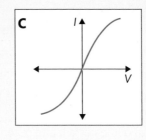

| fixed resistor | filament lamp | diode |

⑩ I–V graphs — Grade 5

1. (a) Explain what the gradient of an *I–V* graph for a fixed resistor tells you. **[2 marks]**

For a resistor, the gradient of an I–V graph is equal to
....

The steeper the line, the
....

(b) The current through a piece of metal wire at a constant temperature is directly proportional to the potential difference across it.

Describe the *I–V* graph for a metal wire at a constant temperature. **[2 marks]**

....

....

(c) The filament in a filament bulb is made from a piece of metal wire.

Explain why the gradient of an *I–V* graph is not constant. **[4 marks]**

A current flowing through the filament causes   The increased current at higher
....

....

....

....

....

⑤ Resistance graphs — Grade 6

2. (a) Sketch a graph of resistance against temperature for a thermistor. **[2 marks]**

(b) Sketch a graph of resistance against light intensity for an LDR. **[2 marks]**

Practical: *I–V* characteristics

 Quick quiz

Number the instructions to show the correct order of how to create an *I–V* graph for a given component. The first one has been done for you.

Plot a graph of current against potential difference.	
Measure the current passing through the component for each potential difference.	
Change the potential difference across the component using a variable resistor.	
Set up a circuit with an ammeter to measure the current through the component and a voltmeter to measure the potential difference across it.	1
Switch the direction of the current and potential difference by swapping the connections on the power supply.	

 Investigating the relationship between current and pd — Grade 6

1. A student investigates how the current in a diode changes with potential difference.

(a) Draw a circuit that could be used to investigate how the current in a diode changes with potential difference. **[3 marks]**

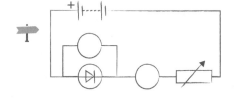

> This will be the standard test circuit with a diode.

(b) Sketch the *I–V* graph the student should expect to obtain. **[2 marks]**

> The resistance of a diode depends on the direction of the current.

 Resistance from an *I–V* graph — Grades 6–7

2. A student investigated the relationship between the current and potential difference of a piece of wire with the temperature kept constant.

(a) State why the circuit the student used included a variable resistor. **[1 mark]**

....

(b) Describe the shape of the *I–V* graph the student should obtain. **[1 mark]**

....

(c) Explain how the *I–V* graph shows that the wire has a fixed resistance. **[2 marks]**

....

....

(d) The student switched the circuit off between readings. Explain why this was a good idea. **[2 marks]**

....

....

 Made a start   Feeling confident   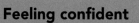 Exam ready

Energy transfer in circuits

② Quick quiz

Complete the sentences using words from the box.

| cools | current | electrons | heats | ions | neutrons | protons |

When there is an electric .... in a resistor, there is an energy transfer which

.... the resistor. This energy transfer is the result of collisions between ....

and .... in the lattice.

(10) Heating effect of a current   Grades 5–6

1. When an electrical appliance is switched on, thermal energy is dissipated to the surroundings.

Explain why.   **[3 marks]**

When the appliance is switched on, an electric current

....

....

....

2. The heating effect of an electrical current can be useful and can be a disadvantage.

(a) Give **three** examples when the heating effect of an electric current is useful.   **[3 marks]**

1 *Heating water in an electric kettle*

....

2 ....

3 ....

(b) Give **three** examples when the heating effect of an electric current is a disadvantage.   **[3 marks]**

1 ....

2 ....

3 ....

(10) Calculating energy transferred   Grade 6

3. A torch is switched on for 2 minutes. During this time 810 J of energy is transferred to the filament in the torch bulb. The current in the filament is 750 mA.

> You will need to select this equation from the list of equations at the end of the exam paper.

(a) Calculate the potential difference of the torch battery.   **[4 marks]**

potential difference = ... V

(b) Explain why the filament gets hot when the torch is switched on.   **[3 marks]**

....

....

....

 Made a start   Feeling confident   ✓ Exam ready   **215**

Electrical power

BBC

② Quick quiz

Draw **one** line from each quantity to match it to its unit.

power	energy	time	current	potential difference	resistance

seconds (s)	volts (V)	joules (J)	amps (A)	ohms (Ω)		watts (W)

⑤ Power   Grade 6

1. An electric kettle transfers 200kJ of energy when it heats water for 3 minutes.

Calculate the power of the kettle.   **[3 marks]**

200 kJ = ... J,   3 minutes = ... s

$P = \dfrac{E}{t} = $ ....

> Convert the energy and time into standard units.

> **Maths skills**
> Always check that the quantities in the question are in the standard units needed for the equation.

power = ... W

⑮ Electrical power equations   Grade 6

2. An electric oven uses a current of 5 A when connected to the mains supply at 230 V.

Calculate the power of the oven.   **[2 marks]**

power = ... W

3. A hairdryer has a power rating of 2000 W. The hairdryer is connected to a mains supply of 230 V.

(a) Calculate the current in the hairdryer.   **[3 marks]**

current = ... A

(b) Calculate the resistance of the hairdryer.   **[3 marks]**

resistance = ... Ω

4. A microwave has a power rating of 800 W. It is connected to the mains supply with a potential difference of 230 V.

(a) Calculate the current in the microwave. Give your answer to 2 significant figures.   **[3 marks]**

current = ... A

(b) The microwave is used for 5 minutes. Calculate the energy transferred when it is used.   **[3 marks]**

energy transferred = ... J

 Made a start   Feeling confident   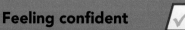 Exam ready

Mains electricity

② Quick quiz

True or false?

Mains electricity is direct current.	**True / False**
There are two or three colour-coded wires in appliance plugs.	**True / False**
The neutral wire in a three-core cable has a blue cover.	**True / False**
The live wire is always at 0 V.	**True / False**

⑤ Earthing   Grade 6

1. (a) Explain why touching the live wire of an appliance is dangerous.   **[2 marks]**

Touching the live wire is dangerous because you complete a
....
                    between
....
and
....

> **Exam focus**
> Check how many marks each question is worth: for 2 marks you must make two distinct points.

(b) All metal-cased appliances should be earthed.

State what it means when an appliance is 'earthed'.   **[1 mark]**

....

....

⑮ Mains supply   Grade 6

2. An appliance plug contains a three-core cable and a fuse.

Which wire is the fuse connected to? Tick **one** box.   **[1 mark]**

earth wire ☐   live wire ☐   neutral wire ☐   case of the appliance ☐

3. A kettle uses mains electricity, while a torch uses a battery.

(a) Explain the difference between these two supplies of electricity.   **[2 marks]**

....

....

(b) Give the frequency of the domestic mains electricity supply in the UK.   **[1 mark]**

....

4. Draw a graph of potential difference against time for the domestic mains electricity supply in the UK.   **[3 marks]**

Energy transfers in appliances

② Quick quiz

Write 'useful' or 'wasted' next to each description of an energy transfer.

A torch transfers energy from its chemical store to its thermal store as light. ....

A drill transfers energy to the thermal store in the environment when it is used. ....

The heating elements in a toaster transfer energy from its thermal store as light when it is turned on.

....

A laptop computer transfers energy from its chemical store to the thermal store in the environment when it is on. ....

⑩ Useful and wasted energy transfers   Grade 5

1. Complete the table for each of these devices.   **[3 marks]**

Device	Energy source or store	Useful energy transfers	Wasted energy transfers
Hair dryer	transfer by electricity	kinetic,	
Electric drill	transfer by electricity		
Mobile phone			

Mains appliances transfer energy from the mains to other energy stores. Battery-powered appliances transfer energy from their chemical stores as electricity to other energy stores. Wasted energy is most commonly transferred to thermal stores in the environment, or kinetic stores of particles (as sound).

⑩ Energy transfers   Grade 5

2. Figure 1 shows a television.

(a) Give the energy transfers that take place when the television is turned on.   **[1 mark]**

....

(b) Identify which of the energy transfers you gave in **(a)** are wasted and which are useful.   **[2 marks]**

....

....

Figure 1

(c) Electricity from the mains carries 2000 J of energy to the television. 1500 J of this energy is usefully transferred to other stores.

Calculate how much energy is wasted.   **[1 mark]**

wasted energy = ...J

(d) Describe what happens to the wasted energy.   **[1 mark]**

....

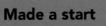 Made a start   Feeling confident   Exam ready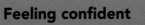

Magnetic fields

② Quick quiz

Draw the magnetic field lines around the bar magnet.

N ▮ S

⑤ Types of magnets   Grade 6

1. **Figure 1** shows paper clips hanging from a bar magnet. The paper clips are induced magnets.

   Describe what is meant by the term 'induced magnet'. **[2 marks]**

   An induced magnet is:
   ....
   * an object that becomes magnetic when placed in a
   ....
   * always .... to a permanent magnet.
   ....

   ### Exam focus
   You can use bullet points in your answer to make sure you have made two different points.

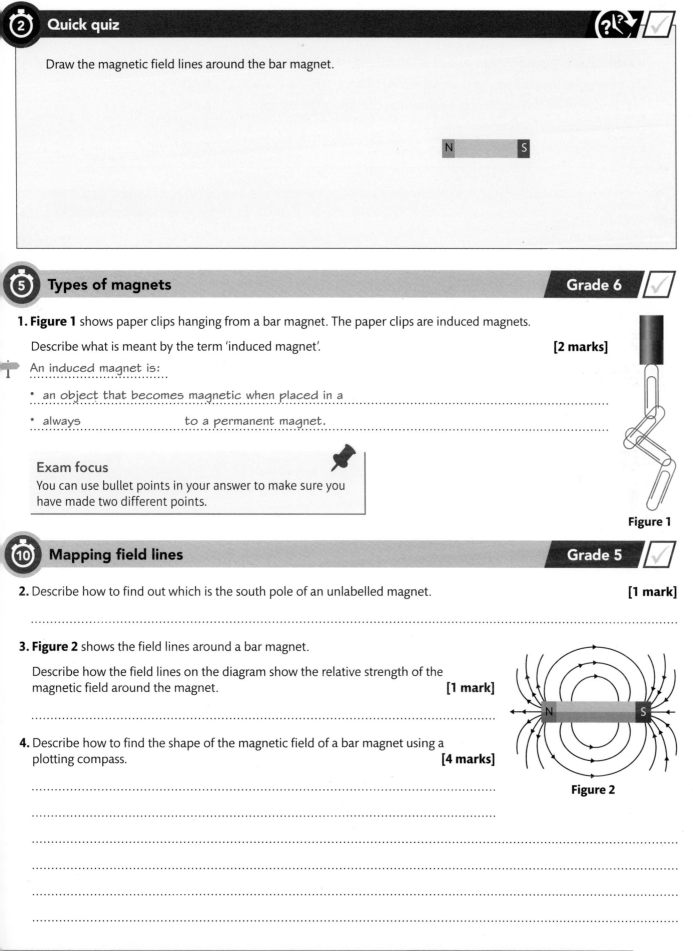

Figure 1

⑩ Mapping field lines   Grade 5

2. Describe how to find out which is the south pole of an unlabelled magnet. **[1 mark]**

   ....

3. **Figure 2** shows the field lines around a bar magnet.

   Describe how the field lines on the diagram show the relative strength of the magnetic field around the magnet. **[1 mark]**

   ....

4. Describe how to find the shape of the magnetic field of a bar magnet using a plotting compass. **[4 marks]**

   ....
   ....
   ....
   ....
   ....
   ....
   ....

Figure 2

Electromagnetism

② Quick quiz

Is each statement an advantage (**A**) or disadvantage (**D**) of an electromagnet?

Electromagnets use electricity and so cost money to run.	A / D
The strength of electromagnets can be altered by controlling the current.	A / D
Electromagnets can be switched on and off.	A / D
Electromagnets can get hot.	A / D

⑤ Solenoids — Grade 5

1. (a) Explain what a solenoid is. **[2 marks]**

🪧 A coil of wire

....

....

(b) Describe how a solenoid is made into an electromagnet. **[1 mark]**

....

⑤ Electromagnets — Grade 5

2. (a) Figure 1 shows a wire carrying a current.

Draw the magnetic field around the wire on the diagram. **[2 marks]**

(b) Give **two** things that affect the strength of the magnetic field around the electromagnet at a particular point. **[2 marks]**

1 ....

2 ....

current

Figure 1

⑤ Using electromagnets — Grade 7

3. Coiling a wire into a solenoid makes a magnetic field, just like that around a bar magnet.

(a) How could you determine the direction of the current in the coil? Tick **one** box. **[1 mark]**

using the right-hand grip rule, the thumb points in the direction of the current ☐

using the right-hand grip rule, the direction of the fingers represents the direction of the current ☐

using the left-hand grip rule, the thumb points in the direction of the current ☐

using the left-hand grip rule, the direction of the fingers represents the direction of the current ☐

(b) How could you determine the north pole of the solenoid? Tick **one** box. **[1 mark]**

using the right-hand grip rule, the thumb points in the direction of the current ☐

using the right-hand grip rule, the direction of the fingers represents the direction of the magnetic field ☐

using the right-hand grip rule, the thumb points in the direction of the magnetic field ☐

using the left-hand grip rule; the direction of the fingers represents the direction of the magnetic field ☐

The motor effect

---

② Quick quiz

For Fleming's left-hand rule, draw lines to match the part of the hand to the information it gives about the force on a current-carrying wire.

thumb		magnetic field, north to south
first finger		current, positive to negative
second finger		motion / direction of force

---

⑤ The motor effect

Grade 5

1. **Figure 1** shows a current-carrying wire in a magnetic field.

   Give **three** ways in which the force on the wire could be increased. **[3 marks]**

   1 increasing the magnetic flux density of the magnetic field

   2 increasing the

   3 ....

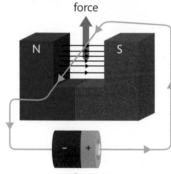

force

N   S

Figure 1

---

⑮ Size of force on a wire

Grade 8

2. **Figure 2** shows a current-carrying wire in a magnetic field. | Use Fleming's left-hand rule. |

   (a) Draw an arrow on the diagram to show the direction of the force on the wire. **[1 mark]**

   (b) The length of wire in the magnetic field is 10 cm and it carries a current of 5.0 A. The magnetic flux density of the magnetic field is 0.5 T.

   Calculate the magnitude of the force on the wire. **[3 marks]**

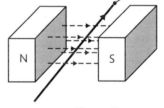

wire carrying current

N   S

Figure 2

   force = ... N

3. A wire of length 0.45 m is placed in a magnetic field, perpendicular to the direction of the field. There is a current of 10.0 A in the wire. The force acting on the wire due to the magnetic field is 0.50 N.

   Calculate the magnetic flux density of the magnetic field. **[3 marks]**

   magnetic flux density = ... T

4. A wire is in a magnetic field where the flux density of the field is 7 T, the current in the wire is 10 A and the wire is 0.1 m long, and is at right angles to the field.

   Calculate the force acting on the wire. **[2 marks]**

   force = ... N

 Made a start   **Feeling confident**   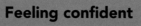 **Exam ready**

Transformers

---

② Quick quiz

True or false?

Transformers increase or decrease the potential difference of a supply.	**True / False**
Transformers only work with an alternating supply.	**True / False**
A transformer consists of a single coil of wire wound on a core.	**True / False**
A transformer core is made from lead.	**True / False**

---

② Transformer construction   **Grades 6–7**

1. Describe the construction of a transformer. **[3 marks]**

A transformer consists of two coils of insulated wire wound onto
....

....

2. (a) State why the core of a transformer is made from soft iron. **[1 mark]**

....

(b) Explain why the coils of wire on a transformer are insulated. **[2 marks]**

....

....

(c) Explain why a transformer only works with alternating current. **[2 marks]**

....

....

....

---

⑩ Transformer function   **Grades 6–7**

3. Explain how a transformer works. **[4 marks]**

....

....

....

....

4. State the factors that affect the size of an induced potential difference. **[4 marks]**

....

....

....

....

....

....

....

 Made a start   **Feeling confident**   **Exam ready**

Transformers and the National Grid

Quick quiz

True or false?

Transformers are used to increase the efficiency of the National Grid.	**True / False**
Step-up transformers increase potential difference.	**True / False**
Step-down transformers increase potential difference.	**True / False**
$\text{power} = \dfrac{\text{potential difference}}{\text{current}}$	**True / False**

Transformer equation | Grade 7

1. In a transformer, the p.d. across the primary coil is 230 V and the current in the primary coil is 0.5 A. The secondary coil output has a potential difference of 10 V.

(a) Explain whether this is a step-up or a step-down transformer. **[1 mark]**

....

> Step-up transformers increase the potential difference.

(b) Calculate the current in the secondary coil. **[3 marks]**

$V_p \times I_p = V_s \times I_s$ so $230 \times 0.5 = \dfrac{V_p \times I_p}{V_s}$

$I_s = \dfrac{\text{............} \times \text{............}}{\text{............}} = \text{............}$

> **Exam focus**
> In the exam, you will need to choose the correct equation from the Physics equation sheet.

current = ... A

The National Grid | Grade 7

2. **Figure 1** shows the National Grid.

(a) Explain why step-up transformers are used to increase the potential difference from about 25 kV to 400 kV. **[2 marks]**

....

....

(b) State why there is a need for a step-down transformer before the electrical supply reaches the consumer. **[1 mark]**

....

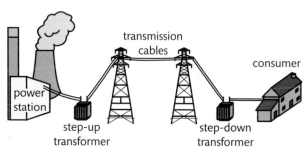

Figure 1

3. In a transformer, the primary coil input is 330 V and the current in the primary coil is 3.0 A. The secondary coil output has a potential difference of 15 000 V.

(a) Explain whether this is a step-up or a step-down transformer. **[1 mark]**

....

(b) Calculate the current in the secondary coil. **[3 marks]**

current = ... A

 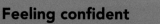

Changes of state

BBC

② Quick quiz

True or false?

The temperature a substance freezes at is called the melting point.	**True / False**
The temperature a substance condenses at is called the boiling point.	**True / False**
Changes of state are reversible.	**True / False**
Density is conserved in a change of state.	**True / False**

⑩ State changes   Grade 8

1. Ethanol has a boiling point of 78 °C. A sample of ethanol is heated from room temperature to its boiling point.

Explain what is happening to the energy in the system as the ethanol is heated.   **[5 marks]**

The energy supplied to the ethanol increases the .... of the particles, so the temperature

of the ethanol sample .... When the ethanol reaches its boiling point, the energy supplied is used to

.... between the particles of the liquid so it .... and becomes a gas.

During the change of state there is no increase in the kinetic energy of the particles so the temperature ....

....

⑩ Cooling curve   Grade 6

2. Stearic acid is a solid at room temperature.

Figure 1 shows a boiling tube containing some stearic acid. The boiling tube is heated until all the stearic acid melts. Then it is allowed to cool.

The temperature is recorded every minute as the liquid stearic acid cools.

The temperature of the stearic acid stays the same between 10 and 12 minutes.

Timing stops after 15 minutes.

(a) Sketch the shape of the temperature–time graph the results would give.   **[2 marks]**

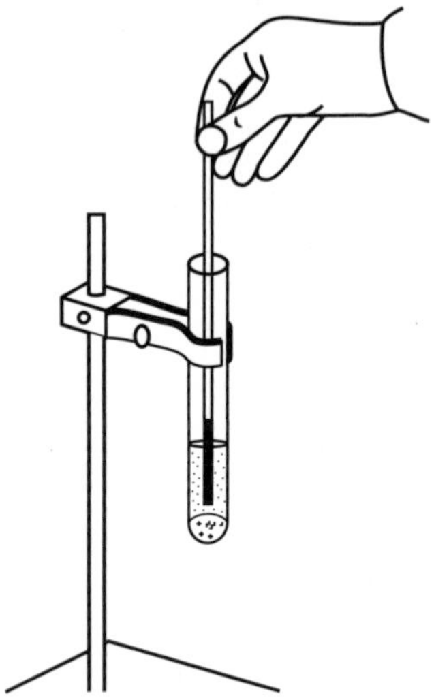

Figure 1

(b) Explain why the temperature of the stearic acid stays the same between 10 and 12 minutes.   **[2 marks]**

....

....

....

 Made a start   Feeling confident   Exam ready

Density

 Quick quiz

Draw **one** line from each quantity to match it to its unit.

mass	m^3
volume	kg/m^3
density	m
length	kg

 **Calculating density** | **Grade 7** |

1. An aluminium block has the following dimensions: height 10 cm; width 15 cm; depth 5.0 cm. It is a cuboid. The block has a mass of 2.0 kg.

> It is easier to convert each dimension from cm to m than to try to convert the final volume from cm^3 to m^3.

(a) Calculate the volume of the block in m^3. Give your answer in standard form. **[2 marks]**

 Convert the dimensions to metres:

height = ... m, width = ... m, depth = ... m

volume = height × width × depth = ... × .... × .... = ...

volume = ... m^3

(b) Calculate the density of the aluminium block. Give your answer to 2 significant figures. **[3 marks]**

 $density = \dfrac{mass}{volume} = \dfrac{............}{............} = ...$

density = ... kg/m^3 (to 2 significant figures)

Maths skills
To convert from cm to m, divide by 100.

(c) A different aluminium block has a mass of 10.50 kg. Calculate the volume of this block. Give your answer in standard form. **[3 marks]**

 $volume = \dfrac{mass}{density} = \dfrac{............}{............} = ...$

volume = ... m^3

 Density and floating | **Grade 7** |

2. The density of cooking oil is 915 kg/m^3.

(a) 10 cm^3 of the cooking oil is added to a pan.
Calculate the volume of the oil in m^3. **[2 marks]**

volume = ... m^3

(b) Calculate the mass of cooking oil that was added to the pan. **[3 marks]**

mass = ... kg

3. A concrete paving slab is 2.5 cm thick and has a mass of 30 kg. The density of concrete is 2400 kg/m^3.
Calculate the area of the paving slab in metres squared. **[4 marks]**

area = ... m^2

 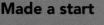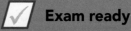

Practical: Density of materials

② Quick quiz

True or false?

A unit of density is g/mm³	**True / False**
Density can be measured with a top-pan balance.	**True / False**
The mass of a sample of a substance can be calculated using mass = $\frac{mass}{volume}$	**True / False**
A unit of density is m²/kg	**True / False**
Volume can be measured using a measuring cylinder.	**True / False**

⑮ Measuring density
Grade 6

1. Describe a method to determine the density of a small irregularly shaped object. **[5 marks]**

Measure the mass of the object using a .... Put some water in a measuring cylinder

and record ....

....

....

....

2. Describe a method to determine the density of milk. **[5 marks]**

....

....

....

....

....

3. A cuboid of mass 0.5 kg has the following measurements: height = 10.0 cm, width = 5.0 cm, depth = 3.0 cm.

Calculate the density of the cuboid in g/cm³. **[4 marks]**

density = ... g/cm³

Make a quick sketch and label the dimensions.

⑤ Experimental design
Grade 5

4. Suggest **three** ways in which errors in the method in Question **1** could be reduced. **[3 marks]**

....

....

....

✓ **Made a start** ✓ **Feeling confident** ✓ **Exam ready**

Specific heat capacity

② Quick quiz

Rearrange this equation, $\Delta Q = mc\Delta\theta$, to make each of the following quantities the subject of the equation.

mass, $m =$

specific heat capacity, $c =$

change in temperature, $\Delta\theta =$

⑤ Calculating energy transfer · Grade 7

1. An electric kettle heats 1500 g of water from 20 °C to 100 °C. The specific heat capacity of water is 4200 J/kg °C.

Calculate the energy transferred from the kettle to the water. **[3 marks]**

$\Delta Q = mc\Delta\theta$

1500 g = ... kg

$\Delta Q =$ .... × 4200 × .... = ...

> **Exam focus** 📌
> Remember that $\Delta\theta$ means change in temperature.

energy transferred = ...J

⑮ Specific heat capacity · Grade 7

2. Figure 1 shows a storage heater.

The storage heater contains 20 kg of concrete.

400 000 J of energy is transferred to heat up the concrete from 15 °C to 40 °C.

(a) State what is meant by 'specific heat capacity'. **[1 mark]**

....

....

(b) Calculate the specific heat capacity of concrete. **[3 marks]**

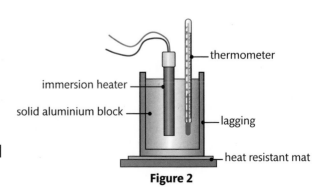

Figure 1

specific heat capacity of concrete = ...J/kg °C

3. Figure 2 shows the equipment used to determine the specific heat capacity of an aluminium block.

The mass of the aluminium block is 1.0 kg. The specific heat capacity of aluminium is 900 J/kg °C. The temperature of the block at the start of the experiment was 20 °C. It increased to 32 °C.

Calculate the energy transferred by the heater to the block. **[2 marks]**

thermometer

immersion heater

solid aluminium block

lagging

heat resistant mat

Figure 2

energy transferred = ...J

 Made a start **Feeling confident** 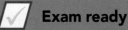 **Exam ready** **227**

Specific latent heat

 Quick quiz

True or false?

The specific latent heat of fusion is the energy required to change 1 kg of a liquid into 1 kg of a gas at constant temperature.   **True / False**

The units of specific latent heat of fusion are J/kg.   **True / False**

The specific latent heat of vaporisation is the energy released when 1 kg of a gas is changed to 1 kg of a liquid at constant temperature.   **True / False**

The units of specific latent heat of vaporisation are J/kg °C.   **True / False**

 Specific latent heat of fusion   Grade 6

1. It takes 1680 kJ of energy to melt 5.0 kg of ice at 0 °C.

Calculate the latent heat of fusion of water.   **[3 marks]**

$Q =$ .... J

$$Q = mL \text{ so } L = \frac{Q}{m} = \frac{\text{..........}}{\text{..........}} = \text{.........................}$$

> **Maths skills**
> To convert from kJ to J, multiply by 1000.

latent heat of fusion = ...J/kg

 Specific latent heat   Grade 7

2. Figure 1 shows some ice cubes in a glass of lemonade.

The specific latent heat of fusion of water is 336 000 J/kg.

(a) State what is meant by 'specific latent heat of fusion'.   **[2 marks]**

....

....

(b) 30 g of ice were added to the lemonade. Calculate how much energy from the lemonade was used in melting the ice.   **[2 marks]**

Figure 1

energy = ...J

3. 5×10^{-2} kg of water is vaporised at 100 °C. 112 000 J of energy are transferred from the thermal store of the water to the thermal store of the vapour.

Calculate the specific latent heat of vaporisation for water. Give your answer in standard form. Give the unit.   **[4 marks]**

specific latent heat = ...

    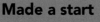 **Made a start**   **Feeling confident**   **Exam ready**

Practical: Properties of water

Quick quiz

Cross out the incorrect **bold** words to make each sentence correct.

The **higher / lower** the specific heat capacity of a substance, the more energy it takes to increase the temperature of a given mass of the substance.

The **higher / lower** the specific latent heat of a substance, the more energy it takes to change the state of a given mass of the substance.

A liquid with a **high / low** specific heat capacity would be the most suitable for use in a central heating system.

Specific heat capacity by electrical heating · Grade 7

1. A student has the following equipment to determine the specific heat capacity of aluminium:

- electric heater
- thermometer
- stopwatch
- 1 kg aluminium block.

Exam focus

When asked a question about a required practical, say what you measured and what you measured it with.

Describe a method the student could use to determine the specific heat capacity of aluminium. **[5 marks]**

1 Measure the start temperature of the aluminium block using the thermometer.

2 Heat the block

3 Measure the highest temperature reached after

4 Calculate the energy input using

5 Calculate the specific heat capacity using

Specific heat capacity using hot water · Grade 7

2. The specific heat capacity of a metal can be found using a method where the block of metal is placed in a beaker containing hot water.

Give **three** ways in which the errors in this method can be reduced. **[3 marks]**

1 .... 2 .... 3 ....

Specific heat capacity data · Grade 7

3. The specific heat capacities of substance X and substance Y are shown in **Table 1**.

(a) Substance X and substance Y are heated by a 2 kW heater. The temperatures of X and Y rise at different rates. Explain which one would rise the slowest. **[2 marks]**

....

....

Table 1

Substance	Specific heat capacity (J/kg °C)
X	300
Y	2200

(b) A 2 kg sample of substance Y is heated from 10 °C to 50 °C.

Calculate how much energy is transferred to the sample. **[2 marks]**

energy = ... J

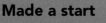

Particle motion in gases

② Quick quiz

True or false?

Metres squared is a unit of volume.	**True / False**	N/m^2 is a unit of pressure.	**True / False**
Kelvin is a unit of temperature.	**True / False**	C is a unit of temperature.	**True / False**
Pascal is a unit of volume.	**True / False**		

⑤ Gas in containers   Grade 4

1. Explain what is meant by the term 'absolute zero'.   **[3 marks]**

Absolute zero is the lowest temperature

....

....

⑮ Gas pressure   Grade 7

2. Figure 1 shows a container of propane gas. Propane gas is used as camping gas. It is important that the container is kept cool.

Explain, using ideas about gas pressure, why it is important that the container is kept cool.   **[4 marks]**

If the gas is heated, the kinetic energy of the particles increases.

This causes the particles to

....

....

....

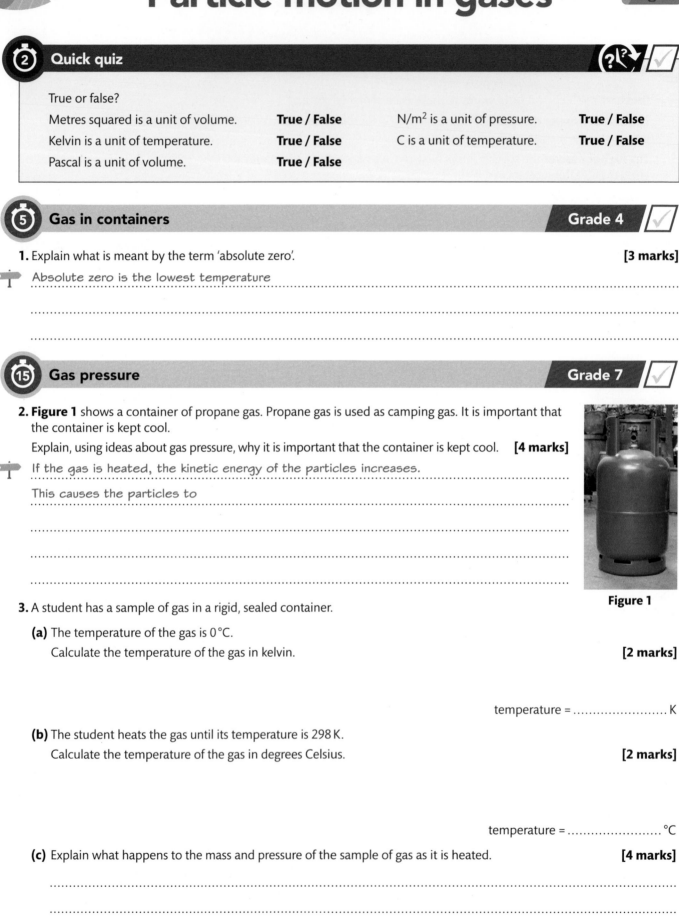

Figure 1

3. A student has a sample of gas in a rigid, sealed container.

(a) The temperature of the gas is 0 °C.
Calculate the temperature of the gas in kelvin.   **[2 marks]**

temperature = ... K

(b) The student heats the gas until its temperature is 298 K.
Calculate the temperature of the gas in degrees Celsius.   **[2 marks]**

temperature = ... °C

(c) Explain what happens to the mass and pressure of the sample of gas as it is heated.   **[4 marks]**

....

....

....

....

Forces and elasticity

 Quick quiz

True or false?

Compression usually involves a single force.	**True / False**
Hooke's law states that the extension of an elastic object is inversely proportional to the force applied to it.	**True / False**
The units for the spring constant are N/m.	**True / False**
force = spring constant × extension	**True / False**

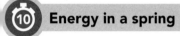 **Energy in a spring**   **Grade 8**

1. A mass of 200 g is added to a spring and it extends by 10 cm.

(a) Calculate the weight added to the spring. Assume $g = 10$ N/kg. **[2 marks]**

> **Maths skills**
> Remember that to convert from cm into m you need to divide by 100. To convert from g to kg you need to divide by 1000.

$$W = m \times g = 0.2 \times 10 = \text{.....................} \text{ N}$$

weight = ... N

(b) Calculate the spring constant of the spring. **[3 marks]**

$$F = k \times x \text{ so } k = \frac{F}{x} = \frac{\text{..........}}{\text{..........}} = \text{.....................}$$

spring constant = ... N/m

(c) Calculate the total elastic potential energy stored in the spring when the mass is hung on it. **[3 marks]**

$$E = \frac{1}{2} kx^2 = \text{.....................} \times \text{.....................} \times 0.1^2 = \text{.....................}$$

total elastic potential energy = ... J

 Stretching a spring   **Grade 8**

2. A student investigated the relationship between force applied and the extension of a spring.

He added 100 g masses, each providing a force of 1 N, one after the other and measured the extension of the spring. Up until 800 g were added, the spring obeyed the equation for linear elastic distortion. Upon adding 900 g, the elastic limit of the spring was exceeded.

(a) Sketch the force–extension graph for this experiment. **[3 marks]**

(b) On the sketch graph, label the limit of linear behaviour using the letter L. **[1 mark]**

(c) How can the force–extension graph be used to determine the spring constant? Tick **one** box. **[1 mark]**

spring constant = the intercept on the y-axis ☐	spring constant = 0.5 × the intercept on the y-axis ☐
spring constant = the gradient of the line ☐	spring constant = 0.5 × the gradient of the line ☐

 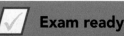

Physics / Forces and matter / Forces / Practical skills

Practical: Force and extension

② Quick quiz

True or false?

The extension of a spring is the final length subtracted from the initial length. **True / False**

The greater the spring constant of a spring, the stiffer the spring. **True / False**

A graph of force applied against extension for a spring will be a straight line through the origin. **True / False**

⑩ Force and extension · Grade 7

1. A student investigated the relationship between the extension of a spring and the force applied to it. She added 100 g masses, each providing a force of 1 N, one by one to the end of a spring and measured the extension of the spring each time. She plotted a graph of 'force added' on the y-axis and 'extension of the spring' on the x-axis.

(a) Give **one** way in which the student could reduce the errors in this investigation. **[1 mark]**

Measure the length of the spring from the .... point on the spring each time.

(b) The student predicted that the extension of the spring would be directly proportional to the force on it. Her results agreed with her prediction.

Suggest how she could use the graph to show this. **[2 marks]**

Maths skills
If two quantities are directly proportional to one another, when one is zero, the other is zero.

(c) Describe how the student can use the graph to determine the spring constant of the spring. **[1 mark]**

spring constant = ... of the graph

(d) The spring constant of the spring is 49 N/m. Calculate the energy stored in the spring when it is extended by 4 cm. **[3 marks]**

energy = ... J

⑩ F = kx · Grade 7

2. A student carried out an experiment to determine the spring constant of a spring. He added 100 g masses to the end of a spring and measured the extension of the spring. **Table 1** shows his results.

(a) Plot a graph of the results with force on the y-axis and extension on the x-axis. **[4 marks]**

Table 1

Force added (N)	0	1	2	3	4	5	6
Extension (cm)	0	4	8	12	16	20	24

(b) Use the graph to determine the spring constant of the spring. Give the units. **[3 marks]**

spring constant = ... units ....

(c) Describe the relationship between the force applied and the extension of the spring. **[1 mark]**

Made a start Feeling confident Exam ready

Practice paper: Biology

> Time: 1 hour 10 minutes
> You must have: calculator, ruler
> The total mark for this paper is 60.
> Answer **all** questions.

1. **Figure 1** is a photograph of three stomata and their guard cells in the lower epidermis of a lily leaf. The photograph was taken using a light microscope.

   (a) Describe the function of stomata and their guard cells in plant leaves. **[2 marks]**

   (b) The magnification of the photograph is ×200. Calculate the real diameter of one stoma using the equation:

   $$\text{magnification} = \frac{\text{image size}}{\text{real size}}$$

   Give your answer in micrometres. **[3 marks]**

   Figure 1

   (c) What is the function of the green sub-cellular structures in the guard cells (labelled A) in **Figure 1**? Tick **one** box. **[1 mark]**

   control what enters and leaves the guard cell ☐

   site of respiration in the guard cell ☐

   site of photosynthesis in the guard cell ☐

   where most cellular reactions take place ☐

   (d) Explain why you need an electron microscope to study the detail inside one of the green sub-cellular structures. **[2 marks]**

   (e) Name **one** other sub-cellular structure you would expect to see in a plant cell that is also found in animal cells. **[1 mark]**

   (f) Name **one** sub-cellular structure you would expect to see in a plant cell that is not found in prokaryotic cells such as bacteria. **[1 mark]**

2. (a) Students carried out an investigation into the effect of sugar solution concentration on the mass of potato chips.

   This is the method they used.

   1. Chips were cut from a potato.

   2. The mass of each chip was measured and recorded.

   3. Two beakers of solution were set up, with different sugar concentrations.

   4. One chip was placed in each beaker.

   5. After 10 minutes each chip was reweighed and the new mass recorded.

   Suggest how this method could be improved to produce valid results. **[4 marks]**

(b) **Table 1** shows results from the investigation.

Table 1

Sugar concentration	Mass of chip at start (g)	Mass of chip at end (g)	Percentage change in mass
0% (pure water)	5.21	5.35	2.69%
30%	5.04	4.28	

Use the measurements in **Table 1** to calculate the percentage change in mass of the chip in the 30% solution to 2 decimal places. **[2 marks]**

(c) Suggest a conclusion that explains the results in **Table 1**. **[2 marks]**

3. Scientists have genetically modified mosquitoes using a gene that affects a cell process and causes young mosquitoes to die before they develop into flying adults.

(a) Explain why the new gene was inserted into a cell of a mosquito embryo. **[2 marks]**

Scientists plan to release adult GM mosquitoes into the environment to mate with wild mosquitoes, to help control the spread of diseases such as malaria.

(b) Describe **one** way that the spread of malaria is being reduced that does not use GM mosquitoes. **[1 mark]**

(c) Explain how the GM mosquitoes could reduce the spread of malaria. **[3 marks]**

(d) Small field trials are being carried out using the GM mosquitoes before they are allowed to be used on a large scale. Give a reason for this approach. **[2 marks]**

4. Students used the apparatus in **Figure 2** to measure the rate of water loss from a plant in still air and moving air. Water loss is measured as the distance the bubble moves over a given time.

(a) Describe how water moves through a plant. **[2 marks]**

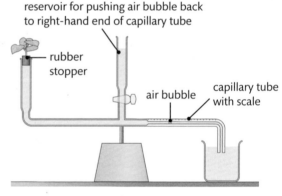

reservoir for pushing air bubble back to right-hand end of capillary tube

rubber stopper

capillary tube with scale

air bubble

Figure 2

Table 2 shows the results of the experiment.

Table 2

	Distance moved by bubble in 5 mins (mm)	Rate of water loss (mm/min)
still air	8	1.6
moving air	27	

(b) Complete the table by calculating the rate of water loss for moving air. **[1 mark]**

(c) Name **two** environmental factors that should be controlled in this experiment, giving a reason for each answer. **[2 marks]**

(d) Students then tested two plants in the same conditions. On plant A they covered the upper surface of each leaf with sticky petroleum jelly. On plant B they covered the lower surface of each leaf with petroleum jelly.

Predict which plant would show the faster rate of water loss, giving a reason for your answer. **[2 marks]**

5. In a transect survey from the top to the bottom of a slope in a meadow, students recorded the number of plants of two buttercup species. They also took measurements of soil moisture using a moisture probe. **Table 3** shows their results.

Table 3

Sample number	1 (top of slope)	2	3	4	5	6 (bottom of slope)
Number of bulbous buttercups in 1 m²	4	4	1	0	0	0
Number of creeping buttercups in 1 m²	0	0	1	2	2	5
Soil moisture value*	1.0	1.5	3.0	5.5	8.5	9.5

*The moisture probe gave a reading of 1 for very dry soil and 10 for very wet soil.

(a) Describe a method for carrying out this survey. [2 marks]

(b) Describe the relationship between the distribution of plants and the measured abiotic factor shown in **Table 3**. [2 marks]

(c) Suggest a biotic factor indicated in **Table 3** that could explain the distribution of the two buttercup species. [1 mark]

6. Cystic fibrosis is an inherited disorder that causes mucus in the lungs and the digestive system to be thick and sticky rather than runny.

(a) Describe how defence systems in the trachea and bronchi of the lungs normally protect against infection. [2 marks]

Figure 3 shows a family tree for a family in which one person has cystic fibrosis.

(b) Cystic fibrosis (CF) is caused by a recessive allele. If F represents the unaffected allele, and f represents the allele that causes CF, what is the genotype of person B in this family? Tick **one** box. [1 mark]

FF ☐   Ff ☐

ff ☐   not possible to tell ☐

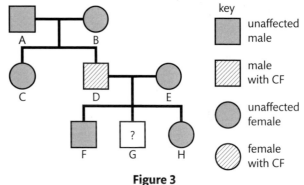

key

■ unaffected male

▨ male with CF

● unaffected female

◉ female with CF

Figure 3

(c) Give a reason for your answer to part (b). [2 marks]

(d) Complete the Punnett square to calculate the probability that person G has CF. [3 marks]

	father's (D) alleles	
mother's (E) alleles	F	
	f	

In a clinical trial for a new gene therapy treatment, 140 cystic fibrosis patients were separated into two groups. The trial was carried out as double-blind. One group inhaled a mixture that contained the replacement allele, while the other group inhaled a placebo mixture. After 12 months, lung function in the allele group had decreased by 0.4% while the decrease in the placebo group was a mean of 4.0%.

(e) Evaluate the trial. [4 marks]

7. **Figure 4** shows the relationship between body mass and type 2 diabetes from a study of UK adults in 2009–10.

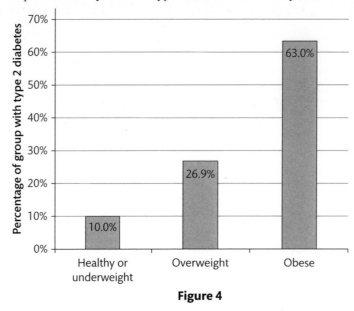

Figure 4

(a) Use **Figure 4** to give a reason why obesity is described as a risk factor for type 2 diabetes. **[1 mark]**

Estimates suggest that 79% of the money spent by the NHS on treating diabetes could be saved by helping people to avoid developing diabetes.

(b) Describe **two** ways that a doctor may advise a person to change their lifestyle to reduce their risk of developing diabetes. **[2 marks]**

(c) Give **one** reason why it may be difficult to reduce the amount spent on treating diabetes. **[1 mark]**

(d) Wearable glucose monitors will soon be prescribed to many thousands of people in England who have type 1 diabetes. The monitor is attached to the skin and transmits information about blood glucose concentration to a nearby reader. Most people who have type 1 diabetes rely on finger-prick blood tests many times a day to monitor their blood glucose concentration.

Evaluate the use of wearable glucose monitors for helping people with type 1 diabetes to monitor and manage their condition. **[6 marks]**

Practice paper: Chemistry

Time: 1 hour 10 minutes
You must have: calculator, ruler
The total number of marks for this paper is 60
Answer **all** questions.

1. **(a)** **Figure 1** shows the physical properties of an unknown substance.

   What type of bonding is present in the unknown substance?
   Tick **one** box.   **[1 mark]**

   covalent bonding ☐   intermolecular force ☐

   ionic bonding ☐   metallic bonding ☐

Physical properties
conducts electricity when molten
high melting and boiling point
soluble in water
cannot conduct when solid
crystalline solid

   Figure 1

   (b) Metals are good conductors of electricity. Explain why. **[2 marks]**

   (c) Describe how a covalent bond is formed. **[1 mark]**

   (d) Graphene is formed from carbon atoms held together by covalent bonds.

   Describe the bonding and structure of graphene. **[2 marks]**

   (e) Complete **Table 1** to give some information about three different ions. **[3 marks]**

   Table 1

Ion	Atomic number	Mass number	Number of protons	Number of electrons	Number of neutrons
Mg^{2+}	12	24			
O^{2-}	8				8
	19	39		18	

   (f) What is the structure of carbon dioxide? Tick **one** box. **[1 mark]**

   ionic ☐   simple molecular (covalent) ☐   giant covalent ☐   metallic ☐

2. Alkanes are a homologous series of hydrocarbons with the general formula C_nH_{2n+2}.

   (a) Which two of the organic molecules in **Figure 2** belong to the alkane homologous series? **[2 marks]**

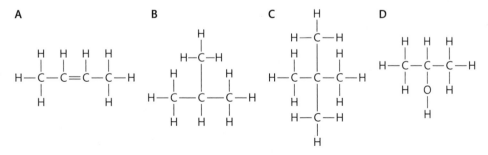

Figure 2

(b) Name the method used to separate crude oil into different fractions. **[1 mark]**

(c) Fractions containing hydrocarbon molecules with longer chains, such as bitumen, have different properties from fractions containing hydrocarbon molecules with shorter chains, such as gases.

   Describe how the properties of hydrocarbons change as the chain length increases. **[3 marks]**

3. Antacids are used to neutralise excess stomach acid and cure indigestion. A student uses the apparatus shown in **Figure 3** to investigate the rate of reaction between an antacid tablet and excess dilute hydrochloric acid.

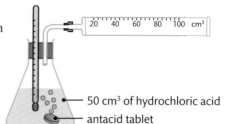

The method for the experiment at room temperature is:

- Add one antacid tablet to $50\,cm^3$ of hydrochloric acid in a conical flask.
- Fit the bung quickly into the neck of the flask.
- Measure the volume of gas produced every 10 seconds until after the reaction finishes.

50 cm³ of hydrochloric acid
antacid tablet

Figure 3

Table 2 shows the results.

Table 2

Time (s)	0	10	20	30	40	50	60
Total volume of gas in syringe (cm³)	0	20	35	45	49	50	50

(a) The reaction produces carbon dioxide gas. Describe the test for carbon dioxide gas. **[2 marks]**

(b) Draw a graph of volume of carbon dioxide gas against time on the grid. **[3 marks]**

(c) Use the graph to calculate the mean rate of the reaction during the first 20 seconds of the reaction. Give the units. **[2 marks]**

(d) The student repeated the experiment but heated the acid to 30 °C before adding it to the flask. All other conditions were the same. Sketch the graph you would expect when the experiment is repeated using a higher temperature. Label your line **A**. **[2 marks]**

(e) The hydrochloric acid solution used contained $7.3\,g$ of hydrochloric acid in $50\,cm^3$ of solution. Calculate the concentration of the hydrochloric acid in $g\,dm^{-3}$. **[1 mark]**

4. Ethene reacts with steam in a reversible reaction to make ethanol. The equation for this reaction is shown below.

   ethene   ethanol

   $C_2H_4(g) + H_2O(g) \rightleftharpoons C_2H_5OH(g)$

   In a sealed container, this reversible reaction can reach equilibrium.

(a) Describe what happens to the forward reaction and reverse reaction at equilibrium. **[2 marks]**

Table 3 shows how the percentage yield of ethene at equilibrium changes as the **temperature** changes and as the **pressure** changes.

Table 3

Temperature in °C	Percentage yield of ethene		
	30 atmospheres	40 atmospheres	50 atmospheres
200	35%	43%	47%
250	26%	35%	39%
300	19%	25%	29%

(b) Describe how changes in the temperature and pressure affect the percentage yield of ethene produced.   [2 marks]

(c) Suggest the conditions needed for a maximum percentage yield of ethene.   [1 mark]

5. The compound CF_3Cl is a refrigerant used in air conditioning systems.

(a) Calculate the relative formula mass of CF_3Cl. (relative atomic masses C = 12.0, F = 19.0, Cl = 35.5)   [1 mark]

(b) A sample of this compound has a mass of 1.65×10^{-3} kg. Calculate the number of moles of molecules in this substance. Give your answer to an appropriate number of significant figures.   [2 marks]

(c) Use the value obtained in (b) to calculate the number of molecules in the sample.   [2 marks]

6. The Earth's atmosphere is a mixture of gases. These gases include carbon dioxide, nitrogen, oxygen and water vapour. The percentages of these gases remain almost constant.

(a) Complete **Table 4** to show the percentage of different gases in clean air.   [2 marks]

Table 4

Gas	% composition
carbon dioxide and other trace gases	<1
	80
oxygen	

(b) The atmosphere today is very different from the atmosphere billions of years ago. Describe the processes that scientists believe led to these changes in the amounts of oxygen, carbon dioxide and water.   [4 marks]

7. Soluble salts can be made by reacting acids with solid insoluble substances, such as metals, metal oxides, hydroxides or carbonates.

(a) Complete the word equation for the reaction between the insoluble base lead oxide and an acid to produce the soluble salt lead nitrate.

lead oxide + ... → .... + ...   [2 marks]

(b) Describe how you could prepare a solution of the salt lead nitrate. In your answer you must name the relevant equipment and techniques used.   [4 marks]

(c) Describe how you could prepare a dry sample of the salt lead nitrate, from the solution produced in (b).   [3 marks]

8. In the periodic table, elements are arranged in order of their atomic number and put into groups and periods.

(a) Explain why the Group 1 elements are arranged together.   [2 marks]

(b) Balance the equation for the reaction of potassium with water.

....K + ...H_2O → .....KOH + H_2 [1 mark]

(c) Compare and contrast the trends in reactivity down Group 1 and Group 7 of the periodic table. Explain these trends in reactivity in terms of electronic configuration.   [6 marks]

Practice paper: Physics

Time: 1 hour 10 minutes
You must have: calculator, ruler
The total mark for this paper is 60.
Answer **all** questions.

1. Specific heat capacity is a property of a material.

   (a) State what is meant by 'specific heat capacity'. **[1 mark]**

   (b) A kettle is used to heat 0.50 kg of water from 20 °C to 80 °C. The specific heat capacity of water is 4200 J/kg °C.

   Calculate the energy transferred to the water, in joules (J).
   Use the correct equation from the Physics equation sheet. **[2 marks]**

   (c) A student measures the temperature of a flask of water as it is heated steadily. The measurements are shown in **Figure 1**.

   Figure 1

Time (seconds)	0	30	60	90	120	150	180	210	240	270
Temperature (°C)	20	30	42	58	63	74	86	97	100	100

   (i) Explain whether any of the readings are anomalous. **[2 marks]**

   (ii) Give **one** way that the student could improve the quality of the data other than by ignoring anomalous readings. **[1 mark]**

   (iii) Explain what is happening to the water after 240 seconds. **[1 mark]**

2. A rubber ball is dropped from the side of a building. Energy is transferred as the ball falls.

   (a) Which of these describes the energy transfer as the ball falls? Tick **one** box. **[1 mark]**

   Kinetic energy decreases, gravitational potential energy decreases ☐

   Kinetic energy decreases, gravitational potential energy increases ☐

   Kinetic energy increases, gravitational potential energy decreases ☐

   Kinetic energy increases, gravitational potential energy increases ☐

   (b) The mass of the ball is 30 g. What is the mass of the ball in kilograms? Tick **one** box. **[1 mark]**

   0.30 kg ☐   3.0 kg ☐   0.030 kg ☐   30 000 kg ☐

   (c) Just before the ball hits the ground, its gravitational potential energy has changed by 0.45 J. Give your answer correct to 3 significant figures.

   (i) Calculate the height, in metres (m), the ball must have been dropped from. The gravitational field strength on Earth is 9.8 N/kg. **[4 marks]**

   (ii) State and explain the kinetic energy of the ball just before it hits the ground. **[2 marks]**

   (d) Calculate the maximum speed, in m/s, reached by the ball. Give your answer correct to 2 significant figures. **[3 marks]**

3. Potential difference is measured using a voltmeter.

    (a) State what is meant by 'potential difference'.   [1 mark]

    (b) A kettle has a power rating of 2000 W. It is connected to the mains supply with a potential difference of 230 V.

        Calculate the current in the element in the kettle. Give your answer correct to 3 significant figures.
        Give the unit.   [3 marks]

    (c) **Figure 2** shows the graph of current against potential difference obtained when a
        particular electrical component is tested.

        (i) State and explain the type of component that was being tested.   [3 marks]

        (ii) Describe the energy transfers taking place in the component at point X.   [2 marks]

current

X

potential
difference

Figure 2

4. The particle model can be used to explain the physical properties of materials.

    (a) Which statement about the particles in a gas is true? Tick **one** box.   [1 mark]

        The particles are close together.   ☐

        The forces between the particles are very small.   ☐

        The particles move very slowly.   ☐

        The forces between the particles keep them in contact. ☐

    (b) Solid aluminium has a density of 2700 kg/m^3. Liquid aluminium has a density of 2400 kg/m^3.

        Explain the difference in density between solid and liquid aluminium.   [3 marks]

    (c) An aluminium block has a mass of 1.5 kg and a volume of 5.0×10^{-4} m^3.

        Calculate the density of the block in kg/m^3.   [2 marks]

    (d) A student wants to determine the density of an irregular shaped piece of rock.

        Describe a method the student could use to determine the density of the rock.   [4 marks]

5. $^{12}_{6}C$ and $^{13}_{6}C$ are two stable isotopes of the element carbon.

    (a) Give **one** similarity and **one** difference between the nuclei of these two isotopes of carbon.   [2 marks]

    (b) $^{14}_{6}C$ is another isotope of carbon. It is radioactive, and an atom of $^{14}_{6}C$ decays to form an atom of nitrogen, as shown.

$$^{14}_{6}C \rightarrow \, ^{14}_{7}N + \text{..............................}$$

        (i) Complete the nuclear equation.   [3 marks]

        (ii) State the type of decay that $^{14}_{6}C$ undergoes in this process.   [2 marks]

    (c) State what is meant by 'half-life'.   [1 mark]

    (d) The amount of $^{14}_{6}C$ measured in rock samples can be used to estimate the age of the rock.

        In one particular sample, the amount of $^{14}_{6}C$ atoms is found to be $\frac{1}{8}$ of the amount expected when the rock was formed.
        $^{14}_{6}C$ has a half-life of 5730 years.

        (i) Deduce the number of half-lives that must have passed since the rock formed.   [2 marks]

        (ii) Estimate the age of the rock sample.   [2 marks]

6. The UK government is committed to reducing carbon dioxide emissions by 80% by 2050. One way of doing this is to increase the use of renewable energy resources.

(a) Which one of the following is a renewable energy resource? Tick **one** box.   **[1 mark]**

oil ☐   nuclear ☐   biofuel ☐   coal ☐

(b) In 2017, 17% of the total electricity usage of the UK was generated by wind turbines. Give **one** advantage and **one** disadvantage of the use of wind turbines to generate electricity.   **[2 marks]**

(c) Give **two** economic considerations that would need to be made before a wind farm could be built.   **[2 marks]**

(d) The UK government is also committed to building new nuclear power stations over the next 30 years. Evaluate the benefits and drawbacks of nuclear power, including whether or not this commitment will help in delivering the target reduction in carbon dioxide emissions.   **[6 marks]**

Answers

Page 1 Levels of organisation

Quick quiz

tissue – a group of similar cells working together; organ system – a group of organs working together; cell – the smallest structural and functional unit of an organism

1. **A**: red blood cell; **B**: blood; **C**: heart; **D**: circulatory system

   [1 for each correct box, total 3]

2. **(a)** An organ is a group of different tissues that work together to perform a role. **[1]**

   (b) The digestive system. **[1]**

   (c) Grouping into systems brings tissues and organs with a related function closer together, **[1]** making it easier / more effective for the body to carry out those functions. **[1]**

3. **(a)** Drawing should be made with clean single lines, no shading, label lines drawn with a ruler and not crossing each other. **[1]** Labels should identify nucleus, cytoplasm, cell membrane. **[1]**

   (b) Measured diameter of white blood cell = X mm, measured diameter of red blood cell = Y mm **[1]**

   Actual diameter of red blood cell = $18 \times \frac{Y}{X} = Z$ mm

Page 2 Eukaryotic and prokaryotic cells

Quick quiz

cells contain a nucleus	E	cells have no nucleus	P
cells are usually smaller	P	cells are usually larger	E
bacterial cells	P	plant, animal and yeast cells	E

1. **(a)** A = cytoplasm **[1]**

   B = cell membrane **[1]**

   C = nucleus **[1]**

   D = mitochondrion **[1]**

   E = ribosomes **[1]**

   F = cell wall **[1]**

   (b) Ribosomes **[1]** because they are too small to be seen using light. **[1]**

   (c) Cell 1 is an animal cell **[1]** because it has a nucleus but no chloroplasts / cell wall / vacuole. **[1]**

   Cell 2 is a prokaryotic / bacterial cell **[1]** because it has no nucleus / its genetic material / chromosomal DNA lies free in the cytoplasm. **[1]**

   (d) The cell wall surrounds and protects the bacterium. **[1]**

2. **(a)** micrometre

   (b) (i) 16 μm = 0.016 mm or 1.6×10^{-2} mm **[1]**

   (ii) 16 μm = 16 000 nm or 1.6×10^4 nm **[1]**

   (iii) 16 μm = 0.0016 cm or 1.6×10^{-3} cm **[1]**

Page 3 Animal and plant cells

Quick quiz

A – plant cell wall;

B – chloroplast;

C – vacuole;

D – ribosome;

E – mitochondrion

1. Nucleus – contains genetic material (DNA) that controls what happens in the cell. **[1]**

   Cell membrane – controls which substances enter and leave the cell. **[1]**

   Cytoplasm – gel-like fluid where most cellular reactions take place. **[1]**

   Ribosomes – where proteins are made in the cell. **[1]**

   Mitochondria – where aerobic respiration takes place, producing energy. **[1]**

2. Cell wall – rigid, made from cellulose, **[1]** provides strength and support to the cell. **[1]**

   Chloroplasts – contain chlorophyll, **[1]** the site of photosynthesis. **[1]**

   (Permanent) vacuole – contains cell sap **[1]** to support the cell structure and store substances. **[1]**

3. **(a)** carbohydrate **[1]**

   (b) From glucose **[1]**, which is made during photosynthesis. **[1]**

Page 4 Specialised animal cells

Quick quiz

muscle
nerve
epithelial

1. **(a)** carries the father's chromosomes to the egg cell **[1]**

   (b) contains enzymes that digest a hole in the egg cell membrane so the sperm nucleus / father's chromosomes can enter **[1]**

   (c) release energy from respiration so that the tail can make swimming movements to reach the egg cell **[1]**

2. **(a)** provide nutrients needed for division and growth of fertilised egg cell before placenta forms **[1]**

   (b) thicken and harden so that other sperm nuclei cannot get into the egg cell **[1]**

3. **(a)** They have tiny hair-like structures on their surface that can wave from side to side. **[1]**

   (b) The movement of the cilia carries the mucus up out of the tubes to the back of the throat. **[1]** This removes pathogens from the lungs so they cannot cause infection. **[1]**

Page 5 Microscopy

Quick quiz

light; sub-cellular structures; lower; more

1. The mitochondria are too small to be seen with a light microscope. **[1]**

2. **(a)** ×160 **[1]**

   (b) ×40 **[1]**

3. Electrons have much shorter wavelength than light **[1]** which means that very small structures such as ribosomes can be seen with greater clarity/in much greater detail. **[1]**

4. **(a)** real size: 36 mm / 10 000 **[1]** = 0.0036 mm **[1]**

   (b) (i) 3.6×10^{-3} **[1]** mm

   (ii) 3.6 **[1]** μm

Page 6 Practical: Using microscopes

Quick quiz

A – objective lens

B – eyepiece

C – adjustment knob

D – stage

E – mirror

1. Image size = 3 cm = $3 \times 10 000$ μm

   = 30 000 μm **[1]**

   real size = 30 000/1000 **[1]**

   size of real object = 30 μm **[1]**
   [Total = 3]

2. **(a)** about 4 μm (about 4 × the scale bar length) **[1]**

   (b) 4 μm = 4×10^{-6} m or 4×10^{-3} mm or 4×10^{-4} cm **[1]**

   (c) quick way to compare sizes of different structures/cells **[1]**

Page 7 Enzyme action

Quick quiz

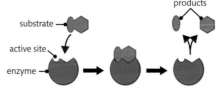

1. **(a)** 40 °C (+/-2 °C) **[1]**

   (b) 30 g (+/-1 g) **[1]**

   (c) As the temperature increases from 0 °C the rate of reaction increases/rises. **[1]**

   This is because at higher temperatures the molecules have more kinetic energy and so collide more often. **[1]**

   (d) As temperature rises above 50 °C the rate of reaction decreases/falls. **[1]**

   This is because the active site changes shape making it more difficult for the substrate molecule to fit tightly/well in the active site and so be broken down. **[1]**

2. **(a)** Only substrate C will fit in the active site of the enzyme **[1]** so it is the only molecule that can be broken down by this enzyme. **[1]**

   (b) At very high temperatures the enzyme is denatured / the active site has changed shape so much **[1]**, so no substrate molecules will fit. **[1]**

Page 8 Practical: Enzymes

Quick quiz

False, True, False, True

1. **(a)** answer should be in the range 20–30 seconds **[1]**

   (b) calculation should be based on time given in part (a), e.g. 20 seconds × 5 spots = 100 seconds **[1]** (not 6, because the first spot was done at time 0)

   (c) 50/answer from 1(b) e.g. 50/80 = 0.625 mg/s **[1]**

   (d) To keep temperature constant **[1]** because temperature also affects rate of enzyme-controlled reactions. **[1]**

2. **(a)** The rate of reaction increases as pH increases up to a maximum at about pH 5.5 **[1]**. Rate of reaction decreases as pH increases above pH 5.5. **[1]**

   (b) The more the pH differs from the optimum value, the more the active site of amylase changes shape. **[1]** This makes it more difficult for the starch to fit into the active site and be broken down by the enzyme. **[1]**

Page 9 Digestion and enzymes

Quick quiz

lipase – fat – fatty acids and glycerol; carbohydrase (e.g. amylase) – carbohydrates (e.g. starch) – glucose; protease – protein – amino acids

1. **(a)** Enzymes break down large food molecules into small soluble molecules. **[1]**

   (b) Food molecules are too large to be absorbed into the blood from the small intestine. **[1]**

   Digestive enzymes break down the large food molecules into smaller ones **[1]** that can be absorbed. **[1]**

   (c) proteins **[1]**

   (d) Enzymes are biological because they are made inside living organisms. **[1]**

   Enzymes are catalysts because they speed up the rate of reactions. **[1]**

   (e) Enzymes make reactions inside living organisms happen more quickly **[1]** so that all the life processes can happen fast enough to sustain life. **[1]**

2. **(a)** At low substrate concentration many enzyme molecules have empty active sites, **[1]** so adding more substrate molecules means more active sites

are filled and breakdown of substrate happens faster. **[1]**

   (b) At high substrate concentration, most active sites are filled most of the time. **[1]** Even if more substrate molecules are added, there are no active sites for them to fill, so the rate of reaction cannot get faster. **[1]**

Page 10 Diffusion

Quick quiz

1. Diffusion is the net movement of particles from an area of their higher concentration to an area of their lower concentration. **[1]**

2. Membrane surface area – The larger the area over which diffusion can occur, the faster the rate; Temperature – Particles with more energy move more quickly; Concentration gradient – The greater the difference in concentration of particles between two areas, the faster the net movement of particles

3. **(a)** Gas A: carbon dioxide **[1]**; Gas B: oxygen **[1]**

   (b) Any two from: millions of air sacs/ alveoli and capillaries **[1]** provide large surface area for exchange **[1]**; thin capillary and alveolar walls **[1]** provide a short diffusion path **[1]**; continual flow of blood through capillary **[1]** maintains the concentration gradient of gases between blood and alveolar air **[1]**; ventilation/breathing refreshes air in alveoli **[1]** maintaining the concentration gradient of gases between blood and alveolar air. **[1]**

Page 11 Osmosis

Quick quiz

osmosis; diffusion; dilute; concentrated; permeable

1. **(a)** The water enters the cell by osmosis causing the cytoplasm to swell **[1]**. This is because the solute concentration of the cytoplasm is higher than the solute concentration of the distilled water. **[1]**

   (b) The water leaves the cell by osmosis causing the cytoplasm to shrink. **[1]** This is because the solute concentration of the surrounding solution is higher than the solute concentration of the cytoplasm. **[1]**

2. **(a)** A membrane that allows small molecules, like water, to pass through but not larger molecules, like sugar. **[1]**

   (b) rate of osmosis = increase in mass / time **[1]**

increase in mass = 16 – 10 = 6.00 g **[1]**
rate of osmosis = 6/60 = 1 g/min **[1]**

   (c) The change in mass would be less **[1]** because the concentration difference between the solutions inside and outside the tubing would be less. **[1]**

Page 12 Practical: Osmosis

Quick quiz

arrow pointing from left to right across the membrane

1. **(a)** Independent variable: sugar solution concentration. **[1]** Dependent variable: change in mass of potato cylinder. **[1]**

   (b) Any two suitable, such as: time left in solution, always mopping up excess water on cylinders before weighing, temperature of solution, volume or surface area of potato cylinders **[2]**

2. **(a)** percentage change in mass = 1.25 –1.13/1.13 × 100 **[1]** = (+)10.6% or 11% **[1]**

   (b) Using percentage change removes any variation in results **[1]** caused by differences in initial mass between potato cylinders. **[1]**

   (c) The mass of the cylinders increased in distilled water **[1]** because water moved by osmosis from the distilled water into the cytoplasm which has a higher solute concentration. **[1]**

   (d) The mass would fall **[1]** because water would move out of the cytoplasm by osmosis into the surrounding solution which has a higher solute concentration. **[1]**

Page 13 Active transport

Quick quiz

Diffusion	Osmosis	Active transport
E, D	B	A, C

1. **(a)** To increase the surface area of the root **[1]** for absorption of water/minerals. **[1]**

   (b) By osmosis. **[1]**

   (c) The concentration of mineral ions is usually higher in the root hair cells than in the surrounding soil solution. **[1]** Therefore the mineral ions need to be moved against their concentration gradient using energy from the cell (so they can't diffuse). **[1]**

2. **(a)** To absorb digested food molecules into the body. **[1]**

   (b) Mitochondria **[1]**

   (c) Energy is required for active transport. **[1]** Mitochondria release energy during respiration. **[1]**

   (d) Highly folded surface **[1]** increases surface area which increases rate of absorption. **[1]**

Page 14 Mitosis and the cell cycle

Quick quiz

prophase – nucleus breaks down and spindle fibres form; metaphase – chromosomes line up across equator of cell; anaphase – chromosome pairs pulled apart to opposite sides of cell; telophase – membrane forms around chromosomes at each side of cell to make nuclei of new cells; cytokinesis – the cell surface membranes of the new cells form

1. Produces genetically identical cells **[1]** for growth, replacement and repair. **[1]**

2. **(a)** The cell increases in size. **[1]** The number of sub-cellular structures, such as mitochondria and ribosomes, increases. **[1]** The chromosomes replicate/ double/are copied. **[1]**

   (b) Two diploid cells **[1]** that are genetically identical to the parent cell. **[1]**

3. **(a)** B **[1]**

   (b) The chromosomes have formed two sets and are being pulled to opposite ends of the cell. **[1]**

4. **[1 mark for correct diagram]**

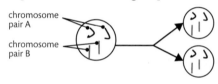

Page 15 Importance of mitosis

Quick quiz

False, True, True, False

1. **(a)** asexual **[1]**

   (b) mitosis **[1]**

   (c) Like those of the parent, **[1]** because the cells produced by mitosis/ asexual reproduction are genetically identical. **[1]**

2. **(a)** mitosis

   (b) Cell division in a cancer is uncontrolled, **[1]** so the cancer/ tumour continues to grow while body cell division is limited and stops when there are enough cells. **[1]**

Page 16 Cell differentiation and growth

Quick quiz

False, True

1. **(a)** Cell differentiation also takes place to produce specialised cells for particular functions. **[1]**

   (b) Cell differentiation produces cells with special features for a particular purpose. **[1]** This make it possible for the organism to carry out many functions more effectively. **[1]**

   (c) For repair of damaged tissue/ replacement of cells. **[1]**

2. **(a)** unspecialised **[1]**

   (b) They elongate/get longer. **[1]**

(c) Cells in meristems can continue to divide throughout the plant's life. **[1]** This means the plant roots can continue to grow and provide more substances from the soil for the parts of the plant above the soil. **[1]**

3. **(a)** The growth of a baby with the median size of the population. / Half of all babies in the population will show growth above this curve and half equal to or below the curve. **[1]**

   (b) It shows whether a baby is growing at a rate that is expected for its birth weight **[1]** and can help medical professionals to identify if there are any growth problems that need looking at more carefully. **[1]**

Page 17 Stem cells

Quick quiz

embryonic stem cell – unspecialised cell that can give rise to most of the different types of cells in a human body; adult stem cell – unspecialised cell in tissue that can produce some types of differentiated cell; meristem – plant cells that divide and differentiate into any type of plant cell

1. New blood cells are produced by division of adult stem cells **[1]** which are found in bone marrow tissue. **[1]**

2. **(a)** A body cell cannot divide to produce other kinds of differentiated cell. **[1]** Embryonic stem cells can divide to produce many kinds of differentiated cell. **[1]**

   (b) Stem cells containing the healthy version of the gene that codes for insulin could be inserted into the pancreas **[1]** so that they start to produce insulin. **[1]**

   (c) The cells will be identified by the immune system as being part of the body **[1]** and so won't be rejected/destroyed. **[1]**

   (d) Any suitable risk, such as: the stem cells may produce the wrong type of differentiated cell / may start to divide uncontrollably and produce a cancer. **[1]**

3. **(a)** meristem **[1]**

   (b) Any suitable benefit such as: identical good characteristics to parent / no viruses / produce large numbers of identical plants. **[1]**

   (c) The stem cells divide by mitosis to produce genetically identical cells. **[1]** This means they all contain a copy of the inserted gene and so will have the new characteristic. **[1]**

Page 18 The human nervous system

Quick quiz

receptor cells	1
relay neurone in spinal cord	3
effector cells	5
motor neurone	4
sensory neurone	2

---

1. 1: The electrical impulse reaches the axon terminal.

   2: The impulse causes the axon terminal to release neurotransmitter into the gap between the neurones. **[1]**

   3: The neurotransmitter diffuses across the gap to the next neurone. **[1]**

   4: This causes a new electrical impulse to start in the next neurone. **[1]**

2. Reflex actions are automatic and rapid because they do not involve the conscious part of the brain. **[1]** This helps protect us from harm, such as by something hitting the eye. **[1]**

3. **(a)** Sensory neurones have many dendrites and terminals to connect with other neurones/receptor cells **[1]**, and a long (myelinated) axon to carry electrical impulses quickly through the body. **[1]**

   (b) Any answer that indicates loss of function of muscles, e.g. muscle weakness / not being able to walk **[1]** because motor neurones stimulate muscles to move. **[1]**

Page 19 Meiosis

Quick quiz

True, False, True, True

1. **(a)** 38/2 = 19 **[1]**

   (b) As two gametes fuse during fertilisation their chromosomes are collected into the new nucleus. **[1]** Halving the chromosome number in gametes restores the full chromosome number/prevents doubling of the chromosome number in the fertilised cell. **[1]**

2. **(a)** genetic material is copied **[1]**

   (b) four **[1]**

3. Any four suitable comparisons, such as: Both are processes of cell division/produce new cells. **[1]** Mitosis is used for growth in body cells, meiosis produces gametes. **[1]** Cells produced by mitosis are genetically identical, cells produced by meiosis are genetically varied. **[1]** Cells produced by mitosis have two sets of chromosomes, cells produced by meiosis have only one set of chromosomes. **[1]** Mitosis produces two daughter cells; meiosis produces four daughter cells. **[1] [max. 4]**

Page 20 The structure of DNA

Quick quiz

Mash up the fruit very thoroughly – makes sure you will be able to get as much DNA out of the fruit as possible; Mix the fruit mash with salt, detergent and water and warm for 15 minutes – breaks down membranes surrounding cells and nuclei; Add two drops of protease enzyme – separates out the proteins that surround the DNA in the chromosomes; Pour ice-cold ethanol down the inside of the tube very carefully – causes the DNA to precipitate out of the mixture

1. **(a)** double helix **[1]**
   (b) A particular base will only pair with one other particular base. **[1]**
   (c) Lots of bonds together make the join between the strands very strong. **[1]**
2. **(a)** nucleotide **[1]**
   (b) It is made of repeating units (nucleotides). **[1]**
   (c) Complementary base-pairing means only a nucleotide with the specific base attaches to each base on the strand **[1]** so you end up with two identical DNA sequences in the new DNA molecules. **[1]**

Page 21 DNA and the genome

Quick quiz

genetic, DNA, polymer, two, helix, chromosomes

1. **(a)** All the genetic material of a human. **[1]**
   (b) A small section of DNA **[1]** that codes for a particular protein. **[1]**
2. **(a)** A change in DNA / a gene. **[1]**
   (b) All non-African people share a mutation/variation in the genome **[1]** that is not present in African people. **[1]**
   (c) The version of a gene that causes an inherited disorder is different / has a mutation **[1]** that is not in the version of the gene which doesn't cause the disorder. **[1]**
   (d) Any suitable advantage such as: they can be treated before the disease develops badly enough to affect quality of life/they can change their lifestyle to reduce risk. **[1]**
   (e) Any suitable disadvantage, such as: knowing may cause the person to worry more than is needed. **[1]**

Page 22 Genetic inheritance

Quick quiz

A homozygous recessive allele pair
B different genes
C alleles of gene A
D homozygous dominant allele pair
E heterozygous allele pair

1. multiple interacting genes **[1]**
2. **(a)** A recessive disorder is caused by having two recessive alleles for the gene related to the disorder. **[1]**
   (b)

		Father's alleles	
		F	f
Mother's alleles	F	FF	Ff
	f	Ff	ff

[1 mark for correct alleles for father, 1 mark for correct offspring genotypes]
   (c) probability expressed in one of the following ways: 0.25, ¼, 25%, 1 in 4 **[1]**

3. **(a)**

		Father's alleles	
		T	t
Mother's alleles	t	Tt	tt
	t	Tt	tt

[1 mark for correct parent alleles, 1 mark for correct offspring genotypes]
   (b) 2 out of 4 = 50% **[1]**

Page 23 Inherited disorders

Quick quiz

inherited disorder – a disorder caused by a faulty allele; recessive allele – affects the phenotype only when there are two copies in the genotype; dominant allele – affects the phenotype when only one copy is present in the genotype; monohybrid inheritance – inheriting a phenotype caused by a single gene

1. **(a)** four **[1]**
   (b) aa **[1]** because if one of the dominant alleles was present person 1 would have the disorder. **[1]**
   (c) The children of couple 6/7 are all homozygous recessive so must have inherited a 'normal'/non-disorder allele from parent 7. **[1]** This means that person 7 could be either homozygous recessive and therefore could only pass on recessive alleles **[1]** or heterozygous and all children inherited the 'normal'/non-disorder allele. **[1]**
2. **(a)** tall **[1]**
   (b) possible gametes, from left: T, t, T, t [1 for all correct]
   possible offspring genotypes, from left: TT, Tt, Tt, tt [1 for all correct]
   possible offspring phenotypes, from left: tall, tall, tall, dwarf [1 for all correct]
   (c) 25% **[1]**

Page 24 Sex determination

Quick quiz

fertilisation, gametes, zygote, genes, XX, XY

1. **(a)** meiosis **[1]**
   (b) **(i)** 100%/all **[1]**
   (ii) half/50% **[1]**
   (c) Egg cells from the mother contain only an X chromosome. **[1]**
   Sperm cells contain either an X chromosome or a Y chromosome. **[1]**
   So it is the father whose gamete determines the sex of the baby. **[1]**
2. **(a)**

		Sperm cells from father	
		X	Y
Egg cells from mother	X	XX	XY
	X	XX	XY

[1 mark for parent's chromosomes, 1 mark for correct genotypes of offspring]

   (b) 50% **[1]**
   (c) 0.5 probability or 50% **[1]**
   (d) The probability of having a boy or a girl is always 50:50 **[1]**, because it depends only on whether the sperm cell contains an X or a Y chromosome. **[1]**

Page 25 Variation and mutation

Quick quiz

genetic; environmental; genetic; environmental

1. **(a)** Variation is the differences in characteristics/features between individuals. **[1]**
   (b) A mutation is a change in the DNA/in a gene. **[1]**
   (c) Mutations cause a change in the DNA. **[1]** This may change a gene/protein. **[1]** Sometimes this leads to a change in an organism's phenotype. **[1]**
   (d) Most or all of the mutations will have no obvious effect on the baby's phenotype. **[1]**
2. **(a)** There are many different alleles for each of the genes, **[1]** and different people have different combinations of alleles. **[1]**
   (b) Each child inherits some alleles from its father and some from its mother. **[1]** Depending on which alleles are inherited and how those alleles interact (e.g. which one is dominant), they may cause different hair colour to develop in the phenotype. **[1]**
   (c) A mutation in a hair colour gene prevents colour developing in the phenotype. **[1]**
   (d) It is a variation that develops in the person's lifetime/is acquired **[1]** as a result of something in the environment/sunlight. **[1]**

Page 26 Evolution by natural selection

Quick quiz

evolution, natural selection, characteristics, adapted, offspring, genes

1. **A** Label should refer to variation in the population due to mutations in genes. **[1]**
   B Label should state that only individuals with the mutation that makes them most resistant to the antibiotic survive. **[1]**
   C Label should state that individuals that survive reproduce and pass on the characteristic for resistance to their offspring. **[1]**
2. Marks awarded for coherent explanation and ordering of ideas as well as scientific knowledge – Level 3 answer **[5–6]**, Level 2 answer **[3–4]**, Level 1 answer **[1–2]**.

Indicative content:

- separation of single population into two by formation of Congo 2 million years ago
- different environmental conditions develop north and south of river
- different adaptations in the north and south populations selected for by different environments
- after 2 million years of separate evolution, bonobos and chimps can no longer breed together to produce fertile offspring
- not being able to breed together means they are separate species

Page 27 Evidence for human evolution

Quick quiz

True, False, True, True

1. **(a)** Lucy's leg bone is nearer in length to a modern chimp **[1]** than a modern human. This suggests she was a similar height to a modern chimp. **[1]**

   (b) The alignment of Lucy's leg bone indicates that her knees were close together **[1]** when she walked. This suggests that she walked upright like a modern human. **[1]**

2. **(a)** The rock or substrate in which they were found was analysed and dated. **[1]**

   (b) The more recent hand axe shows an obvious point and more careful working than the older hand axe. **[1]** This suggests an evolution in brain structure / passing on of more cultural knowledge / more learning in *Homo erectus* than *Homo habilis*. **[1]**

Page 28 Classification

Quick quiz

prokaryotes – single cells with genetic material free in cytoplasm; protists – usually single cells with nucleus and other sub-cellular structures; fungi – usually multi-celled organisms that digest food outside their bodies; plants – usually multi-celled organisms that are able to photosynthesise; animals – multi-celled organisms that digest food inside their bodies

1. **(a)** characteristics **[1]**

   (b) kingdoms **[1]**

   (c) species **[1]**

   (d) genetics **[1]**

   (e) domains **[1]**

2. **(a)** Any two from: protists, fungi, animals, plants **[2]**

   (b) prokaryotes **[1]**

   (c) They have similarities to both bacteria and eukaryota **[1]** which the other groups do not share with each other. **[1]**

Page 29 Selective breeding

Quick quiz

Any suitable responses, such as: dog – markings, size, gentle nature; cow – high milk yield, high meat yield; flower – unusual or large flowers, brightly-coloured flowers, attractive scent, disease resistance

1. **(a)** Selective breeding is the process by which humans choose and breed plants and animals for particular genetic characteristics. **[1]**

   (b) 1: To make the chicken grow faster. **[1]**

   2: To make the chicken grow larger or lay more eggs. **[1]**

   (c) Select male and female cattle that produce the most meat and breed them together. **[1]** Then breed together the offspring that produce the largest amount of meat. **[1]** Repeat this over many generations to produce individuals with the largest meat production. **[1]**

2. **(a)** Breeding closely related individuals together. **[1]**

   (b) Inbreeding produces individuals with limited genetic variation **[1]** which can make them more likely to suffer particular inherited diseases or other defects. **[1]**

   (c) If more of the molecules that the cow is absorbing from its food are used to make milk **[1]** then less are available to produce other substances needed by the body for healthy growth (e.g. more bone, healthy immune system). **[1]**

   (d) Selective breeding produces benefits (more food) but also problems for the animals. **[1]** Different people will have different priorities and therefore different ideas of what is right or wrong. **[1]**

Page 30 Genetic engineering

Quick quiz

(a) restriction enzymes   **(d)** ligase

(b) sticky ends   **(e)** vectors

(c) bacteria

1. **(a)** The gene for human insulin is cut out of a human chromosome (using enzymes). **[1]**

   The gene is then inserted into a bacterium in a way that means it produces human insulin. **[1]**

   (b) The healthy version of the CF gene is inserted into a cell in an early embryo. **[1]** All the cells produced by mitosis from the GM cell will produce cells that don't have the CF disorder. **[1]**

2. **(a)** The toxin gene is cut out of the bacterial DNA using restriction enzymes that leave sticky ends. **[1]**

   The DNA of a bacterial plasmid is cut open with the same enzyme to leave the same sticky ends. **[1]**

   The toxin gene is inserted into the plasmid and the sticky ends joined together using a ligase enzyme. **[1]**

   The plasmid is used as a vector to carry the toxin gene into the nucleus of a plant cell and join the toxin gene to the plant cell DNA. **[1]**

   (b) This type of GM maize kills caterpillars that try to eat it **[1]** so there is less damage to the plant and it can grow better/produce more food. **[1]**

   (c) Any suitable explanation that shows how the inserted gene could lead to harm in the environment, such as: the poison gene could transfer to wild plants nearby by pollination. **[1]** Wild plants growing from the seed will also kill caterpillars, leaving less food for insect-eating birds. **[1]**

Page 31 Health issues

Quick quiz

lung cancer, cardiovascular disease

1. Any suitable reason linking mental and physical health, such as: disease is only one factor in health, how you feel both physically and mentally are also important. **[1]**

2. Communicable diseases are caused by a pathogen and can be passed from an infected person to others. **[1]**

   Non-communicable diseases have other causes, such as genes or faults in the way cells work, and cannot be passed to another person by infection. **[1]**

3. Any suitable argument that uses information from the question in support, such as: treating 100 people costs £20 000 less to get rid of their dependency than treating any illness or injury linked to their drinking. **[1]** So it will be cheaper in the long term for the health service to increase dependency treatment. **[1]**

4. **(a)** Asthma reduces the amount of oxygen getting into the body, and carbon dioxide getting out **[1]** which can harm cells and could cause death. **[1]**

   (b) The peaks in asthma cases match the peaks in flu cases well. **[1]** This suggests a strong positive correlation between flu and asthma/This suggests that an outbreak in flu infections increases the risk of asthma attacks. **[1]**

Page 32 Communicable diseases

Quick quiz

pathogens, fungus, bacterium, protist

1. **(a)** The irritation will cause coughs and sneezes **[1]** spreading the viruses though the air in droplets that other people may breathe in. **[1]**

   (b) Catching the droplets from a sneeze or cough in a tissue and binning the tissue **[1]** reduces the chance that other people will come into contact with the flu viruses. **[1]**

2. **(a)** Removing and burning damaged parts kills the pathogens inside them. **[1]**

   (b) Killing insects that suck plant sap will stop them taking viruses from an infected plant **[1]** to an uninfected plant and causing a new infection. **[1]**

3. (a) Any one suitable symptom, such as: damage to the lungs / coughing up blood. [1]

   (b) 3.2(%) [1]

   (c) Smoking fewer than 10 cigarettes a day does not increase the chance of recurrent tuberculosis. [1] Smoking more than 10 cigarettes increases the chance of recurrent tuberculosis [1] by more than double / any appropriate use of numbers in table. [1]

Page 33 Viral diseases

Quick quiz

True, False, True, False

1. (a) virus

   (b) Any one suitable method such as: exchange of blood/sexual fluids / sexual activity / sharing injection needles. [1]

   (c) Any one suitable way such as: using a male condom during sexual activity / not sharing injection needles. [1]

   (d) White blood cell. [1]

   (e) White blood cells are part of the immune system [1] and attack and destroy pathogens that enter the body. [1]

2. (a) As the proportion of people with HIV increases, the proportion of people with TB also increases. / There is a positive correlation between proportion of people with HIV and proportion with TB. [1]

   (b) HIV infection damages the immune system/destroys white blood cells [1], which increases the chance of a person being infected with other diseases such as TB. [1]

Page 34 Bacterial diseases

Quick quiz

chlamydia, cholera

1. (a) The infection rates in the two under-25 age groups are higher than in the three over-25 groups.

   (b) The age groups most likely to be infected are tested. [1] The tests cost money to carry out, so it is more cost-effective to focus on younger age groups. [1]

   (c) Tests mean a person is more likely to get treatment to clear the infection [1] and to use methods to prevent spread of infection such as male condom during sex. [1]

2. (a) diarrhoea [1]

   (b) Loss of water and minerals in diarrhoea [1] can affect how cells work and stop reactions happening properly. [1]

   (c) The cholera pathogen is in the human waste and passes to drinking and cooking water. [1] It infects another person who drinks the contaminated water. [1]

   (d) Any suitable method that prevents ingestion of pathogen, such as: only drink bottled water, boil water to kill pathogens before drinking. [1]

Page 35 Fungal diseases

Quick quiz

Eukaryota

1. (a) Lesions/breaks in bark and dieback of branches. [1]

   (b) If water and nutrients cannot reach the leaf and stem cells, [1] the cells cannot carry out the processes needed for life. [1]

   (c) Any two suitable suggestions, such as: transporting infected young trees to other parts of the UK, spores dispersed from infected leaf stalks by wind/animals/humans in autumn and winter

      [1 mark per suggestion to a max. of 2]

2. (a) Clearing dead wood and leaves will remove the fruiting bodies that release spores. [1]

   (b) Clearing large numbers of trees will remove food and shelter for some of the animals that live in the wood [1] and so could reduce biodiversity. [1]

Page 36 Protist diseases

Quick quiz

True, False, False, True

1. A: When a mosquito bites a person who has malaria, it takes in protist pathogens in the blood that it sucks from the person. [1]

   B: When that mosquito then bites a person who doesn't have malaria, the protists get into the blood of the person being bitten and cause disease. [1]

2. (a) Recurrent bouts of fever. [1]

   (b) It causes many deaths each year. [1]

   (c) Any two suitable ways from the information given, with a reason, such as: spray water with chemicals to kill young/larval mosquitoes [1] as then they won't develop into adults that bite humans [1]; spray resting areas with insecticide/chemicals that kill mosquitoes [1] so then they won't bite humans [1]; sleep inside mosquito net [1] to prevent night-flying females from getting to skin to bite. [1]

Page 37 Human defence systems

Quick quiz

False, True, False, False

1. (a) Thick skin makes it difficult for pathogens to get into the body. [1]

      Sticky mucus in the nose traps pathogens before they can attack cells lining the nose. [1]

      Cells lining the trachea and bronchi have cilia (tiny hairs) on their surface that move pathogens out of the lungs

   (to the throat where they can be swallowed). [1]

      Stomach acid destroys pathogens that enter the body in food and drink. [1]

   (b) Lysozymes made in the eyes [1] break down/digest pathogens that enter the eyes. [1]

2. (a) immune system [1]

   (b) white blood cells/phagocytes/ lymphocytes [1]

   (c) (Phagocytes) ingest/engulf pathogens by phagocytosis, [1] (lymphocytes) produce antibodies that attack and destroy specific pathogens, [1] produce memory lymphocytes that respond rapidly after a second infection by the same pathogen. [1]

3. (a) Rapidly increasing as pathogen divides. [1]

   (b) Just before the top of the peak in antibody concentration. [1]

   (c) This would be when pathogen numbers are greatest [1], before antibody concentration is high enough to start killing off the pathogens. [1]

Page 38 Immunisation

Quick quiz

antigens, communicable, specific, illness

1. (a) Using dead, inactive or weakened form of the pathogen that contains its antigens. [1]

   (b) The vaccine triggers the immune system to produce antibodies to the pathogen. [1]

      This means that if the child is infected later with the polio virus antibodies will be produced rapidly. [1] This will prevent the child developing (symptoms of) polio disease. [1]

2. (a) Any two suitable reasons, such as: to prevent lots of people dying from smallpox [1]; to reduce the spread of smallpox to people who hadn't had the vaccine or disease [1]; some people don't like being immunised. [1]

   (b) There is no risk of them being infected by the smallpox pathogen. [1]

   (c) The eradication programme cost a lot of money which could have been spent in other ways [1] but getting rid of smallpox has saved a lot of money because people no longer need to be vaccinated to prevent infection [1] or be treated after catching the infection. [1] So overall eradication could have saved money in the long-term. [1]

Page 39 Antibiotics

Quick quiz

antibiotic – medicine used to cure bacterial disease; antibody – produced by immune system in response to infection; painkiller – medicine used to reduce some symptoms of disease; antigen – stimulates the immune system to attack a pathogen

1. **(a)** Antibiotics only kill bacteria **[1]** so they will have no effect on a disease caused by viruses. **[1]**

   (b) Processes in the bacteria that cause pneumonia are disrupted, which stops the bacteria growing **[1]** but human cells are not damaged by the antibiotic. **[1]**

2. **(a)** Improved cleanliness reduced the number of deaths before 1940 **[1]** but the number of deaths continued to fall after the introduction of antibiotics. **[1]** This suggests that antibiotics have played an important role in controlling infections. **[1]**

   (b) Antibiotic-resistant strains cannot be killed by using antibiotics, **[1]** so the number of deaths from infections is likely to increase. **[1]**

Page 40 Development of drugs

Quick quiz

cell culture – cells grown in the lab for testing a new drug

side effect – unintended harm caused by a drug

dose – how much drug to use at a time

1. plants **[1]**, antibiotics **[1]**, development **[1]**, computers **[1]**

2. **(a)** 1: The drug is tested on human cells and tissues. **[1]**

   2: The drug is tested on animals. **[1]**

   (b) To make sure it is safe to use in living cells and systems / to make sure it won't poison human cells. **[1]**

   (c) Phase 1: Test the drug on a small group of healthy volunteers **[1]** to make sure it is safe. **[1]**

   Phase 2: Test the drug on a large number of people who have the disease that the drug will be used for **[1]** to find the optimum dose and check for side-effects. **[1]**

   (d) Advantage: Any one suitable answer such as: ensures drug is thoroughly tested for safety etc., before doctors can give it to patients. **[1]** Disadvantage: Any one suitable answer such as: makes the process of producing new drugs very slow/costly. **[1]**

3. So the patient doesn't know what they've had **[1]** because how you feel about something can affect how your body responds to it. **[1]**

Page 41 Non-communicable diseases

Quick quiz

False, False, True, True

1. **(a)** Waist: hip ratio is a person's waist measurement divided by their hip measurement. **[1]**

   (b) It means that the person's waist is larger than their hips. **[1]**

   (c) A description that makes reference to the following points: deaths from cardiovascular disease increase as waist: hip ratio increases **[1]**; percentage of women dying from cardiovascular disease is greater than for men at waist: hip ratios above 0.79. **[1]**

   (d) Any reasoning that makes reference to the following points: as waist: hip ratio increases, the amount of fat around the waist/heart increases **[1]**; increased amount of fat is related to increased risk of blood vessel blockage. **[1]**

   (e) Any suitable suggestion that will reduce the percentage of body fat such as: increase amount of exercise/ adjust diet to reduce calorie intake **[1]**

2. **(a)** Any suitable answer that indicates the cancer won't develop until after the cell has been infected by the HPV virus. **[1]**

   (b) The number of cases of cervical cancer should decrease **[1]** because fewer women should be infected with the virus that triggers the cancer. **[1]**

Page 42 Effects of lifestyle

Quick quiz

lung cancer, type 2 diabetes, liver disease, skin cancer

1. **(a)** Smoking 1–14 g/day has a risk of 1.60 of having a heart attack compared with a risk of 1.0 for someone who never smoked. **[1]** This means their risk of heart attack is 1.6 times greater. **[1]**

   (b) As the mass of tobacco smoked per day increases the risk of having a heart attack increases. **[1]**

   (c) Substances inhaled in smoke are absorbed into the blood. **[1]** Some of these substances cause fatty plaques to form in blood vessels and block them. **[1]**

   (d) The study included 13 000 men which means the results are more likely to be reproducible. **[1]**

   The study was carried out only with men from Copenhagen, which means the results may not be reproducible with different groups (such as women/ men from other countries). **[1]**

2. **(a)** Alcohol consumption increased from about 7 dm^3 per person per year in 1970 to about 10 dm^3 per person per year in 2009. **[1]** Deaths from liver disease increased from about 3 per 100 000 people in 1970 to about 11 per 100 000 in 2009. **[1]**

   (b) High alcohol consumption can damage the liver **[1]** so increasing consumption could be the cause of the increased deaths. **[1]**

Page 43 Cardiovascular disease

Quick quiz

circulatory, arteries, fat, oxygen

1. If blood flow through the heart is affected, it could reduce the amount of oxygen and glucose getting to cells for respiration. **[1]** This will reduce the amount of energy available for movement, other cell processes, etc. **[1]**

2. The left graph shows that the risk of death over 15 years from surgery is the same for both types of valve. **[1]** The right graph shows that the risk of having to replace a biological valve increases much faster over 15 years than for a mechanical valve. **[1]** This suggests a mechanical valve is a better replacement for a faulty valve. **[1]**

3. **(a)** Any two suitable lifestyle changes with appropriate reasons, such as: stopping smoking **[1]** as smoking is a major risk factor for cardiovascular disease so this will reduce the risk of further disease **[1]**; taking more exercise suitable for the stage of recovery **[1]** as this will help to strengthen the heart muscle and improve circulation **[1]**; adjusting the diet **[1]** to increase the proportion of foods that help protect against cardiovascular disease (e.g. fruit and vegetables) and reduce the proportion of foods linked to CVD (e.g. fatty red meats). **[1]**

   (b) A person with a high blood cholesterol concentration would need to keep taking statins to keep their blood cholesterol concentration at a safe level. **[1]**

Page 44 Photosynthesis

Quick quiz

water + carbon dioxide → oxygen + glucose

1. **(a)** Plants are producers that use photosynthesis to make glucose/ food/biomass. **[1]**

   This is the source of food for the animals/ consumers in the food chain. **[1]**

   (b) More energy is transferred to the reaction from the environment **[1]** than is transferred from the reaction to the environment. **[1]**

   (c) There is less light on a cloudy day than a sunny day **[1]** so less energy is transferred to the chloroplasts/ chlorophyll **[1]** so the rate of photosynthesis is slower. **[1]**

2. **(a)** chloroplast **[1]**

   (b) chlorophyll **[1]**

   (c) Palisade layer **[1]** because these cells contain the most chloroplasts. **[1]**

   (d) It is near to the upper surface of the leaf/below the transparent epidermis **[1]** so will receive the most light. **[1]**

Page 45 Rate of photosynthesis

Quick quiz

intensity of light, carbon dioxide concentration, temperature

1. A factor that limits the rate of photosynthesis when there is not enough of it. **[1]**

2. **(a)** Point X **[1]** because on this part of the graph, as carbon dioxide concentration increases rate of photosynthesis increases. **[1]**

   (b) Carbon dioxide is one of the reactants in photosynthesis **[1]** so if there is not enough of it photosynthesis will be slower. **[1]**

3. The rate of photosynthesis increases between 5 °C and 25 °C **[1]** because enzyme and substrate molecules collide more often and the reaction is faster. **[1]** The rate of photosynthesis falls above 25 °C **[1]** because the shape of the active site of the enzymes changes / the enzymes are denatured, so the substrate molecules don't fit so well. **[1]**

4. **(a)** Light intensity, temperature and carbon dioxide concentration are all limiting **[1]** because increasing any one of them increases the rate of photosynthesis. **[1]**

   (b) Burning oil would be better **[1]** because it would increase temperature as well as increasing carbon dioxide concentration. **[1]**

Page 46 Practical: Photosynthesis

Quick quiz

false, true

1. **(a)** carbon dioxide **[1]**

   (b) Independent variable: light intensity/ distance from light source. **[1]**

   Dependent variable: change in pH/ colour of indicator **[1]**

   (c) This reduces energy transfer from the lamp **[1]** which helps because temperature change affects the rate of photosynthesis. **[1]**

   (d) Any two suitable control variables such as: length of time to record change, **[1]** mass/number of algal balls, **[1]** volume of indicator solution in each bottle **[1] [max. of 2]**

2. **(a)** $1/(10 \times 10) = 0.0100$ **[1]**

   (b) Graph similar to below, axes correctly labelled **[1]**, points correctly drawn and joined by straight lines or line of best fit. **[1]**

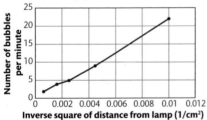

   (c) The relationship between number of bubbles produced and inverse square of distance from lamp is directly proportional. **[1]**

Page 47 Specialised plant cells

Quick quiz

A lower epidermis

B palisade mesophyll

1. **(a)** To absorb water and mineral ions from the soil. **[1]**

   (b) Root hair cells have a large surface area. **[1]** This increases the rate at which substances can be absorbed into the plant. **[1]**

   (c) Mitochondria are where respiration is carried out. **[1]** This provides the energy the cell needs for active transport. **[1]**

2. **(a)** Transports water and dissolved mineral ions through plant. **[1]**

   (b) Strong walls don't burst or collapse as fluid/water flows through them, **[1]** dead cells contain no cytoplasm so fluid can flow easily, **[1]** pores in walls allow water and dissolved ions to move freely into and out of vessel. **[1]**

3. **(a)** Transports dissolved sucrose around plant. **[1]**

   (b) Energy is needed to pump sucrose into and out of phloem tissue. **[1]** This energy is released by respiration in mitochondria in living cells. **[1]**

Page 48 Transport in plants

Quick quiz

water and dissolved mineral ions, xylem, sucrose, phloem

1. **(a)** roots **[1]**

   (b) osmosis **[1]**

   (c) transpiration **[1]**

   (d) leaves **[1]**, evaporation **[1]**

2. Mineral ions are absorbed from the soil **[1]** through root hair cells **[1]** by active transport because they are in a more dilute solution in the soil than in the cytoplasm. **[1]**

3. **(a)** Allow gases to diffuse into and out of the leaf. **[1]**

   (b) The guard cells change shape, **[1]** so changing the size of the stoma between them. **[1]**

   (c) Opening during the day allows carbon dioxide to diffuse more rapidly into the leaf and reach palisade cells for photosynthesis. **[1]** Closing at night when photosynthesis doesn't happen reduces water loss from the leaf. **[1]**

Page 49 Water uptake in plants

Quick quiz

False, True, True

1. **(a)** Stomata open more as light intensity increases **[1]** so more water molecules can evaporate from the leaf at the same time when it is sunnier. **[1]**

   (b) The movement of water molecules by air movement will be faster when it is windier **[1]** causing a steeper concentration gradient for water molecules so a faster evaporation rate. **[1]**

2. **(a)** $(28.5 + 26.4 + 29.1)/3 = 28.0$ mm/ 5 min **[1]**

   (b) $38.9/5 = 7.78$ mm/min **[1]**

   (c) Water molecules evaporate faster from the leaves at a higher temperature **[1]** so water uptake is faster. **[1]**

   (d) A different surface area would mean a different number of stomata. **[1]** More stomata would allow a faster rate of evaporation of water from the leaf. **[1]**

   (e) Any one factor that can affect rate of evaporation of water from leaves, such as: light intensity, air humidity, temperature. **[1]**

Page 50 Human endocrine system

Quick quiz

A thyroid

B adrenal glands

C pituitary

D pancreas

1. **(a)** Muscle/liver **[1]** because cells in them respond to insulin (by taking in glucose from the blood). **[1]**

   (b) It is released from an endocrine gland **[1]** directly into the blood which carries it round the body **[1]** and it changes the way target organs function. **[1]**

2. The pituitary secretes several hormones into the blood stream (in response to a change in the body). **[1]** These hormones act on other glands to bring about the release of other hormones which then have an effect on the body. **[1]**

3. Endocrine system slower to respond than nervous system. **[1]** Effects of hormones usually last much longer than effects of nervous responses. **[1]**

4. Increasing hormone levels released from the ovaries and testes during puberty **[1]** cause many parts of the body to change, e.g. production of sperm in testes, start of menstrual cycle. **[1]**

Page 51 Adrenalin and thyroxine

Quick quiz

A: adrenal glands; T: thyroid gland

1. **(a)** The heart rate increases. **[1]**

   (b) Increasing heart rate pumps blood containing oxygen and glucose around the body more quickly. **[1]**

   Increased blood flow to the brain and muscles allows a quicker response. **[1]**

2. **(a)** Any effect of low metabolic rate, such as low level of activity/slow growth in a child **[1]** due to low metabolic rate. **[1]**

(b) TSH concentration would rise **[1]** because the pituitary gland would be stimulated by low TSH concentration due to the low concentration of thyroxine. **[1]**

(c) Negative feedback is where a change in a system causes the opposite change to happen. **[1]** When thyroxine concentration falls it stimulates the release of TRH from the hypothalamus, which stimulates the release of TSH from the pituitary which stimulates the release of more thyroxine. **[1]** When thyroxine concentration rises it inhibits/slows down the release of TSH from the pituitary which inhibits/slows down release of thyroxine from the thyroid gland. **[1]**

Page 52 Hormones in reproduction

Quick quiz

puberty – time when the body starts developing in ways that will allow reproduction; oestrogen – female hormone that causes development of breasts and start of menstrual cycle; testosterone – male hormone that stimulates sperm production; secondary sexual characteristics – features that develop in response to increasing sex hormone concentrations

1. FSH causes an egg to mature in an ovary. **[1]**

LH causes an egg to be released from an ovary/ovulation. **[1]**

Oestrogen and progesterone repair and maintain the uterus lining. **[1]**

2. (a) When an egg is released from an ovary. **[1]**

(b) 28 **[1]**

(c) ovary **[1]**

3. (a) Oestrogen concentration rises triggering release of more LH. **[1]** A surge in LH release triggers ovulation on day 14 of the cycle. **[1]**

(b) A fall in progesterone and oestrogen concentration towards day 28 of the cycle. **[1]**

Page 53 Contraception

Quick quiz

oral contraceptive, implant

1. (a) Progesterone inhibits the release of FSH/LH. **[1]**

Keeping a constant high level of progesterone in the body means that the menstrual cycle stops/FSH doesn't increase, so no eggs mature/are released from the ovary which could then be fertilised. **[1]**

(b) 100 – 82 = 18 **[1]**

(c) Any one from: doesn't cause hormonal side-effects, protects against infection with sexually transmitted infections. **[1]**

2. (a) A physical barrier placed at the top of the uterus prevents sperm getting to the egg. **[1]**

(b) No sperm will be released into the woman's reproductive system during sex. **[1]**

(c) The middle of the menstrual cycle is when an egg is most likely to be in the oviduct. **[1]**

(d) This prevents any fertilised egg implanting in the uterus lining (which it needs to do to develop into an embryo). **[1]**

Page 54 Hormones to treat infertility

Quick quiz

LH/luteinising hormone, fertilisation, IVF/in vitro fertilisation, embryo

1. (a) Hormone A is FSH **[1]** because it stimulates eggs to mature in the ovaries. **[1]**

Hormone B is LH **[1]** because it stimulates the ovaries to release the mature eggs. **[1]**

(b) Progesterone (possibly with oestrogen) **[1]** to thicken the uterus lining so that the embryo can embed in the lining. **[1]**

(c) Any suitable stage where there is a need to see inside cells, e.g. during insertion of a sperm into an egg cell **[1]** to make sure it enters the nucleus **[1]**; to check health of embryos **[1]** so that only healthy ones are placed in mother's uterus. **[1]**

2. (a) Clomifene stimulates the release of more LH and FSH than normal. **[1]** This increases the chance that an egg will mature and be released at ovulation. **[1]**

(b) Higher concentrations of FSH and LH than normal **[1]** can cause more than one egg to mature and be released at the same time. **[1]**

(c) Multiple births can cause problems for the babies (e.g. low birth weight) and for the mother. **[1]**

Page 55 Control of blood glucose

Quick quiz

internal, external, blood glucose, constant, cells

1. (a) **Figure 1** shows that after each meal the blood glucose concentration rises. **[1]**

(b) **Figure 1** shows an increase in blood glucose concentration is accompanied by an increase in blood insulin concentration. **[1]**

(c) Blood glucose concentration rises as glucose is absorbed from the small intestine. **[1]** This triggers cells in the pancreas to release more insulin into the blood. **[1]**

(d) Insulin prevents blood glucose concentration increasing

to high levels **[1]** which could be damaging for cells and tissues. **[1]**

2. (a) Blood glucose concentration falls during exercise **[1]** because muscle cells break down glucose during respiration to release energy. **[1]** The fall in blood glucose concentration stimulates cells in the pancreas to release glucagon into the blood. **[1]**

(b) Insulin prevents blood glucose concentration rising too high after meals which is dangerous. **[1]** Glucagon prevents blood glucose concentration falling too low at other times, which is also dangerous for cells and tissues. **[1]** Alternatively: The two hormones keep blood glucose concentration within a narrow range **[1]** which protects cells from damage and makes glucose available when they need it. **[1]**

Page 56 Diabetes

Quick quiz

True, True, False, False

1. (a) Between 1990 and 2000, mean body mass and the percentage of people with type 2 diabetes increased. **[1]**

This means that mean body weight and percentage with type 2 diabetes show a positive correlation. **[1]**

(b) BMI removes the effect of height on body mass **[1]** so is a better measure of the amount of fat in a person's body. **[1]**

(c) The lower value indicates someone with a larger hip measurement than waist measurement **[1]** and the higher value indicates someone with a larger waist measurement than hip measurement. **[1]**

(d) The man should lose weight/eat a healthier diet/do more exercise **[1]** because this should reduce their risk of developing type 2 diabetes **[1]**.

2. Type 1 is caused by failure to produce insulin so injections of insulin are needed to keep blood glucose concentration at a safe level. **[1]** Type 2 is caused by failure to respond to insulin produced by the body or by failure to produce enough insulin. **[1]** Type 2 usually doesn't need insulin injections. **[1]** Type 2 is usually controlled by low-sugar / carbohydrate-controlled diet and exercise to keep blood glucose concentrations lower. **[1]**

Page 57 Transport in animals

Quick quiz

urea, oxygen, out of, lungs

1. (a) Surface area = 6×4^2 = 96 **[1]**
Volume = 4^3 = 64 **[1]**
Surface area : volume ratio = surface area/volume = 96/64 = 1.5 **[1]**

(b) As length increases, surface area : volume ratio decreases. **[1]**

2. **(a)** Absorbs dissolved food molecules into the blood. **[1]**

(b) They greatly increase the surface area of the small intestine **[1]** so that more dissolved food molecules can be absorbed at the same time/rate of absorption of dissolved food molecules is greater. **[1]**

(c) Each villus has a capillary network inside it which carries absorbed food molecules away quickly. **[1]** This maintains a steep concentration gradient / makes sure the concentration of food molecules in the small intestine is much higher than in the blood in the capillary **[1]** so the rate of diffusion/absorption of food molecules into the blood is as high as possible. **[1]**

Page 58 Alveoli

Quick quiz

lungs, alveoli, oxygen, carbon dioxide, air

1. **(a)** diffusion **[1]**

(b) Higher in the blood **[1]** because the blood is coming from cells where respiration has taken place. **[1]**

(c) They increase the surface area for exchange **[1]** which increases the rate of exchange / means more gas molecules can cross the surface at the same time. **[1]**

2. **(a)** The walls are both one cell thick, which reduces the distance across which gases are exchanged **[1]** and increases the rate of exchange of gases across the walls. **[1]**

(b) An explanation that makes reference to the following points: Ventilation replaces air in the alveoli with air that has a higher carbon dioxide concentration and lower oxygen concentration. **[1]** Blood flow replaces blood in the capillaries with blood that has a higher concentration of carbon dioxide and lower concentration of oxygen than blood leaving the capillaries. **[1]** This maintains steep concentration gradients for oxygen and carbon dioxide between the blood and air in the alveoli, **[1]** which increases the rate of diffusion of gases between blood and air. **[1]**

Page 59 The blood

Quick quiz

red blood cell – carries oxygen; white blood cell – attacks and destroys pathogens; plasma – carries dissolved substances; platelet – causes blood to clot where blood vessels are damaged

1. **(a)** The red colour is caused by the pigment haemoglobin. **[1]**

(b) The red pigment binds to oxygen and so carries it round the body in the blood. **[1]**

(c) This means there is more space for haemoglobin so the cell can carry more oxygen. **[1]**

(d) The shape gives the cell a large surface area. **[1]** This means that exchange of gases is faster. **[1]**

2. **(a)** Platelets cause the formation of protein fibres at the wound site **[1]** which help to block the wound and prevent loss of blood and pathogens from entering the body. **[1]**

(b) Phagocytes engulf pathogens **[1]** and lymphocytes release antibodies to destroy pathogens **[1]**, reducing the risk of infection at the wound site. **[1]**

(c) Plasma contains dissolved substances such as glucose/nutrients **[1]** and red blood cells bring oxygen **[1]**. These substances are needed for respiration to release energy to build new cells. **[1]**

Page 60 Blood vessels

Quick quiz

capillary, vein, capillary, artery

1. Veins have a wide space inside **[1]** which allows blood to flow easily with little friction/resistance. **[1]** Veins also have valves on the inside of their walls **[1]** that close to prevent blood flowing backwards in the vessel. **[1]**

2. **(a)** The aorta is the first artery that blood enters as it leaves the heart **[1]** so it is most affected by the difference in blood pressure caused by heart contraction and relaxation. **[1]**

(b) The artery walls are elastic and contain muscle that stretches when the pulse of blood enters and relaxes when the pulse slows. **[1]** This helps to even out the variation of blood pressure caused by the heartbeat. **[1]**

(c) Capillaries are where substances are exchanged between blood and tissues/cells. **[1]** Thin walls decrease diffusion distance/increase the rate of diffusion. **[1]**

(d) There is greater pressure in capillaries than veins because the lumen of the vein is wider and flow is easier. **[1]**

Page 61 The heart

Quick quiz

labels top to bottom: vena cava, (left) atrium, (left) ventricle

1. **(a)** vena cava **[1]**

(b) right atrium **[1]**

(c) right ventricle **[1]**

(d) pulmonary arteries **[1]**

(e) pulmonary veins **[1]**

(f) aorta **[1]**

2. **(a)** Valves close when the chamber walls contract **[1]** preventing blood flowing backwards through the heart. **[1]**

(b) The atria pump blood only as far as the ventricle. **[1]** The ventricles need to generate a larger force to push blood out of the heart (to the lungs and body). **[1]**

(c) The left ventricle needs to generate a much larger force to push blood all through the body, **[1]** while the right ventricle only pumps blood through the lungs. **[1]**

(d) The aorta has a large diameter as it receives all the blood that is pumped out of the heart at the same time. **[1]** It needs the thickest muscular walls to withstand the highest pressure of blood as it is pumped out of the heart. **[1]**

Page 62 Aerobic and anaerobic respiration

Quick quiz

oxygen, glucose – aerobic – carbon dioxide, water; glucose – anaerobic (in muscle cells) – lactic acid

1. **(a)** Mitochondria **[1]**

(b) glucose + oxygen **[1]** → carbon dioxide + water **[1]**

(c) More energy is released from the reaction than is transferred to the products. **[1]**

(d) Cellular respiration releases energy for all the life processes/metabolic reactions in a cell. **[1]** If this doesn't happen continuously the cell will die. **[1]**

2. **(a)** glucose → lactic acid **[1]**

(b) glucose → ethanol **[1]** + carbon dioxide **[1]**

3. A comparison that makes reference to the following points: Aerobic respiration occurs when there is sufficient oxygen. **[1]** Anaerobic respiration occurs when oxygen is lacking. **[1]** Anaerobic respiration releases less energy from each glucose molecule than aerobic respiration **[1]** because the breakdown/oxidation of glucose is incomplete. **[1]**

Page 63 Practical: Rate of respiration

Quick quiz

True, False, True

1. **(a)** It moves to the left. **[1]**

(b) Soda lime absorbs carbon dioxide. **[1]**

(c) Volume of gas in respirometer decreases because oxygen is taken up by the organisms for aerobic respiration **[1]** and carbon dioxide produced by respiration in the organisms is absorbed by the soda lime. **[1]**

(d) Any suitable answer that keeps temperature constant, such as placing the tube in a water bath. **[1]**

2. **(a)** The measurement at 20 °C **[1]** seems too low to fit the pattern of the other results. **[1]**

(b) 22/5 **[1]** = 4.4 mm/min **[1]**

(c) As temperature increases, **[1]** the rate of respiration increases. **[1]**

(d) Increasing temperature increases the rate at which enzyme-controlled reactions happen. **[1]** Reactions in respiration are controlled by enzymes. **[1]**

(e) Repeating the experiment at each temperature several times and calculating a mean at each temperature. **[1]**

Page 64 Response to exercise

Quick quiz

Organ	Blood flow during rest (cm³/min)	Blood flow during exercise (cm³/min)
Heart	300	890
Muscles	1500	2500

1. Breathing rate increases so that more oxygen is taken into the body for aerobic respiration **[1]** and more carbon dioxide from respiration is removed. **[1]**

   Breath volume increases **[1]** which means that gas is exchanged with the environment more rapidly. **[1]**

   Heart rate increases **[1]** so that blood transports oxygen and glucose faster to cells and removes carbon dioxide from cells more rapidly. **[1]**

2. **(a)** cardiac output = 0.081 × 55 **[1]** = 4.46 (l/min) **[1]**

   (b) stroke volume = 4.46 / 69 **[1]** = 0.065 (l) **[1]**

   (c) Exercise increases the strength of the heart muscle **[1]** so it pumps out more blood each time it contracts. **[1]**

3. **(a)** Anaerobic respiration makes it possible for exercise/muscle contraction to continue **[1]** when there is not enough oxygen for aerobic respiration. **[1]**

   (b) Muscles stop contracting efficiently. **[1]**

Page 65 Communities

Quick quiz

the same, the same area, different, the same area

1. ecosystem **[1]**

2. **(a)** Blackbirds depend on blackberry plants for food/shelter/nest sites. [any one for 1 mark] Blackberry plants depend on blackbirds for seed dispersal. **[1]**

   (b) If the number of blackberry plants in the area increased, the number of blackbirds might increase **[1]** because they would have more food/places to nest. **[1]** (or the opposite)

3. **(a)** rabbits and field mice **[1]**

   (b) food/grass **[1]**

   (c) Rabbit numbers would decrease **[1]** because more deer would eat more

grass/would mean less grass for rabbits. **[1]**

(d) Foxes eat rabbits. **[1]** If rabbit numbers decrease then fox numbers could decrease too. **[1]**

Page 66 Abiotic factors

Quick quiz

light intensity, temperature, water availability, soil nutrient concentration, carbon dioxide concentration in air, pollutants

1. **(a)** The trend is a continuing rise in temperature. **[1]**

   (b) As the temperature increases this could cause more male insects to become sterile/have reduced fertility **[1]** which could cause insect population sizes to fall. **[1]**

   (c) If insect population size falls, there will be less food for their predators **[1]** so predator population sizes could also fall. **[1]**

2. **(a)** Pollution is something added to the environment that causes harm to living organisms. **[1]**

   (b) If corals are killed by the pollution this will reduce the amount of shelter and food the reefs provide for other animals **[1]** so biodiversity will decrease. **[1]**

3. An explanation that makes reference to the following points:
   - loss of leaves on trees increases light intensity nearer the ground **[1]**
   - low-growing plants will be able to photosynthesise more when tree leaves are gone **[1]**
   - more photosynthesis means more sugars made/better growth **[1]**
   - populations of low-growing plants will increase in number through sexual or asexual reproduction **[1]**

Page 67 Biotic factors

Quick quiz

parasitism, mutualism

1. **(a)** Larger white-clawed crayfish are found in populations that contain no signal crayfish. **[1]**

   (b) Signal crayfish compete more successfully than white-clawed for same food. **[1]** Predation by signal crayfish on white-clawed crayfish. **[1]**

   (c) More likely to be competition than predation **[1]** because predation would more likely be of smaller white-clawed not larger, whereas competition leaves less food so larger white-clawed likely to starve first. **[1]**

2. **(a)** If they eat the same food there will be competition. **[1]** Less food for red squirrels will mean they are likely to starve and have fewer offspring. **[1]**

(b) Grey squirrels have evolved resistance to the virus so they don't get ill. **[1]** Red squirrels are not resistant to the virus and are killed by it so their numbers fall rapidly. **[1]**

Page 68 Practical: Population studies

Quick quiz

distribution, abundance

1. **(a)** The buttercups are not spread evenly through the area. **[1]** Random sampling will help to avoid bias in the results such as by choosing positions for the quadrat where there are many / few buttercup plants. **[1]**

   (b) (3+2+0+0+2+1)/6 = 1.3 **[1]**

   (c) total area of field = 25 × 34 = 850 m² **[1]**

   total area of quadrat in m² = 100 cm²
   $= \frac{100}{100 \times 100} = 0.01\,m^2$ **[1]**
   population size = 850/0.01 × 1.3 **[1]**
   = 110 500 plants **[1]**

2. **(a)** Under the tree there are very few daisies, but there are many more out in the open. **[1]**

   (b) Any factor that is affected by the presence of the tree, with an explanation, such as:
   - light intensity, **[1]** because daisy plants need light for photosynthesis and so will grow less well under the tree canopy where there is less light **[1]**
   - soil moisture **[1]** because daisy plants need to absorb water from the soil for cell processes and the tree canopy prevents some rain water reaching the soil under the tree **[1]**
   - competition with tree roots **[1]** such as competition for soil nutrients as daisy plants need these to grow well. **[1]**

Page 69 Biodiversity

Quick quiz

species, ecosystem, depend, food, less

1. **(a)** From 1955 to 1971, oxygen concentration decreased from 8 mg/l to 5 mg/l. **[1]**

   From 1971 to 1997, oxygen concentration rose from 5 mg/l to 10 mg/l. **[1]**

   (b) As oxygen concentration decreases, the number of species also decreases. **[1]**

   When oxygen concentration increases, the number of species rises. **[1]**

   (c) Fertiliser causes eutrophication and rapid growth of algae. **[1]** Death of algae and other plants leads to decay by bacteria **[1]** and fall in oxygen concentration as bacteria respire. **[1]** Animals that need lots of oxygen from the water for respiration cannot carry out metabolic processes so well and may die. **[1]**

2. (a)
Eating farmed fish should reduce the amount of fish taken from the wild for human food. **[1]** Therefore, communities/food webs in the sea will be less affected. **[1]**

(b) Any suitable answer with appropriate reason, such as: excess nutrients from the fish farm enter the surrounding water **[1]** causing eutrophication/changing the native community **[1]**; chemicals used to keep fish healthy could enter surrounding water **[1]** killing some native species and affecting community through changing biodiversity **[1]**; food for the farmed fish may be taken from natural ecosystems, **[1]** harming food chains. **[1]**

Page 70 Maintaining biodiversity

Quick quiz

False, False, True, True

1. (a) The national trend for skylarks is a decreasing population. **[1]**

   The trend on the farm for skylarks is an increasing population. **[1]**

   (b) More yield means the farmer has more to sell/can earn more money. **[1]**

   (c) Planting field edges with a greater diversity of plants **[1]** means that skylarks can find food in the area all year round. **[1]**

2. Marks awarded for coherent explanation and ordering of ideas as well as scientific knowledge – Level 3 answer **[5–6]**, Level 2 answer **[3–4]**, Level 1 answer **[1–2]**.

   Indicative content:

   - planting a large variety of trees will increase biodiversity of trees
   - biodiversity of trees will provide a greater range of habitats and food which will increase biodiversity of animals
   - creating different habitats, such as open areas within the forest, wetter/drier areas, will also increase plant and animal biodiversity
   - consideration should be given to species that are in need of conservation in the UK and the type of habitat/community that they require
   - consideration should be given to plants and animals that may be displaced by the forest, especially if they need conservation

Page 71 Carbon cycle

Quick quiz

increases, decreases, increases

1. (a) carbon dioxide **[1]**

   (b) photosynthesis **[1]**

   (c) Any two from the following: proteins, carbohydrates, fats, nucleic acid/DNA. **[2]**

   (d) respiration **[1]**

(e) It is broken down by microorganisms/bacteria **[1]** that release carbon dioxide into the air from respiration. **[1]**

2. The leaves decay due to the action of microorganisms **[1]**. As the microorganisms break down the leaves, they are respiring **[1]** and so releasing carbon dioxide. **[1]**

Page 72 Water cycle

Quick quiz

cytoplasm, reactions, vacuole, dissolved, plasma, xylem, phloem

1. (a) The water cycle provides fresh water that organisms living on land need to absorb into their cells for many cell processes. **[1]** The water also dissolves mineral ions from the soil that plants absorb to make proteins and other substances. **[1]**

   (b) A: Evaporation is when liquid water in the sea changes to water vapour in the air. **[1]** B: Condensation is when water vapour cools and forms liquid water droplets in clouds. **[1]** C: Precipitation is when liquid or solid water (ice, snow) falls from clouds onto land or sea. **[1]**

2. (a) Water that is suitable for drinking. **[1]**

   (b) Water evaporates from the seawater due to energy from sunlight. **[1]** The water vapour condenses on the cooler cover and is collected in a separate container. **[1]**

   (c) Only the water evaporates from the seawater leaving the dissolved salts behind, so separating the water and salt. **[1]**

   (d) These places are hot and dry/suffer drought and so do not get enough fresh water from rain or rivers. **[1]**

Page 73 Nitrogen cycle

Quick quiz

True, False, False, True

1. (a) As the mass of nitrogen is increased, the yield increases.

   (b) Plants absorb nitrogen from the soil and use it to make substances such as proteins needed in new cells. **[1]** More nitrogen means the plants can make more cells which increases yield. **[1]**

2. (a) (i) Soil bacteria will break down dead plant material **[1]** releasing nitrates into the soil. **[1]**

       (ii) Beans/legumes have root nodules that contain nitrogen-fixing bacteria. **[1]** Nitrogen from the air is converted to nitrogen compounds and some will enter the soil while the bean/legume crop is growing. **[1]**

   (b) The nitrogen in manure is in proteins and other substances that plants cannot absorb. **[1]** Over time, these

substances are broken down by bacteria in the soil into forms that plants can absorb. **[1]**

Page 74 Atoms, elements and compounds

Quick quiz

atom – the smallest part of an element that can exist

element – made of only one type of atom; cannot be broken down into simpler substances by chemical methods

compound – consists of two or more elements chemically combined

1. calcium + oxygen → calcium oxide **[1]**

2. magnesium hydrogencarbonate → magnesium carbonate + water + carbon dioxide **[1]**

3.

Element name	Element symbol
sodium **[1]**	Na
bromine	Br **[1]**
lead **[1]**	Pb
iron	Fe **[1]**
chlorine **[1]**	Cl
potassium	K **[1]**

4. carbon dioxide **[1]**

5. barium chloride **[1]**

6. 2 **[1]**

7. copper carbonate → carbon dioxide + copper oxide **[1]**

Page 75 The model of the atom

Quick quiz

5, 2, 4, 1, 3

1. Marks awarded for coherent explanation and ordering of ideas as well as scientific knowledge – Level 3 answer **[5–6]**, Level 2 answer **[3–4]**, Level 1 answer **[1–2]**.

   Indicative content:

   - In both models, the atom contains positive charges.
   - However, the plum pudding model describes a ball of positive charge whereas the nuclear model contains separate positive charges within a central nucleus.
   - Both models have negative particles called electrons.
   - The plum pudding model has electrons arranged randomly whereas the nuclear model has electrons in shells.
   - The plum pudding model has no nucleus unlike the nuclear model.
   - The plum pudding model has no neutrons but the nuclear model has neutrons located within the nucleus.

2. The experiment showed that:

   some particles were repelled so must have encountered a positive charge **[1]**

   most particles passed through undeflected so could not have passed close to any charge **[1]** therefore, most of the atom is empty space [1]

the positive charges in the atom must be located in a small area (the nucleus) [1]

Page 76 Subatomic particles

Quick quiz

A electron **B** neutron **C** proton

nucleus

1. Completed table, 1 mark for each correct row:

Name of subatomic particle	Position in the atom
proton	nucleus
neutron	nucleus
electron	shell

2. Proton [1]

3. Atoms contain equal numbers of protons and electrons. [1]

4. $\dfrac{1 \times 10^{-10}\,\text{m}}{1 \times 10^{-14}\,\text{m}}$ [1] $= 1 \times 10^4$ [1]

5. 0.000 000 000 1 m [1]

Page 77 Size and mass of atoms

Quick quiz

True; False; False

1. Atomic number is the number of protons in an atom. [1] Mass number is the total number of protons and neutrons in an atom. [1]

2. There are 79 protons because the atomic number is 79. [1] There are 79 electrons because atoms have an equal number of protons and electrons. [1] There are 197 − 79 = 118 neutrons [1] because the mass number is the total number of protons and neutrons. [1]

3. 26 protons [1], 56 − 26 = 30 neutrons [1], 26 − 3 = 23 electrons [1]

4. Atomic number = 4 [1], mass number = 4 + 5 = 9 [1]

5. **(a)** carbon [1]
   (b) The atom has 6 protons [1] so its atomic number is 6. [1]
   (c) Fluorine has 3 more protons/9 protons compared to 6 protons [1], 4 more neutrons/10 neutrons compared to 6 neutrons [1] and 3 more electrons/9 electrons compared to 6 electrons/7 electrons in outer shell compared to 4 [1] than the atom in **Figure 1**.

Page 78 Isotopes and relative atomic mass

Quick quiz

False; True; False; True

1. **(a)** protons 8 [1]; neutrons 8 [1]; electrons 8 [1]
   (b) Both have the same number of protons [1] but they have different

numbers of neutrons. [1] Oxygen-16 has 8 neutrons, oxygen-18 has 10. [1]

(c) relative atomic mass
$= \dfrac{(63 \times 69.2) + (65 \times 30.8)}{100}$ [1]
$= 63.616$ [1] $= 63.6$ to 3 significant figures [1]

2. **(a)** protons 2 [1]; neutrons 1 [1]; electrons 2 [1]
   (b) There are other isotopes of helium (which are heavier). [1]

Page 79 Developing the periodic table

Quick quiz

Mendeleev, atomic mass, similar, groups, elements

1. **(a)** Metals and non-metals were mixed together rather than being on separate sides of the table [1]; more than one element in some boxes. [1]
   (b) Elements with similar properties are grouped together [1], with only one element per box. [1]

2. Three from: Elements with similar properties were grouped together [1]; elements in atomic weight order [1]; gaps in the table for unknown elements when the pattern suggested it [1]; some elements swapped position to fit the group trend better [1]

3. **(a)** He grouped elements with similar properties together [1] and left gaps where elements did not fit the pattern. [1]
   (b) Any one for 1 mark from: Some elements were not in the correct group/elements with similar properties were not under each other, e.g. Te and Ir. [1]

Page 80 The periodic table

Quick quiz

potassium – Group 1; nitrogen – Group 5; argon – Group 0

True; True; True; False

1. **(a)** chlorine/fluorine/bromine/astatine/iodine [1]
   (b) Cl/F/Br/At/I [1]

2. **(a)** 6 [1]
   (b) 4 [1]

3. **(a)** Group 3 [1], Period 3 [1]
   (b) aluminium [1]

4. **(a)** Hydrogen and the Group 1 elements all have one electron in the outer shell. [1]
   (b) Hydrogen is a non-metal but Group 1 elements are metals. [1] At room temperature hydrogen is a gas but Group 1 elements are solid. [1]
   (c) An alkaline solution [1] because francium is in the same group as rubidium and will have similar chemistry. [1]
   (d) RbCl [1]

Page 81 Electronic structure

Quick quiz

Shell	Maximum number of electrons
1	2
2	8
3	8

Group 6

Period 3

sulfur

1. **(a)**
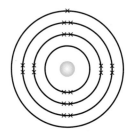
   [1] for correct inner shells 2, 8, 8 and [1] for 1 electron in outer shell.
   (b) If there are 19 electrons there must be 19 protons. [1]

2. Group 3 [1] because there are 3 electrons in the outer shell. [1] Period 3 [1] because there are 3 occupied shells of electrons. [1]

3. **(a)** **(i)** 2, 6 [1]
   (ii) 1 [1]
   (b) The number of outer electrons is the same as the group. [1]
   (c) 2.4 [1]; carbon [1]

4. [1 mark for correct inner shells; 1 mark for correct outer shells]
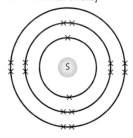

Page 82 Metals and non-metals

Quick quiz

Completed table:

Property	Metals	Non-metals
poor conductor of electricity		✓
good conductor of heat	✓	
strong	✓	
brittle		✓
dull		✓
malleable	✓	

1. To the right [1]

2. Metals usually have high melting points so they are solid at room temperature [1] but mercury is liquid. [1]

3. Metals lose electrons (to gain a full outer shell) [1] forming positive ions. [1] Non-metals gain electrons (to fill their outer shell) [1] forming negative ions. [1]

4. Non-metals are usually poor conductors of electricity [1] and have low melting points [1] but graphite conducts electricity [1] and has a high melting point. [1]

Page 83 Chemical bonds

Quick quiz

True, False, False, False, True

Metallic bonds form between atoms of metals, either the same type of metal atom or different metal atoms.

Covalent bonding involves sharing of electrons.

Metallic bonding involves delocalised electrons, while ionic bonding involves transfer of electrons.

1. (a) Both hydrogen and chlorine are non-metals and so can only form covalent bonds with each other. [1]

   (b) Hydrogen has 1 electron in its outer shell and shares one electron to obtain a full outer shell. [1] Chlorine has 7 electrons in its outer shell and can share one electron with hydrogen to obtain a full outer shell. [1]

2. Ticks for: oxygen and carbon; phosphorus and oxygen; carbon and chlorine. [1 mark for each correct answer; deduct 1 mark for each extra tick]

3. A bond formed between oppositely charged ions [1] attracted to each other by electrostatic attraction. [1]

4. Metallic bonding has attraction [1] between the delocalised electrons [1] and positively charged nuclei of metal ions. [1]

Page 84 Ionic bonding

Quick quiz

magnesium Mg^{2+}; oxygen O^{2-}; sodium Na^+; aluminium Al^{3+}; fluorine F^-; calcium Ca^{2+}

1. All atoms of elements in Group 2 have 2 electrons in their outer shell. [1] To be stable, they lose these two outer electrons [1] to gain a full outer shell. [1]

2. (a) Lithium is in Group 1 so when it reacts it loses its outer electron [1] to form a Li^+ ion. [1] Chlorine is in Group 7 so when it reacts its outer shell gains an electron (to make a stable outer shell) [1] forming a Cl^- ion. [1]

   (b)

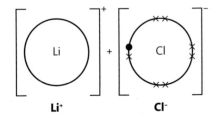

[1 mark per correct structure]

3.

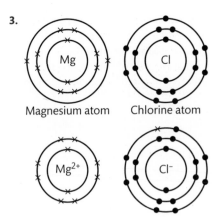

Magnesium atom Chlorine atom

Magnesium ion Chlorine ion

[1 mark per correct structure]

Page 85 Ionic compounds

Quick quiz

two-dimensional; three-dimensional; ball and stick; dot and cross

1. Advantages: The different ion sizes can be seen. [1] Gives an idea of the position of the ions. [1] Disadvantages: Does not show the bonds between the ions. [1] The internal structure cannot be seen. [1]

2. Marks awarded for coherent explanation and ordering of ideas as well as scientific knowledge – Level 3 answer [5–6], Level 2 answer [3–4], Level 1 answer [1–2].

   Indicative content:
   - The ball and stick model shows a 3D structure.
   - Whereas the dot and cross model only shows a 2D structure.
   - The ball and stick model indicates the position of the bonds.
   - And so the arrangement of the atoms or ions.
   - The dot and cross diagram only shows the atoms or ions involved in one molecule or bond.
   - Ball and stick can show many atoms or ions.
   - Both models do not show the correct size of the atoms or ions.
   - Both models are not to scale.
   - Ball and stick show spaces between atoms/ions.

3. (a) There is a regular arrangement of ions [1] held by strong electrostatic forces between oppositely charged ions. [1]

   (b) MgO [1]

   (c) In the diagram there are 13 ions of one type and 14 ions of the other type (not 1:1) [1] because the diagram shows only a part of the lattice structure. [1]

Page 86 Properties of ionic compounds

Quick quiz

Ionic compounds conduct electricity when liquefied.

Ionic compounds have a high melting point because there are strong forces of attraction between ions.

1. A giant ionic lattice forms [1] held together by the electrostatic attraction [1] between the oppositely charged ions. [1]

2. The ions in a solid are in fixed positions. [1] In order to conduct electricity, the ions need to be free to move. [1]

3. The ions are free to move [1] and carry the charge. [1]

4. Check the compound to see if it conducts electricity [1]; it should conduct electricity when dissolved in water (or when molten) but not when solid. [1] Heat the compound to see if it melts easily [1]; its melting point should be high. [1]

Page 87 Covalent bonding

Quick quiz

covalent – a bond formed when a pair of electrons is shared between atoms; ion – an atom or group of atoms with a positive or negative charge; ionic – a bond formed by the transfer of electrons between atoms; molecule – a group of atoms bonded together

1. (a) Oxygen has six electrons in its outer shell so it can share two electrons to gain a full outer shell and become stable. [1] Each hydrogen atom has one electron in its outer shell and it shares with oxygen so it obtains a full outer shell and becomes stable. [1]

   (b) B [1]

   (c) NH_3 [1]

   (d) A [1]

   (e) water [1]

2. double bond/two shared pairs of electrons [1], rest of molecule correct/four unpaired electrons in each oxygen [1]

3. two double bonds [1], rest of molecule correct/four unpaired electrons in each oxygen atom and no unpaired electrons in the carbon atom [1]

Page 88 Properties of simple molecular substances

Quick quiz

liquids, low, poor, insoluble, covalent

1. Carbon dioxide is a gas at room temperature because the forces of attraction between the molecules are weak/easily overcome, [1] therefore little energy is needed to separate the molecules and the boiling point of carbon dioxide is low. [1]

2. **(a)** As the size of the molecule increases, the boiling point increases. **[1]**

   (b) Value given in the range 80–100 °C **[1]**

   (c) As the size of the molecule increases the intermolecular forces increase **[1]** and more energy is needed to separate the molecules. **[1]**

3. Carbon dioxide gas has a simple molecular structure and does not have an overall electric charge/mobile charged particles/electrons **[1]** so they cannot carry electric charge from place to place. **[1]**

4. There are weak intermolecular forces/forces between molecules **[1]** and so it takes little energy to separate the molecules. **[1]**

Page 89 Giant covalent structures

Quick quiz

simple molecular; simple molecular; simple molecular; giant covalent

1. **(a)** Covalent bonds are formed between atoms by shared pairs of electrons **[1]**.

   (b) Any three for 3 marks from: Very high melting point/boiling point (as a lot of energy is needed to break the many strong covalent bonds **[1]**; does not conduct electricity as there are no mobile charge carriers **[1]**; insoluble in water as the attraction to the water molecules is not strong enough to overcome the strong covalent bonds **[1]**; very hard due to the strong covalent bonding in the three dimensional structure. **[1]**

2. It has a high melting point and is a good conductor of electricity. **[1]**

3. In diamond there are strong covalent bonds between all atoms. **[1]**

   These require a lot of energy. **[1]**

   To break all the bonds and separate the atoms so the melting point is high. **[1]**

   In carbon dioxide there are weak forces between molecules/weak intermolecular forces. **[1]**

   Little energy is needed to separate the molecules. **[1]**

Page 90 Diamond

Quick quiz

four, covalent, hard, high

1. **(a)** Diamond has a giant covalent structure **[1]** with many strong covalent bonds **[1]** arranged in a tetrahedral arrangement/in the shape of a tetrahedron to give a strong rigid structure. **[1]** This makes diamond very hard and therefore suitable for cutting tools **[1]**

   (b) It has no free electrons/ions. **[1]**

   (c) Any two for 2 marks from: solid at room temperature **[1]**; transparent **[1]**; high melting point/high boiling point **[1]**; brittle **[1]**; insoluble **[1]**; hard. **[1]**

   (d) Much energy is needed **[1]** to break the many **[1]** strong covalent bonds and separate the atoms. **[1]**

2. It is made of carbon atoms. **[1]** Each carbon atom forms 4 bonds. **[1]** The bonds are covalent. **[1]** Diamond has a giant covalent/lattice/tetrahedral structure. **[1]**

Page 91 Graphite

Quick quiz

A: covalent bond, **B:** carbon atom, **C:** intermolecular force of attraction

1. **(a)** covalent **[1]**

   (b) 3 **[1]**

2. Graphite forms layers of carbon atoms. **[1]** These are arranged in hexagons. **[1]** Between the layers there are weak forces of attraction. **[1]**

3. Between the layers of carbon atoms there are only weak forces of attraction **[1]** so the layers can easily slide past each other and deposit on the paper. **[1]**

4. The weak attraction between the water and carbon atoms **[1]** does not overcome the strong bonds in graphite/does not separate the atoms. **[1]**

5. Only three out of each carbon atom's four outer electrons are used in covalent bonds **[1]** so each carbon atom has one delocalised electron which can move and carry charge. **[1]**

6. Graphite: The atoms are in layers that can slide over each other **[1]** because the forces of attraction between the layers are weak. **[1]**

   Diamond: Each carbon atom forms four strong covalent bonds. **[1]** Strong tetrahedral arrangement/in the shape of a tetrahedron. **[1]**

Page 92 Graphene and fullerenes

Quick quiz

True, False, True, False

1. **(a)** 3 **[1]**

   (b) Both have high melting and boiling points so are solid at room temperature. **[1]** Both conduct electricity. **[1]**

2. Graphene is a giant covalent structure. **[1]** It has covalent bonds between the atoms. **[1]** These bonds are very strong/need a lot of energy to break. **[1]**

3. Any three for 3 marks from: strong **[1]**; conduct electricity **[1]**; high tensile strength **[1]**; high length to diameter ratio **[1]**; high melting and boiling points. **[1]**

4. Marks awarded for coherent explanation and ordering of ideas as well as scientific knowledge – Level 3 answer **[5–6]**, Level 2 answer **[3–4]**, Level 1 answer **[1–2]**.

   Indicative content:
   - Graphene is only one layer thick.
   - Therefore, it can be used in very small electrical components.

   - The carbon atoms in graphene are only covalently bonded to three other carbon atoms
   - so graphene has delocalised electrons which can move and carry charge
   - and so it can conduct electricity.
   - Graphene is very strong
   - due to the strong covalent bonds between all atoms.
   - Graphene is transparent and flexible
   - so it can be used in touch screens in a variety of electrical appliances.

Page 93 Polymers

Quick quiz

large, stronger, high

1. **(a)** A polymer is a large molecule made from smaller molecules/monomers joined together. **[1]**

   (b) covalent **[1]**

   (c) Polymer chains are large molecules and the intermolecular forces between them are relatively strong, **[1]** therefore the melting points of polymers are higher than room temperature. **[1]**

2. **(a)** C_3H_6 **[1]**

   (b) covalent **[1]**

   (c) The intermolecular forces **[1]** between molecules of polypropene are greater **[1]** than those between molecules of propene.

3. PVC does not conduct electricity because there are no free electrons or ions in the structure. **[1]**

Page 94 Metallic bonding

Quick quiz

(a) One large grey circle labelled 'metal atom'; one small green circle labelled 'electron'

(b) negative / –1

(c) In a regular arrangement.

(d) They can move/are delocalised.

1. **(a)** Metals consist of a regular arrangement of metal atoms **[1]** surrounded by delocalised electrons. **[1]** There is strong attraction between the positive metal nuclei and the negatively charged electrons, **[1]** so bonding in metals is strong.

   (b) The metallic bonds are formed from the strong attraction **[1]** between positively charged nuclei and the negatively charged electrons. **[1]** Sodium has one delocalised electron per metal particle, **[1]** magnesium has two delocalised electrons per metal particle. **[1]**

2. **(a)** The electrons in the outer shell. **[1]**

   (b) Aluminium atoms have three electrons in their outer shell (because it is in Group 3) **[1]** and so there are three delocalised electrons per aluminium atom. **[1]**

3. Layers of positive metal nuclei attracted to delocalised electrons. **[1]**

Page 95 Properties of metals

Quick quiz

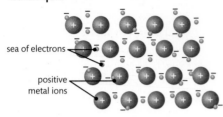

sea of electrons

positive metal ions

The delocalised electrons move and carry charge.

1. Malleable means that metals can be hammered into shape without breaking. **[1]**

2. **1** X has a high melting point. **[1]**

   2 It is a good conductor of electricity. **[1]**

   3 It is shiny/it has a high density/it is malleable. **[1]**

3. It is a liquid/has a low boiling point **[1]**; it does not conduct electricity. **[1]**

4. The layers of ions **[1]** can slide over each other. **[1]** The delocalised electrons hold the atoms together and so the metal changes shape instead of breaking. **[1]**

5. Metals have strong bonds **[1]** between positive nuclei of metal atoms and delocalised electrons. **[1]** It takes a lot of energy **[1]** to break these bonds. **[1]**

Page 96 Relative formula mass

Quick quiz

True, False, False, False

1. **(a)** Carbon 12 **[1]**; Sodium 23 **[1]**; Mercury 201 **[1]**

   (b) Oxygen 32 **[1]**; Fluorine 38 **[1]**; Chlorine 71 **[1]**

2. $CuSO_4$: Cu + S + (4 × O) = 159.5 **[1]**; Na_2CO_3: 2 × Na + C + 3 × O = 106 **[1]**; NaCl 58.5 **[1]**; NH_4OH 35 **[1]**; $Ca(NO_3)_2$ 164 **[1]**

3. **(a)** 152 **[1]**

   (b) 158 **[1]**

   (c) 80 **[1]**

   (d) 187.5 **[1]**

   (e) 342 **[1]**

4. If the equation is balanced the total relative formula mass of reactants will equal the total relative formula mass of the products. **[1]**

5. Relative formula mass of NO_3 = 14 + 16 + 16 + 16 = 62 **[1]**; Relative atomic mass of X = 101 − 62 = 39 **[1]**. (Using the periodic table) X = K/potassium **[1]**

Page 97 Empirical formulae

Quick quiz

CH CH_4 CH_3 C_2H_6O CH_2 $CaCl_2$

1. M_r = 12 + 2 + 16 = 30 **[1]**

   180/30 = 6 **[1]**

   Empirical formula is $C_6H_{12}O_6$ **[1]**

2. Hg = 55.5/201 = 0.276 **[1]**; Br = 44.5/80 = 0.556 **[1]**

   Ratio Hg:Br = 0.276:0.556 = 1:2 so empirical formula = $HgBr_2$ **[1]**

3. **(a)** Marks awarded for coherent explanation and ordering of ideas as well as scientific knowledge – Level 3 answer **[5–6]**, Level 2 answer **[3–4]**, Level 1 answer **[1–2]**.

   Indicative content:
   - find mass of crucible/suitable container (+ lid)
   - find mass of container (+ lid) + titanium
   - heat container (+ lid) + titanium
   - lift lid occasionally to allow oxygen in
   - minimise loss of titanium oxide
   - heat until no further change
   - allow to cool
   - find mass of container (+ lid) + titanium oxide
   - repeat heating
   - until constant mass

   (b) mass of oxygen = mass of titanium oxide − mass of titanium

   1.700 − 1.020 = 0.680 g

   moles of oxygen = 0.680/16 = 0.0425 **[1]**

   moles of titanium atoms = 1.020/48 = 0.02125 **[1]**

   ratio titanium atoms:oxygen atoms = 0.02125:0.0425 = 1:2

   empirical formula = TiO_2 **[1]**

Page 98 Balancing equations

Quick quiz

$2Na + Cl_2 \rightarrow 2NaCl$

$2Mg + O_2 \rightarrow 2MgO$

1. **(a)** $BaO + 2HCl \rightarrow BaCl_2 + H_2O$ **[1]**

   (b) $2Na + Br_2 \rightarrow 2NaBr$ **[1]**

   (c) $Mg + CuSO_4 \rightarrow MgSO_4 + Cu$ **[1]**

   (d) $Li_2CO_3 + 2HNO_3 \rightarrow 2LiNO_3 + H_2O + CO_2$ **[1]**

   (e) $N_2 + 3H_2 \rightarrow 2NH_3$ **[1]**

   (f) $4Al + 3O_2 \rightarrow 2Al_2O_3$ **[1]**

   (g) $2Fe + 3CuSO_4 \rightarrow Fe_2(SO_4)_3 + 3Cu$ **[1]**

2. **(a)** $CuO + H_2 \rightarrow Cu + H_2O$ [1 mark for correct formulae; 1 mark for correct balancing]

   (b) $2SO_2 + O_2 \rightarrow 2SO_3$ [1 mark for correct formulae; 1 mark for correct balancing]

   (c) $Fe_2O_3 + 3CO \rightarrow 2Fe + 3CO_2$ [1 mark for correct formulae; 1 mark for correct balancing]

   (d) $6CO_2 + 6H_2O \rightarrow C_6H_{12}O_6 + 6O_2$ [1 mark for correct formulae; 1 mark for correct balancing]

   (e) $2C_4H_{10} + 13O_2 \rightarrow 8CO_2 + 10H_2O$ [1 mark for correct formulae; 1 mark for correct balancing]

Page 99 Conservation of mass

Quick quiz

Heating copper carbonate; Reacting hydrochloric acid and magnesium

1. **(a)** $2Ag_2O \rightarrow 4Ag + O_2$ [1 mark for correct formulae; 1 mark for correct balancing]

   (b) 6.22 − 5.79 = 0.43 g **[1]**

   (c) If the gas produced in a reaction is not collected or fully collected, **[1]** the total mass of the products will appear less. **[1]**

2. **(a)** The mass of the pack increases. **[1]**

   (b) The iron nails oxidise (react with water and oxygen in the air) to make rust (iron oxide). **[1]** Since the oxygen chemically combines with the iron of the nails, their mass increases. **[1]**

3. mass of magnesium = 0.24 g; mass of magnesium oxide = 0.40 g; **[1]** mass of oxygen = 0.16 g **[1]**

4. **(a)** copper + iodine → copper iodide **[1]**

   (b) The mass would increase because copper combines with iodine in the reaction **[1]** so the mass is due to copper and iodine, not just copper **[1]**.

Page 100 Calculating masses in reactions

Quick quiz

128 g

1. **(a)** Student 1: The reaction produces a gas. **[1]** Unless the gas is collected, the mass of the products will appear less than that of the reactants as the gas has escaped. **[1]**

   Student 2: If a closed system is used, all of the products will be collected. **[1]**

   (b) $CaCO_3(s) + 2HCl(aq) \rightarrow CaCl_2(aq) + H_2O(l) + CO_2(g)$ [1 mark for correct formulae, 1 mark for balancing, 1 mark for correct state symbols]

   (c) The carbon dioxide is a gas, **[1]** which escaped from the beaker so the measured mass was lower than expected **[1]**.

2. 24 + 2 × (1 + 35.5) = 97 left hand side **[1]**

   24 + (2 × 35.5) + (2 × 1) = 97 right hand side **[1]**

3. The total mass after a reaction is the same as the total mass before the reaction. **[1]**

4. A closed system means the reactants and products cannot escape to the surroundings. **[1]**

5. 50 − 28 = 22 g **[1]**

   (22/50) × 100% **[1]** = 44% **[1]** correct answer without working is 2 marks

Page 101 Concentrations of solutions

Quick quiz

g dm^{-3}, g, dm^3

concentration = mass/volume

1. (a) $0.020\,dm^3$ **[1]**

(b) $0.150\,dm^3$ **[1]**

(c) $0.025\,dm^3$ **[1]**

2. (a) $100/1000 = 0.1\,dm^3$ **[1]**

(b) concentration = mass/volume **[1]**
$= 3.7/0.1$ **[1]** $= 37\,g\,dm^{-3}$ **[1]**

3. mass = concentration × volume **[1]**;
mass $= 65 × 2.5$ **[1]** $= 162.5\,g$ **[1]**

4. $5\,cm^3 = 5/1000 = 0.005\,dm^3$ **[1]**

mass = concentration × volume **[1]** =
$0.2 × 0.005 = 0.001$ **[1]** $= 1 × 10^{-3}\,g$ **[1]**

5. volume = mass/concentration **[1]**
$= 2/20$ **[1]** $= 0.1\,dm^3$ **[1]**

Page 102 Moles

Quick quiz

number of moles = mass/relative formula
mass OR mass/M_r

32g

1. $M_r = (1 × 12) + (2 × 16) = 44$ **[1]**.
Mass $= 2 × 44 = 88\,g$ **[1]**

2. number of moles $= 15/60$ **[1]** $= 0.25\,mol$ **[1]**

3. 98 **[1]**

4. $M_r = (2 × 23 + 12 + 3 × 16) = 106$ **[1]**
moles of $Na_2CO_3 = 5.3/106 = 0.05$ **[1]**

5. $M_r\,(NH_4)_2SO_4 = (14 + 4) × 2 + 32 + (4 × 16)$
$= 132$ **[1]**

mass = moles × $M_r = 2 × 132 = 264\,g$ **[1]**

Page 103 Amounts of substances

Quick quiz

$M_r \rightarrow$ relative formula mass; mol $\rightarrow$ unit for
amount of matter; $A_r \rightarrow$ relative atomic mass;
g $\rightarrow$ unit for mass

$6.02 × 10^{23}$

1. (a) $6.02 × 10^{23}$ **[1]**

(b) $0.83 × 6.02 × 10^{23}$ **[1]** $= 5.0 × 10^{23}$ **[1]**

2. moles $= 6.4/16 = 0.4$ **[1]**

Number of molecules $= 0.4 × 6.02 × 10^{23}$
$= 2.408 × 10^{23}$ **[1]**

3. Number of moles of water $= 12.0/18$
$= 0.667\,mol.$ **[1]** (3 atoms in 1 molecule) so
number of moles of atoms $= 0.667 × 3$
$= 2\,mol.$ **[1]** Number of atoms $= 2 × 6.02$
$× 10^{23} = 1.204 × 10^{24}.$ **[1]** This is
$1.20 × 10^{24}$ to 3 significant figures. **[1]**

4. M_r = mass/moles $= 480/3$ **[1]** $= 160$ **[1]**

Page 104 Using mass to balance equations

Quick quiz

F_2 – 38; $SrCO_3$ – 148; $BaCl_2$ – 208;
$AgNO_3$ – 170

M_r = mass/moles

1. (a) mass of oxygen = mass of copper
oxide – mass of copper $= 6.36 – 5.08$
$= 1.28\,g$ **[1]**

(b) $M_r\,Cu = 63.5; O_2 = 32; CuO = 79.5$ **[1]**;
$Cu = 0.08\,mol; O_2 = 0.04\,mol; CuO =$
$0.08\,mol$ **[1]**

$Cu = 2; O_2 = 1; CuO = 2$ **[1]**; $2Cu + O_2$
$\rightarrow 2CuO$ **[1]**

2. $M_r\,CH_4 = 16; O_2 = 32; CO_2 = 44; H_2O = 18$ **[1]**

Mass of O_2 used $= 4.85 + 3.96 – 1.76$
$= 7.05\,g$ **[1]**

$CH_4 = 0.11\,mol; O_2 = 0.22\,mol; CO_2 =$
$0.11\,mol; H_2O = 0.22\,mol$ **[1]**

mole ratio $CH_4 : 2O_2 : CO_2 : 2H_2O$ **[1]**

$CH_4 + 2O_2 \rightarrow CO_2 + 2H_2O$ **[1]**

Page 105 States of matter

Quick quiz

State	Particle arrangement	Particle movement	Forces of attraction
solid	close together regular lattice arrangement	vibrate in one place	strong
liquid	close together random arrangement	move around each other	weak
gas	far apart random arrangement	move around freely in all directions	very weak/none

1. (a) Any three from: the particles move
further apart **[1]**; the strength of
the forces between the particles
decreases **[1]**; the particles move
faster as they have more energy **[1]**;
the solid melts/changes to a liquid. **[1]**

(b) liquid **[1]**

2. The state symbol (aq) means it is aqueous,
a solution in water. **[1]**

3. (a) Any two from the following: The
model represents all particles as
spheres **[1]**; The spheres are solid **[1]**;
It does not show the forces that exist
between the particles **[1]**; The model
is not to scale/there are spaces
between the particles **[1]**.

(b) The stronger the forces of attraction
[1] the higher the boiling point. **[1]**

(c) Marks awarded for coherent
explanation and ordering of ideas as
well as scientific knowledge – Level
3 answer **[5–6]**, Level 2 answer **[3–4]**,
Level 1 answer **[1–2]**.

Indicative content:

In a solid the forces of attraction are
very strong **[1]**; The particles do not
have enough energy to overcome the
forces and so can only vibrate in one
place **[1]**; and so are close (regularly
arranged) **[1]**; In a liquid the particles
are close together but are free to
move **[1]**; This is because the forces of
attraction are strong enough to hold
the particles closely together but not
as strong as in a solid **[1]**; In a gas the
forces of attraction are negligible **[1]**;
and so the particles can move around
freely/random arrangement **[1]**; and
are far apart. **[1]**

Page 106 Pure substances

Quick quiz

A, B, D

1. Sample D is the most pure **[1]** as its
melting point is closest to the melting
point of benzoic acid. **[1]**

2. A pure substance contains only a single
element or compound. Oxygen is made
of atoms/molecules of oxygen only, **[1]**
but air contains different gases/atoms/
molecules and so is not pure. **[1]**

3. Salty water **[1]**

4. C, **[1]** sharp melting point **[1]**

5. Orange juice straight from the orange
contains several different substances
(water, sugars, flavour compounds,
vitamins and so on) **[1]** and so is not made
up of a single element or compound. **[1]**

Page 107 Mixtures

Quick quiz

coal from slurry (a mixture of solid coal dust
and water) – filtration and drying; ethanol from
a mixture of alcohols – fractional distillation;
water from coal slurry – filtration; salts from
seawater (a solution of salts) – crystallisation;
pure water from seawater – simple distillation;
coloured substances from leaves, dissolved in
ethanol – paper chromatography

1. (a) A mixture consists of two or more
elements/compounds/substances not
chemically bonded. **[1]**

(b) Marks awarded for coherent
explanation and ordering of ideas as
well as scientific knowledge – Level
3 answer **[5–6]**, Level 2 answer **[3–4]**,
Level 1 answer **[1–2]**.

Indicative content:

Pour the copper sulfate solution into
the evaporating basin. **[1]** Then place
the basin on a tripod and gauze. **[1]**
Use the Bunsen burner to heat
the solution. **[1]** Continue until about
half of the water has evaporated. **[1]**
Leave the basin on a windowsill/to
cool down (so that the copper
sulfate crystallises). **[1]** Safety
suggestion, e.g. heat solution
gently to prevent spitting; wear eye
protection; tie long hair back. **[1]**

2. (a) fractional distillation **[1]**

(b) The liquids have different
boiling points. **[1]**

3. (a) Sand is insoluble in water **[1]** so its
particles are too large to pass through
the filter paper. **[1]** The particles in
seawater are small enough to pass
through the filter paper. **[1]**

(b) Any two from the following:
use simple distillation **[1]**; heat
the seawater so that the water
evaporates/boils **[1]**; cool the water
vapour so that it condenses to the
liquid state. **[1]**

Page 108 Chromatography

Quick quiz

True, False, False

1. Vertical line of three dots above the black ink cross and at the same heights as those for the blue, yellow and red inks. [2 marks for all correct, 1 mark if two correct, as long as green dot not included]

2. R_f = 3.7/7.3 = 0.506849 [1] = 0.51 (2 significant figures) [1]

3. The paper contains the stationary phase. [1]

   The mobile phase/solvent moves through the paper. [1]

   The substances in the sample are attracted to the two phases. [1]

   The separation depends on how the substances distribute between the two phases. [1]

   Substances travel further if they are more strongly attracted to the mobile phase than to the stationary phase. [1]

Page 109 Practical: Investigating inks

Quick quiz

distillation – the separation of a solution by evaporation and condensation; R_f value – the distance a substance travels relative to the solvent; mobile phase – the liquid solvent; solvent front – the level reached by the solvent

1. Step 1: Draw the base line using a ruler and pencil on chromatography paper. [1]

   Step 2: Put small spots of ink onto the start line (with spaces between). [1]

   Step 3: Pour water (the mobile phase) into a beaker. [1]

   Step 4: Fix the chromatography paper (the stationary phase) in the beaker so that the bottom edge of the paper dips into the water with the water level below the pencil line. [1]

2. The original green ink and the ink from the suspected forgery have different numbers of spots. [1] One of the spots is the same in both paints but the other spots are different. [1] So, the forgery is not written in the same ink as the original green ink. [1]

3. (a) Place 1 cm depth of solvent in a beaker [1] and lower the chromatography paper into the solvent ensuring the level of solvent is below the base line. [1]

   Leave to allow the solvent to rise up the paper and remove when solvent is near the top; mark the solvent front. [1]

   Measure the distance moved from the base line by each spot. [1]

   Measure the distance from base line to solvent front. [1]

   (b) Calculate the R_f values using the equation

   $$R_f = \frac{\text{distance moved by substance}}{\text{distance moved by solvent}}$$ [1]

Page 110 Potable water

Quick quiz

1 – filtration; 2 – sedimentation; 3 – chlorination

1. (a) Potable water contains dissolved substances but pure water does not. [1]

   (b) The seawater is heated to evaporate the water (leaving the salt behind). [1] The water vapour is then condensed to give pure water. [1]

   (c) It needs a lot of (heat) energy to evaporate the water and this is expensive. [1]

2. Seawater is purified by distillation – evaporation and condensation. [1]

   Groundwater treatment involves three main stages – filtration, sedimentation and sterilisation. [1]

   Filtration – the water is passed through filters to remove solid particles. [1]

   Sedimentation – insoluble particles settle to the bottom of the tank. [1]

   Chlorination, to kill microorganisms. [1]

3. Tap water contains dissolved ions [1]; they may react in the analysis test and give incorrect results [1]; deionised water does not contain any ions which may interfere with the tests. [1]

Page 111 The pH scale and neutralisation

Quick quiz

left-hand end 0–6 labelled 'acidic', 7 labelled 'neutral', right-hand end 8–14 labelled 'alkaline'

1. Bases are substances that react with acids to produce a salt and water. [1] Both substances react with acids in this way, [1] but only sodium hydroxide is soluble/copper oxide is insoluble. [1]

2. sulfuric acid + magnesium hydroxide → magnesium sulfate [1] + water [1]

3. (a) battery acid, cola drink, vinegar, tomatoes, shampoo, baking soda, toothpaste, bleach, drain cleaner [3 marks for all 9 correct; 2 marks for 6–8 correct; 1 mark for 4–5 correct]

   (b) (i) colourless [1]

   (ii) pink [1]

   (iii) pink [1]

4. H^+ [1]

5. (a) $HCl(aq) + NaOH(aq) \rightarrow NaCl(aq) + H_2O(l)$ [1 mark for correct formulae, 1 mark for correctly balanced, 1 mark for correct state symbols]

   (b) pH 7 (neutral) [1]

   (c) $H^+(aq) + OH^-(aq) \rightarrow H_2O(l)$ [1 mark for correct formulae, 1 mark for correct state symbols]

Page 112 Strong and weak acids

Quick quiz

Strong acids: hydrochloric acid, sulfuric acid, nitric acid

Weak acids: ethanoic acid, carbonic acid, citric acid

1. The concentration of an acid is related to the amount of acid dissolved in a given volume. [1] The more acid dissolved, the more concentrated the acid is. [1] The strength of an acid is related to its degree of ionisation. [1] The more an acid ionises in water, the stronger it is. [1]

2. (a) As the pH decreases by one unit, [1] the concentration of hydrogen ions in the solution increases by a factor of 10. [1]

   (b) 1×10^{-9} g dm^{-3} [1 mark for correct answer, 1 mark for correct use of standard form]

3. A strong acid is completely ionised in solution [1]; a weak acid is partially ionised in solution. [1]

4. If an acid is dilute, there will be only a small number of moles of the acid in the solution. [1] The acid's strength is not determined by the amount of acid in solution but by its ability to dissociate. [1]

5. They are the same because they have the same pH [1] and pH is determined by the hydrogen ion concentration. [1]

Page 113 Practical: pH change

Quick quiz

True, False, True, True

1. (a) calcium chloride + water [1]

   (b) calcium chloride + water [1]

2. (a) hydrogen ion [1]

   (b) hydroxide ion [1]

3. universal indicator [1]

4. (a) pipette/burette [1]

   (b) Dip a piece of pH paper/universal indicator paper into the beaker. [1] Compare the colour to the pH colour chart. [1]

   (c) To make sure the calcium hydroxide reacted with the acid. [1]

   (d) Use a pH probe which measures to 1 decimal place. [1]

   (e) Hydroxide ions react with hydrogen ions in the acid [1] to reduce the hydrogen ion concentration and so increase the pH. [1]

Page 114 Salt production

Quick quiz

sulfate, nitrate, chloride

1. (a) magnesium oxide + sulfuric acid → magnesium sulfate + water [1]

   (b) magnesium hydroxide + sulfuric acid → magnesium sulfate + water [1]

   (c) copper carbonate + nitric acid → copper nitrate + water + carbon dioxide [1]

   (d) iron oxide + hydrochloric acid → iron chloride + water [1]

(e) zinc carbonate + hydrochloric acid → zinc chloride + water + carbon dioxide [1]

2. Limewater/calcium hydroxide [1] turns cloudy. [1]

3. (a) Mg^{2+} and Cl^- [1]

   (b) Ag^+ and NO_3^- [1]

   (c) Na^+ and SO_4^{2-} [1]

4. (a) $CaCl_2$, calcium chloride [1]

   (b) Li_2SO_4, lithium sulfate [1]

   (c) $(NH_4)_2SO_4$, ammonium sulfate [1]

5. (a) $2HCl(aq) + MgO(s) → MgCl_2(s) + H_2O(l)$ [1 mark for correct formulae, 1 mark for correctly balanced, 1 mark for correct state symbols]

   (b) $CaCO_3(s) + H_2SO_4(aq) → CaSO_4(aq) + H_2O(l) + CO_2(g)$ [1 mark for correct formulae, 1 mark for correctly balanced, 1 mark for correct state symbols]

   (c) $CuO(s) + 2HNO_3(aq) → Cu(NO_3)_2(aq) + H_2O(l)$ [1 mark for correct formulae, 1 mark for correctly balanced, 1 mark for correct state symbols]

   (d) $H_2SO_4(aq) + 2KOH(aq) → K_2SO_4(aq) + 2H_2O(l)$ [1 mark for correct formulae, 1 mark for correctly balanced, 1 mark for correct state symbols]

Page 115 Reactions of acid with metals

Quick quiz

metal + acid → salt + hydrogen

magnesium + hydrochloric acid → magnesium chloride + hydrogen

magnesium + sulfuric acid → magnesium sulfate + hydrogen

zinc + nitric acid → zinc nitrate + hydrogen

1. (a) magnesium chloride [1]

   (b) Magnesium has lost two electrons. [1] It has been oxidised from Mg to Mg^{2+}. [1]

   (c) The hydrogen ions in the acid have gained electrons. [1]

2. (a) $Zn + H_2SO_4 → ZnSO_4 + H_2$ [1 mark for correct formulae, 1 mark for correctly balanced]

   (b) Zinc is oxidised [1] as it loses (two) electrons to form Zn^{2+}. [1]

   (c) Hydrogen is reduced [1] as H^+ ions gain electrons to form H_2. [1]

   (d) Apply a lighted splint [1] and there will be a (squeaky) pop. [1]

   (e) One species (zinc) is oxidised as the other species (hydrogen ions) is reduced. [1]

Page 116 Soluble salts

Quick quiz

True, True, False, True

1. (a) zinc chloride [1]

   (b) $ZnCO_3(s) + 2HCl(aq) → ZnCl_2(aq) + H_2O(l) + CO_2(g)$ [1 mark for correct formulae, 1 mark for correct

balancing, 1 mark for correct state symbols]

   (c) crystallisation [1]

   (d) Heat the salt solution in an evaporating basin [1] using a Bunsen, tripod and gauze until about half/two-thirds of the water has evaporated. [1] Then leave to cool and crystallise. [1]

2. Add an excess of the metal oxide to the acid [1] until no more disappears. [1]

3. (a) nitric acid [1]

   (b) neutralisation [1]

   (c) To make sure all the acid is used up. [1]

   (d) filtration [1]

Page 117 Practical: Making salts

Quick quiz

evaporating dish, filter funnel, beaker, tripod, Bunsen burner

1. Measure out 25 cm³ of dilute hydrochloric acid into a beaker. Place on a tripod over a Bunsen burner and warm gently. [1]

   Add sodium carbonate and stir with a glass rod until no more solid dissolves. [1]

   Filter using the filter funnel to remove excess solid sodium carbonate. [1]

   Heat in an evaporating basin to evaporate most of the water. Stop heating when crystals start to form. [1]

   Cool and crystallise. Dry the crystals by patting them between two pieces of filter paper. [1]

2. Marks awarded for coherent explanation and ordering of ideas as well as scientific knowledge – Level 3 answer [5–6], Level 2 answer [3–4], Level 1 answer [1–2].

   Indicative content:
   - Suitable acid: sulfuric
   - Suitable substance: zinc carbonate/ zinc oxide/ zinc hydroxide
   - Measure out acid into beaker and add solid, heating and stirring until it is in excess
   - Filter off the solid
   - Pour solution into evaporating basin and evaporate to half volume
   - Cool and crystallise
   - Pat crystals dry between filter paper

3. (a) copper oxide [1]

   (b) blue solution [1]

   (c) To allow large crystals to form. [1]

Page 118 Titration

Quick quiz

red to yellow

1. (a) From top to bottom: pipette filler [1] pipette [1] conical flask [1]

   (b) This makes the colour change at the end point easier to see. [1]

   (c) burette [1]

   (d) pink [1] to colourless [1]

   (e) Repeat the titration using the same volume of acid but no indicator. [1]

   Heat the solution to remove half its volume. [1]

   Cool and crystallise. [1]

   (f) $NaOH + HCl → NaCl + H_2O$ [1]

2. Marks awarded for coherent explanation and ordering of ideas as well as scientific knowledge – Level 3 answer [5–6], Level 2 answer [3–4], Level 1 answer [1–2].

   Indicative content:

   Start of method
   - pipette
   - burette
   - wash with appropriate solution
   - acid or alkali in flask
   - indicator
   - swirling
   - use white tile

   End point
   - correct starting colour of indicator
   - controlled addition until indicator changes colour
   - add dropwise near endpoint
   - correct end colour of indicator
   - repeat titration until concordant results

   Obtaining crystals
   - mix volumes without indicator
   - evaporate to half volume/ until crystallisation starts
   - leave to crystallise
   - dry between filter paper

Page 119 Solubility rules

Quick quiz

solid	Sodium sulfate	Copper hydroxide	Silver nitrate	Calcium carbonate	Barium sulfate	Potassium chloride
soluble	✓		✓			✓
insoluble		✓		✓	✓	

1. (a) $Na_2SO_4 + BaCl_2 → BaSO_4 + 2NaCl$ [1]

   (b) barium sulfate [1]

   (c) residue = barium sulfate [1] filtrate = sodium chloride solution [1]

2. (a) $K_2CO_3(aq) + Mg(NO_3)_2(aq) → 2KNO_3(aq) + MgCO_3(s)$ [1 mark for correct formulae, 1 mark for correct balancing, 1 mark for correct state symbols]

   (b) $2KCl(aq) + Pb(NO_3)_2(aq) → 2KNO_3(aq) + PbCl_2(s)$ [1 mark for correct formulae, 1 mark for correct balancing, 1 mark for correct state symbols]

   (c) $NaCl(aq) + AgNO_3(aq) → AgCl(s) + NaNO_3(aq)$ [1 mark for correct formulae, 1 mark for correct balancing, 1 mark for correct state symbols]

3. lead chloride [1]

4. (a) $K_2CO_3(aq) + ZnCl_2(aq) \rightarrow 2KCl(aq) + ZnCO_3(s)$ [1 mark for correct formulae, 1 mark for correct balancing, 1 mark for correct state symbols]

   (b) Filter the mixture [1]; wash/rinse the residue/solid with water [1]; dry between filter paper/dry in a warm oven. [1]

Page 120 Oxidation and reduction

Quick quiz

(a) magnesium   (b) bromine

(c) zinc   (d) carbon

1. magnesium atom [1]

2. (a) gaining electrons [1]

   (b) iodide [1]

   (c) $Cl_2 + 2I^- \rightarrow I_2 + 2Cl^-$ [1 mark for correct formulae, 1 mark for correctly balanced]

   (d) Reduction: $Cl_2 + 2e^- \rightarrow 2Cl^-$ [1 mark for correct formulae, 1 mark for correctly balanced]

   Oxidation: $2I^- \rightarrow I_2 + 2e^-$ [1 mark for correct formulae, 1 mark for correctly balanced]

3. (a) lead oxide + carbon → lead + carbon dioxide [1]

   (b) $Pb^{2+} + 2e^- \rightarrow Pb$ or $Pb^{2+} \rightarrow Pb - 2e^-$ [1 mark for correct formulae, 1 mark for correctly balanced]

4. (a) $Zn + Pb^{2+} \rightarrow Zn^{2+} + Pb$ [1 mark for correct formulae, 1 mark for correctly balanced]

   (b) Oxidised: zinc [1] Reduced: lead/lead(II)/Pb^{2+} [1]

Page 121 Electrolysis

Quick quiz

False, True, False, False

1. (a)

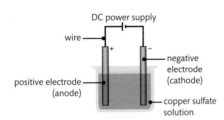

Power supply and wires correctly labelled [1]; electrodes labelled anode (+) and cathode (–) [1]; electrodes dipping into copper sulfate solution in a beaker [1]

   (b) Any one from: it will not take part in the reaction/it is inert; it conducts electricity. [1]

   (c) cathode (negative electrode) [1]

2. (a) positive electrode (anode) [1]

   (b) oxygen [1]

3. Using electricity [1] to break a substance down into simpler substances/decompose a substance. [1]

4. The silver ions have a positive charge [1] so they move towards the negative electrode (the ring). [1]

Page 122 Electrolysis of molten ionic compounds

Quick quiz

solid, an electrolyte, cathode, oxidation

1. (a) Magnesium ions have a positive charge, [1] so they are attracted to the negative charge of the cathode/the opposite charge [1] where they gain electrons to form magnesium metal. [1]

   (b) chlorine [1]

   (c) The ions in solid magnesium chloride are held tightly and cannot move, [1] so they cannot carry a charge/current cannot flow. [1]

2. (a) cathode/negative electrode [1]

   (b) bromine/Br_2 [1]

   (c) At the negative electrode: $Pb^{2+} + 2e^- \rightarrow Pb$ [1 mark for correct formulae, 1 mark for correctly balanced]; reduction [3]

   At the positive electrode: $2Br^- \rightarrow Br_2 + 2e^-$ [1 mark for correct formulae, 1 mark for correctly balanced]; oxidation [3]

   (d) The lead/bromine produced is toxic/corrosive. [1]

Page 123 Electrolysis of aqueous solutions

Quick quiz

anode, cathode, an atom or group of atoms with a positive or negative charge, the solution used in electrolysis, the decomposition of a substance using electricity

1. (a) Na^+ [1], OH^- [1], H^+ [1] and SO_4^{2-} [1]

   (b) Cathode: hydrogen gas [1]; Anode: oxygen gas [1]

   (c) Place a lighted splint in the gas [1]; if hydrogen is present there is a squeaky pop [1]. Place a glowing splint in the gas [1]; if oxygen is present the splint will relight. [1]

2. At the anode, chlorine gas is produced; negative ions Cl^- and OH^- are attracted to the positive electrode; the chloride ions give up electrons more readily than OH^- ions and produce chlorine. Two chloride ions each lose one electron to form a chlorine molecule, Cl_2. [3]

   At the cathode, copper metal is produced because positive ions are attracted to the negative electrode, and copper is less reactive than hydrogen so the Cu^{2+} ions accept the electrons. One copper ion accepts 2 electrons to form Cu. [3]

Page 124 Half equations

Quick quiz

$2Cl^- \rightarrow 2e^- + Cl_2$, $H_2 \rightarrow 2H^+ + 2e^-$, correct, $Br^- \rightarrow Br + e^-$, correct

1. $Zn^{2+} + 2e^- \rightarrow Zn$ [1 mark for correct formula, 1 mark for correct balancing]

2. For each half-equation: 1 mark for correct formulae, 1 mark for correct balancing.

   (a) $2Br^- \rightarrow Br_2 + 2e^-$; $Cl_2 + 2e^- \rightarrow 2Cl^-$

   (b) $Zn \rightarrow Zn^{2+} + 2e^-$; $2H^+ + 2e^- \rightarrow H_2$

   (c) $Mg \rightarrow Mg^{2+} + 2e^-$; $Cu^{2+} + 2e^- \rightarrow Cu$

3. Negative electrode: $Zn^{2+} + 2e^- \rightarrow Zn$ [1 mark for correct formulae, 1 mark for correct balancing]

   Positive electrode: $2Cl^- \rightarrow Cl_2 + 2e^-$ [1 mark for correct formulae, 1 mark for correct balancing]

4. (a) Mg^{2+} [1], H^+ [1], SO_4^{2-} [1], OH^- [1]

   (b) Anode: $4OH^- \rightarrow 2H_2O + O_2 + 4e^-$ [1 mark for correct formulae, 1 mark for correct balancing]

   Cathode: $2H^+ + 2e^- \rightarrow H_2$ [1 mark for correct formulae, 1 mark for correct balancing]

Page 125 Practical: Electrolysis of copper sulfate

Quick quiz

A cell; B cathode; C anode; D electrolyte

1. (a) oxygen [1]

   (b) Graphite electrodes [1] are placed in the electrolyte, which is copper sulfate solution. [1] The electrodes are connected to a dc power supply [1] and left to run for a few minutes. [1]

   (c) The solution contains copper ions. [1] Copper ions have a positive charge. [1] When electricity is passed through the solution the copper ions are attracted to the cathode [1] where they gain electrons and become copper atoms. [1]

   (d) Inert electrodes will not react with the substances in the electrolysis cell [1] so copper metal is obtained. [1]

2. Marks awarded for coherent explanation and ordering of ideas as well as scientific knowledge – Level 3 answer [5–6], Level 2 answer [3–4], Level 1 answer [1–2].

   Indicative content:

   • The impure copper is the anode

   • A strip of pure copper is the cathode

   • At the anode: copper atoms lose electrons, forming copper ions, $Cu^{2+}(aq)$

   • The electrode/anode gets smaller in size as the ions form

   • Copper ions move to the negative cathode

   • At the cathode, copper ions gain electrons to form copper metal

   • The electrode/cathode increases in size as copper is deposited

Page 126 The reactivity series

Quick quiz

sodium

magnesium

iron

1. (a) There was no reaction. [1]

   (b) Metal A reacts with two out of the three salt solutions and so must be the most reactive. [1] Metal D doesn't react with any of the salt solutions and so must be the least reactive. [1] Metals B and C both react with copper chloride so have a similar reactivity. [1] The temperature rise with C was greater than with B so C is more reactive. [1] Order of reactivity is A C B D. [1]

2. (a) Both produce bubbles of gas [1]; both reaction mixtures get hot [1]; the reaction is faster/more vigorous in dilute hydrochloric acid. [1]

   (b) calcium + water → calcium hydroxide + hydrogen [1]

   (c) $Ca + 2HCl \rightarrow CaCl_2 + H_2$ [1 mark for correct formulae, 1 mark for correct balancing]

3. The more easily a metal can lose its outer electrons (to gain a full outer shell/stable arrangement) [1] the more reactive the metal is. [1]

Page 127 Extraction of metals and reduction

Quick quiz
Fe_2O_3
MgO
H_2
SO^4
PbO

1. (a) reduction [1]

   (b) Heat the copper oxide with carbon [1] because carbon is more reactive than copper [1] so it can displace copper from copper oxide/reduce copper oxide. [1]

   (c) Silver or gold.

2. (a) Carbon is less reactive than aluminium [1] so carbon cannot displace aluminium from aluminium oxide/reduce aluminium oxide. [1]

   (b) Potassium is more reactive than aluminium [1] so it can displace aluminium from its compounds. [1]

   (c) Reduced [1] because aluminium ions gain electrons. [1]

3. (a) carbon [1]

   (b) Magnesium is more reactive than carbon [1] so carbon cannot reduce magnesium oxide. [1]

Page 128 Electrolysis to extract metals

Quick quiz
A graphite electrode

B cathode

C steel case

D anode

E aluminium oxide dissolved in molten cryolite

F aluminium

1. The ions move towards the negative electrode. [1] This is because the charge on aluminium ions is positive [1] and so they are attracted to the negative charge of the cathode/opposite charges attract. [1]

2. (a) (molten) cryolite [1]

   (b) Cryolite melts at a lower temperature than aluminium oxide, [1] so less energy is needed to form the electrolyte. [1]

3. Any two from the following: large amounts of electricity are needed [1]; electricity is expensive [1]; a lot of energy is needed to melt the oxide/produce the molten electrolyte. [1]

4. (a) Negative electrode: $Al^{3+} + 3e^- \rightarrow Al$ [1 mark for correct formulae, 1 mark for correctly balanced]

   Positive electrode: $2O^{2-} \rightarrow O_2 + 4e^-$ [1 mark for correct formulae, 1 mark for correctly balanced]

   (b) Hot carbon reacts with oxygen to produce carbon dioxide, [1] $C + O_2 \rightarrow CO_2$ [1] which wears/burns away the anodes. [1]

Page 129 Alternative methods of extracting metals

Quick quiz

2, 4, 1, 3

1. (a) Plants grow on the soil containing copper. [1] As they grow they absorb copper compounds. [1] The plants are burned. [1] The ash produced contains copper compounds. [1]

   (b) There is very little copper in low-grade ores. [1]

   (c) electrolysis [1]

   (d) Iron is more reactive than copper [1] so it can be used to displace the copper from a solution of copper ions. [1]

2. Any two from: reduction by carbon [1]; phytoextraction [1]; bioleaching [1]

3. Bacteria feed on the copper ore. [1] Biological/chemical processes produce a solution of copper ions (leachate). [1]

4. Copper reserves are running out/limited. [1] Copper can be recycled/reused. [1] It is a waste of landfill space. [1] It is potentially toxic to plants and animals. [1]

Page 130 Metal oxides

Quick quiz

True, False, True, False, False

1. (a) calcium oxide [1]

   (b) iron oxide [1]

   (c) magnesium oxide [1]

2. (a) Oxidation is loss of electrons [1] Reduction is gain of electrons [1]

   (b) The metal is oxidised [1]; oxygen is reduced. [1]

3. (a) ionic bonding [1]

   (b) Any two from: high melting point [1]; high boiling point [1]; solid at room temperature [1]; do not conduct electricity when solid. [1]

4. (a) It is oxidised as it loses electrons. [1]

   (b) $Fe \rightarrow Fe^{3+} + 3e^-$ [1 mark for correct formulae; 1 mark for correct balancing]

   (c) aluminium + oxygen → aluminium oxide [1]

   (d) $2Al + 3O_2 \rightarrow 2Al_2O_3$ [1 mark for correct formulae; 1 mark for correct balancing]

5. Giant ionic structure, [1] containing ionic bonds/bonds formed between oppositely charged ions/bonds formed between positive metal ions and negative non-metal ions. [1]

Page 131 Recycling and life-cycle assessment

Quick quiz

extracting the raw materials; manufacture and packaging of the product; use of the product; disposal of the product

1. LCAs assess the impact of the product at every stage [1] to see how it affects the environment. [1]

2. Any three from: energy used to extract the raw materials [1]; amount of waste produced/toxicity of water produced during manufacture [1]; amount of carbon dioxide/greenhouse gases produced [1]; cost of any added resources [1]; renewability of raw materials. [1]

3. Recycle [1] – the bags are collected and melted to make new items. [1] Burn [1] – bags are burned to release energy. [1] Reuse [1] – bags can be used several times by the consumer. [1]

4. Answers could include the following points in a logical order for 6 marks. Your answer must include a conclusion with justification.

   Paper cups – made from a renewable resource; can be made to be biodegradable; produce more carbon dioxide in their manufacture than plastic; produce more solid waste than plastic (although data given doesn't show whether this waste is biodegradable/able to be recycled); require more energy to manufacture than plastic; require more fresh water than plastic.

   Plastic cups – are made from a non-renewable/finite resource; produce less carbon dioxide in their manufacture than paper, produce less solid waste than paper; require less energy than paper to manufacture; require less fresh water than paper.

   Conclusion - paper cups in some respects are more damaging to the environment but the raw materials are renewable and the end result can be made to be biodegradable. Plastic cups may be less damaging in terms of their manufacture but the raw materials are non-renewable and the end product cannot be recycled/not biodegradable.

Page 132 Reversible reactions

Quick quiz

reversible – a reaction that can proceed in either direction; reactants – substances found to the left of the arrow in an equation; equilibrium – rate of forward reaction is equal to rate of backward reaction; products – substances found to the right of the arrow in an equation

1. (a) reversible [1]
   (b) hydrated [1]
   (c) blue anhydrous cobalt chloride + water [1] $\rightleftharpoons$ [1] pink hydrated cobalt chloride [1]
   (d) Change in pressure, [1] change in concentration, [1] change in temperature. [1]

2. reversible reaction [1]

3. $NH_3(g) + HCl(g) \rightleftharpoons NH_4Cl(s)$ [1 mark for correct formulae, 1 mark for correct balancing, 1 mark for correct formulae with correct state symbols]

4. The mixture would change from colourless to red. [1]

Page 133 Dynamic equilibrium and the Haber process

Quick quiz

The rate of the forward and reverse reaction is equal; The reaction mixture must be in a closed system.

1. (a) Dynamic equilibrium occurs in a closed system when the rates of the forward and reverse reactions are equal [1] and the amounts of reactants and products remain constant. [1]
   (b) On the left-hand side of the equation there are 4 moles of gas and on the right-hand side there are 2 moles of gas. [1] Hence increasing the pressure causes the equilibrium position to move to the right side (fewer gas moles). [1] This increases the yield of ammonia. [1]
   (c) Higher pressure gives higher yield, [1] but low pressure is cheaper. [1]

2. (a) nitrogen – air [1]; hydrogen – natural gas [1]
   (b) $N_2 + 3H_2 \rightleftharpoons 2NH_3$ [1 mark for correct formulae, 1 mark for correctly balanced, 1 mark for reversible arrows]
   (c) 450 °C temperature, [1] 200 atmospheric pressure, [1] catalyst of iron [1]

Page 134 Temperature and equilibrium

Quick quiz

fewer, fewer, less

1. (a) $3H_2(g) + N_2(g) \rightleftharpoons 2NH_3(g)$ [1 mark for correct formulae, 1 mark for correctly balanced, 1 mark for correct state symbols]
   (b) To move the equilibrium to the right, temperature should be decreased. [1]

2. If the temperature is increased the equilibrium will move in the endothermic direction. [1]
   Therefore, less SO_3 is produced. [1]
   If the temperature is decreased, then equilibrium will move in the exothermic direction. [1]
   So more SO_3 is produced. [1]

3. (a) endothermic [1]
   (b) The ice bath cools the gases, [1] causing the equilibrium position to move in the direction of the exothermic reaction. [1] The forward reaction is exothermic, so the ice bath means that more ammonium chloride is formed. [1]

Page 135 Pressure and equilibrium

Quick quiz

| Right | Right |
| Left | Stays the same |

1. (a) As pressure increases, the percentage yield of ammonia increases. [1]
   (b) There are fewer moles/molecules of gas on the right-hand side of the equation [1]; when the pressure is increased, the position of equilibrium moves to the side with fewer molecules, increasing the yield. [1]
   (c) Two from: very high pressures could be dangerous/increased risk of explosion [1]; it is very expensive to build a vessel to withstand high pressure [1]; the cost benefit of increasing the yield may not outweigh the cost of building the vessel needed. [1]

2. (a) As pressure increases, the yield decreases. [1]
   (b) The pressure must be kept low. [1] This will ensure the position of equilibrium moves towards the side with the desired product. [1]

3. Changing the pressure will have no effect on the equilibrium position [1] because the number of moles/molecules of gas is the same on both sides of the equation. [1]

Page 136 Concentration and equilibrium

Quick quiz

right; left; right; left

1. (a) The arrow must be reversible/$\rightleftharpoons$. [1]
   (b) $NH_3(g) + HCl(g) \rightleftharpoons NH_4Cl(s)$ [1 mark for correct formulae, 1 mark for correctly balanced, 1 mark for correct state symbols]
   (c) Increase the concentration of one of the reactants [1]; remove the product as it forms. [1]

2. (a) A stoppered flask is used. [1]
   (b) The equilibrium position will move to the right, [1] because the calcium chloride removes water and so

reduces the amount/concentration of water. [1]
   (c) The equilibrium position moves right [1] to oppose the change and decrease the concentration of ethanoic acid, until equilibrium is reached again. [1]

Page 137 Group 1

Quick quiz

They float on the surface of the water; They fizz in water.

1. Lithium has electronic configuration 2.1 and potassium has electronic configuration 2.8.8.1. [1] The outer electron is further from the nucleus in K [1] so there is less attraction between nucleus and outer electron and it is easier to remove. [1]

2. (a) potassium + water → potassium hydroxide + hydrogen [1]
   (b) $2Li(s) + 2H_2O(l) \rightarrow 2LiOH(aq) + H_2(g)$ [1 mark for correct formulae, 1 mark for correctly balanced, 1 mark for correct state symbols]
   (c) Two from the following: potassium produces a lilac flame [1]; lithium does not produce a flame [1]; potassium produces more bubbles/moves faster than lithium [1]; potassium reacts more quickly than lithium [1]; potassium explodes at the end, lithium does not. [1]

3. (a) They form alkaline solutions when they react with water. [1]
   (b) $2K + 2H_2O \rightarrow 2KOH + H_2$ [1 mark for correct formulae, 1 mark for correctly balanced]
   (c) Three of: effervescence/bubbles/hydrogen gas [1]; K disappears [1]; lilac flame [1]; K moves on surface [1]; pop/smoke at end. [1]

Page 138 Group 7

Quick quiz

low; non-metals; poor; coloured; molecules

1. C [1]

2. (a) F 2.7 [1] Cl 2.8.7 [1]
   (b) The outer electron shell [1] is closer to the nucleus in fluorine, [1] so the nucleus can attract an electron more easily. [1]
   (c) $Cl_2 + 2 e^- \rightarrow 2Cl^-$ [1 mark for correct formulae, 1 mark for correctly balanced]
   (d) $2Na + Cl_2 \rightarrow 2NaCl$ [1 mark for correct formulae, 1 mark for correctly balanced]

3. The relative formula mass increases down the group/the molecules get larger down the group, [1] leading to stronger intermolecular forces/stronger forces between molecules [1] which need more energy to break. [1]

4. Damp litmus paper [1] bleaches white [1]

Page 139 Group 7 reactivity

Quick quiz

chlorine + sodium bromide

potassium iodide + bromine

sodium iodide + chlorine

1. **(a)** potassium bromide and iodine: cross (no) **[1]**; potassium iodide and bromine: tick (yes) **[1]**

   (b) The more reactive the halogen the more reactions will take place. **[1]** Chlorine has two ticks in the table and so is the most reactive, as it can displace bromine and iodine. **[1]** Bromine has one tick in the table and so is the next most reactive, as it can displace iodine but not chlorine. **[1]** Iodine has no ticks and so is the least reactive as it cannot displace chlorine or bromine. **[1]**

2. **(a)** The bromide ions lose electrons and form bromine. **[1]** Loss of electrons is oxidation. **[1]** The chlorine gains electrons and forms chloride ions. **[1]** Gain of electrons is reduction. **[1]** Redox because oxidation and reduction are both occurring. **[1]**

   (b) colourless to orange **[1]**

3. Marks awarded for coherent explanation and ordering of ideas as well as scientific knowledge – Level 3 answer **[5–6]**, Level 2 answer **[3–4]**, Level 1 answer **[1–2]**.

   Indicative content:

   - Add bromine to a solution of potassium iodide. **[1]**
   - Solution turns brown. **[1]**
   - Bromine is more reactive than iodine. **[1]**
   - Add iodine to a solution of potassium bromide. **[1]**
   - No reaction. **[1]**
   - Iodine is less reactive than bromine. **[1]**

Page 140 Group 0

Quick quiz

Correct: The noble gases are inert, or unreactive; Neon exists as single atoms; The size of the atoms increases down the group.

Corrected: Helium is placed at the top of Group 0; The noble gases all have a full outer shell; helium has 2 electrons in its outer shell, the others have 8.

1. He 2 **[1]**; Ar 2.8.8 **[1]**

2.

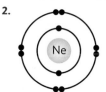

   [1 mark for two shells, 1 mark for correct number in each shell]

3. Their atoms have a full outer shell of electrons. **[1]**

4. The atoms of noble gases have stable electron arrangements/full outer shells **[1]** so they cannot (easily) share electrons. **[1]**

5. **(a)** melting point in range −180 to −210 °C (−189 °C) **[1]**; boiling point only slightly higher than melting point and in range −175 to −205 °C (−186 °C) **[1]**

   (b) The boiling point increases down the group. **[1]**

   (c) The size of the atoms increases **[1]** so there are stronger forces between the atoms and more energy is needed to separate the atoms. **[1]**

   (d) It is low density, **[1]** non-flammable/inert. **[1]**

Page 141 Calculating rate of reaction

Quick quiz

mol/s; cm^3/s

1.

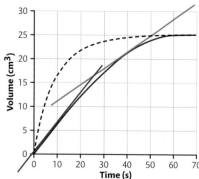

rate of reaction = change in volume (cm^3)/ change in time (s) **[1]** = 15/24 (red line on graph) **[1]** = 0.63 **[1]** cm^3/s **[1]** [allow other equivalent working out depending on tangent drawn, and value ±0.07]

2. **(a)** rate of reaction = change in volume (cm^3)/change in time (s) = $\dfrac{(28 - 11)}{(60 - 10)}$

   [1 mark for top line of fraction, 1 mark for bottom line] (blue line on graph) = 0.34 **[1]** cm^3/s **[1]** [allow other equivalent working out depending on tangent drawn, and value ±0.05]

   (b) The rate decreases **[1]** and becomes 0 (cm^3/s) at 60 s. **[1]**

   (c) Curve shown should be steeper initially **[1]** then level off at the same volume of gas **[1]** to show the rate of reaction has sped up (dashed black line on graph).

Page 142 Factors affecting rate of reaction

Quick quiz

increase; decrease; increase; decrease

1. As temperature is increased the particles will have more (kinetic) energy **[1]** and so will move faster **[1]** leading to more frequent **[1]** successful collisions. **[1]**

2. They provide a pathway of lower activation energy. **[1]** This increases the frequency of successful collisions because more particles have energy greater than

the activation energy so there are more successful collisions. **[1]**

3. **(a)**

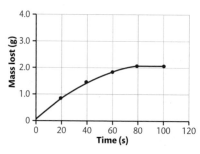

   [1 mark for axes correctly spaced and using over half the grid, 1 mark for correct plots, 1 mark for correct line of best fit]

   (b) The graph would be steeper **[1]** and the reaction would complete at an earlier time with 2.1 g of mass lost. **[1]**

   (c) Size/surface area/surface area to volume ratio of the marble chips. **[1]**

Page 143 Practical: Monitoring rate of reaction - colour change

Quick quiz

volume of gas produced, change in mass, change in colour

1. **(a)** sulfur **[1]**

   (b) $Na_2S_2O_3(aq) + 2HCl(aq) \rightarrow 2NaCl(aq) + H_2O(l) + SO_2(g) + S(s)$ [1 mark for correct formulae, 1 mark for correctly balanced, 1 mark for state symbols]

   (c) Precaution for 1 mark with reason for 1 mark, e.g. avoid contact with dilute hydrochloric acid **[1]** because it is irritant/harms skin **[1]**; avoid breathing in fumes from the flask/use a fume cupboard **[1]** because sulfur dioxide is harmful/has a choking smell. **[1]**

2. **(a)**

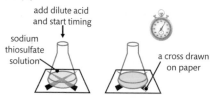

   Conical flask **[1]** on paper with a cross drawn **[1]**; solution labelled **[1]**; stopclock. **[1]**

   (b) Heat the acid in a water bath. **[1]**

   (c) The rate of the reaction would increase **[1]** because the reactant particles have more energy. **[1]** This means they move faster and collide more often/more frequently **[1]** and a greater proportion of the collisions are successful/have the activation energy. **[1]**

   (d) Any two from: keep the volume the same **[1]**; keep the concentrations the same **[1]**; use the same flask and cross each time **[1]**; use the same person to judge when the cross can no longer be seen. **[1]**

Page 144 Practical: Monitoring rate of reaction – gas production

Quick quiz

magnesium and hydrochloric acid

calcium carbonate and hydrochloric acid

zinc and sulfuric acid

1. (a) $CaCO_3(s) + 2HCl(aq) \rightarrow CaCl_2(aq) + H_2O(l) + CO_2(g)$ [1 mark for correct formulae, 1 mark for correctly balanced, 1 mark for state symbols]

   (b) Recognizable apparatus is expected.
   gas syringe label [1]; conical flask label [1]; hydrochloric acid + calcium carbonate label [1]

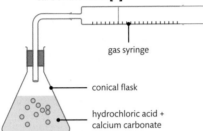

   (c) Otherwise, some carbon dioxide may escape/not be collected. [1]

   (d) Carbon dioxide is slightly soluble and may dissolve in the water (so a smaller volume will be measured). [1]

2. (a) calcium carbonate [1]

   (b) bubbles [1]; calcium carbonate disappears/gets smaller [1]

   (c) Any 2 from: mass of calcium carbonate [1]; size of marble chips [1]; volume of acid [1]; temperature. [1]

   (d) Calcium carbonate disappears or fizzing stops/same volume on syringe. [1]

Page 145 Collision theory and activation energy

Quick quiz

temperature – Particles have more energy and move faster, colliding more frequently; concentration – There are more particles present in the same volume and so a higher chance of collisions; pressure – The volume in which the particles are located is reduced, therefore the particles are more likely to collide

1. It is the minimum amount of energy needed for a reaction to occur. [1]

2. (a)

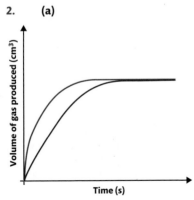

[1 mark for curve is steeper, 1 mark for flattens at same volume of gas as original curve]

   (b) The higher temperature provides the particles with more energy. [1]

   This causes them to move around faster/they are more likely to collide. [1]

   The collisions will be more frequent. [1]

   More collisions will be successful/have the activation energy to react. [1]

3. During the reaction the acid particles are used up, so the concentration of acid decreases, [1] so successful collisions are less frequent. [1]

4. Increasing the pressure reduces the volume in which the particles can move. [1] Increasing the concentration puts more solute particles into a given volume, [1] so in both cases the reactant particles will be closer together and more likely to collide. [1]

Page 146 Reaction profiles

Quick quiz

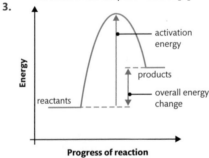

1. (a) The products have less energy than the reactants. [1]

   (b) X is the overall energy change of the reaction/the difference between the energy of the reactants and the energy of the products. [1]

   (c) activation energy [1]

2. (a) exothermic [1]

   (b) It is given out to the surroundings. [1]

   (c) The reaction can only occur if the reactant particles collide [1] and have sufficient energy/at least the activation energy. [1] In this reaction the reactants only gain enough energy to react when they are heated. [1]

3.

Both axes on a correct profile line, labelled relative energies of the reactants and products, [1] and the overall energy change [1] activation energy correctly identified. [1]

Page 147 Catalysts

Quick quiz

True, False, True, False, True

1. (a) Catalysts provide a different pathway for the reaction [1] which has a lower activation energy. [1] This means there are more successful collisions between particles [1] per second/minute. [1]

   (b) iron [1]

2. The mass of catalyst remains unchanged. [1]

3. (a)

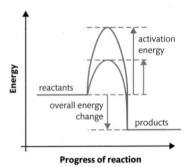

On a correct profile line, labelled relative energies of the reactants and products, [1] and the overall energy change, [1] activation energy (red arrow) correctly identified. [1]

   (b) Top of activation energy curve is lower (green arrow), with no change to positions of lines for reactants and products. [1]

   (c) The reactants will have higher energy than the products. [1] Energy is taken in so the energy change arrow will point up. [1]

Page 148 Exothermic and endothermic reactions

Quick quiz

Endothermic reactions take in heat energy so temperature decreases.

Exothermic reactions give out heat energy so temperature increases.

1. (a) Exothermic, [1] because the temperature of the surroundings increased. [1]

   (b) Any three from: combustion [1]; oxidation [1]; metal displacement [1]; neutralisation/some salts dissolving. [1]

2. (a) A reaction in which heat energy is taken in. [1]

   (b) Record initial temperature of acid using thermometer, [1] add sodium hydrogencarbonate and record temperature. [1] Decrease shows endothermic reaction. [1]

3. (a) Temperature increase (°C): 17, 5, 37, 12 [1]

   (b) The greater the temperature increase, the more reactive the metal is. [1]
   Order of reactivity: C, A, D, B. [1]

Page 149 Temperature changes

Quick quiz

Exothermic – neutralisation, combustion, metal displacement, HCl + NaOH

Endothermic – photosynthesis, dissolving sodium hydroxide

1. All points correct to ±½ small square [2 marks, but 1 mark if 6 points correct]; best fit line [1]

2. Marks awarded for coherent explanation and ordering of ideas as well as scientific knowledge - Level 3 answer [5-6], Level 2 answer [3-4], Level 1 answer [1-2].

   Indicative content:
   - Use the measuring cylinder to measure out a volume of hydrochloric acid.
   - Pour the acid into the polystyrene cup.
   - Take the initial temperature with the thermometer.
   - Weigh out a given mass of powdered zinc, using a balance.
   - Add the zinc to the polystyrene cup and stir.
   - Monitor the temperature and record it when it remains constant.
   - If the temperature increases – exothermic, if it decreases – endothermic.

Page 150 Energy changes in reactions

Quick quiz

exothermic, negative, endothermic, positive

1. Bond breaking = $2459\,kJ\,mol^{-1}$ [1]

   Bond making = $348 + (4 \times 413) + (2 \times 276)$ = $2552\,kJ\,mol^{-1}$ [1]

   Energy change = $2459 - 2552$ = $-93\,kJ\,mol^{-1}$ [1]

2. Energy is taken in to break the bonds, [1] but less than the energy given out when bonds are made. [1]

3. Bond breaking: $(1 \times C=C) + (1 \times C–C) + (1 \times Br–Br) + (6 \times C–H) = 614 + 348 + 193 + 2478 = 3633\,kJ\,mol^{-1}$ [1]

   Bond making: $(2 \times C–C) + (2 \times C–Br) + (6 \times C–H) = 696 + 552 + 2478$ = $3726\,kJ\,mol^{-1}$ [1]

   Energy change = $3633 - 3726$ = $-93\,kJ\,mol^{-1}$ [1]

Page 151 Crude oil and hydrocarbons

Quick quiz

alkane – a series of molecules with general formula C_nH_{2n+2}; homologous series – family of molecules with the same general formula; methane – the simplest hydrocarbon molecule

1. (a) It is a resource made slowly over millions of years and supplies will run out. [1]

   (b) petrochemical [1]

   (c) crude oil is a mixture of hydrocarbons [1]

2. (a) covalent [1]

   (b) They have the same general formula [1]; differ by CH_2 in molecular formulae from neighbouring compounds [1]; show a gradation in physical properties [1]; have similar chemical properties. [1]

3. (a) C_nH_{2n+2} [1]

   (b) if C = 22 then H = $(22 \times 2) + 2 = 46$ hydrogen atoms [1]

   (c) (i) C_2H_6 [1]   (ii) C_6H_{14} [1]

   (d) It contains oxygen [1] and not only carbon and hydrogen. [1]

Page 152 Fractional distillation

Quick quiz

False, True, False, False

1. (a) The fraction at the top of the column contains the shortest hydrocarbon molecules (least number of carbon atoms). As you go down the column the length of the hydrocarbon molecules/the number of carbon atoms increases. [1]

   (b) The crude oil is heated in order to evaporate the hydrocarbons. [1] The gaseous hydrocarbons travel up a fractionating column from hot to cooler till each one reaches the region just below its boiling point [1] where it condenses. [1] The fractions with higher boiling points travel further up the column than the fractions with a lower boiling point. [1]

2. Blank cells from top to bottom: fuel for cars [1]; kerosene [1]; fuel oil [1]; to surface roads/roofs [1]

3. (a) They have a boiling point range [1] but pure substances have an exact boiling point [1].

   (b) petrol [1]; lowest boiling point [1]

   (c) evaporation [1]; condensation [1]

Page 153 Properties of hydrocarbons

Quick quiz

C_3H_8, $C_{12}H_{24}$, $C_{100}H_{202}$, $CH_3CH_2CH_3$, CH_2CHCH_3

1. (a) carbon dioxide [1]; water [1]

   (b) Droplets of water/colourless liquid would appear. [1]

   (c) limewater [1]; The solution would change from colourless to cloudy white/milky. [1]

   (d) carbon monoxide [1]; carbon [1]

   (e) Carbon monoxide is produced [1]; it is toxic [1]; OR Carbon is produced [1]; it causes breathing problems. [1]

2. (a) nonane [1]

   (b) nonane [1]

   (c) propane [1]

   (d) $C_3H_8 + 5O_2 \rightarrow 3CO_2 + 4H_2O$ [1 mark for correct reactants, 1 mark for correct products, 1 mark for correct formulae correctly balanced]

3. So the fuel flows easily, and can be transported to and through the engine easily, [1] and so it can catch fire easily when the engine is turned on. [1]

Page 154 Atmospheric pollutants

Quick quiz

carbon dioxide → greenhouse effect

sulfur dioxide → acid rain

carbon monoxide → toxic gas

1. (a) carbon [1]

   (b) There was a limited supply of oxygen [1] so carbon (soot) formed due to incomplete combustion. [1]

2. (a) natural gas + oxygen → carbon monoxide + water + carbon [1]

   (b) Carbon monoxide is toxic. [1] / Carbon blackens buildings/is a fire risk/causes breathing problems. [1]

3. (a) Sulfur is an impurity which burns [1] to form sulfur dioxide [1] which dissolves in rain water, forming acid rain/sulfurous acid/sulfuric acid. [1]

   (b) Any two from: damages carbonate statues and buildings [1]; corrodes metals [1]; acidifies soil, preventing healthy crops from growing and killing trees [1]; acidifies water and kills fish. [1]

4. (a) The temperature is so high [1] that it can enable atmospheric oxygen and nitrogen to react together. [1]

   (b) $2NO_2 \rightarrow N_2 + 2O_2$ [1 mark for correct formula, 1 mark for correct balancing]

5. diesel + oxygen → carbon dioxide + carbon + water [1]

Page 155 Comparing fuels

Quick quiz

Non-renewable: coal, diesel oil, natural gas, petrol

Renewable: vegetable oil, wood

1. (a) $CH_4(g) + H_2O(g) \rightarrow CO(g) + 3H_2(g)$ [1 mark for correct formulae, 1 mark for correct balancing, 1 mark for state symbols]

   (b) No, because methane is obtained from natural gas [1] which is non-renewable. [1]

   (c) cathode/negative electrode [1]

   (d) It is renewable [1] as water can be replaced in a human lifetime. [1]

   (e) Hydrogen is flammable [1] and so difficult to store safely in a car. [1]

2. renewable [1]

3. Advantage: ethanol is renewable/saves resources of crude oil. [1] Disadvantage: produces less energy per litre so more must be burnt. [1] The advantages outweigh the disadvantages.

Page 156 Cracking and alkenes

Quick quiz

$C_{18}H_{36}$; $C_{22}H_{44}$;
$C_{28}H_{58}$; $C_{14}H_{28}$

1. **(a)** Cracking involves breaking down larger saturated hydrocarbon molecules **[1]** into smaller more useful ones some of which are unsaturated (alkenes). **[1]**

   (b) Some fractions obtained from crude oil contain larger hydrocarbon molecules, so they have limited use **[1]** and need to be broken down into smaller more useful molecules. **[1]**

2. **(a)** The molecules are made of carbon and hydrogen only **[1]** and contain no C=C (carbon-to-carbon double bonds). **[1]**

   (b) alkene **[1]**

3. thermal decomposition **[1]**

4. **(a)** $C_8H_{18} \rightarrow 2C_2H_4$ **[1]** + C_4H_{10} **[1]**

   (b) More useful to make polymers/ plastics/big demand for plastics/more useful as fuels. **[1]**

5. Large saturated molecules **[1]** are broken down (by heating) **[1]** into smaller more useful (unsaturated) molecules. **[1]**

Page 157 Earth's early atmosphere

Quick quiz

nitrogen increased; oxygen increased; carbon dioxide decreased

1. nitrogen: volcanic activity **[1]**; oxygen: photosynthesis (by plants and algae) **[1]**; carbon dioxide: photosynthesis/dissolved into oceans/formation of carbonate rocks. **[1]**

2. **(a)** Argon is an inert gas, so has remained unreacted in the atmosphere. **[1]**

   (b) There are no green plants or algae / there is no photosynthesis on Mars. **[1]**

   (c) Carbon dioxide is used up by plants and algae for photosynthesis **[1]** but there are no plants on Mars / only Earth has plants. **[1]**

3. Marks awarded for coherent explanation and ordering of ideas as well as scientific knowledge – Level 3 answer **[5–6]**, Level 2 answer **[3–4]**, Level 1 answer **[1–2]**.

   Indicative content:
   - Carbon dioxide levels decreased because plants and/or algae developed, using up the carbon dioxide for photosynthesis.
   - The process of photosynthesis causes an increase in the levels of oxygen in the atmosphere.
   - Carbon dioxide levels decreased because oceans formed, absorbing carbon dioxide.
   - Carbon dioxide became locked up in carbonate rocks and fossil fuels.
   - As the Earth cooled, the number of volcanoes decreased as the crust formed as it cooled.
   - When the Earth cooled, water vapour in the atmosphere condensed to form the oceans.
   - Nitrogen was given out by volcanoes.

Page 158 Oxygen and carbon dioxide levels

Quick quiz

False, True, False

1. **(a)** 35% **[1]**

   (b) Algae and plants carried out photosynthesis **[1]** which released oxygen into the atmosphere. **[1]**

2. carbon dioxide + water $\rightarrow$ glucose + oxygen **[1]**

3. **(a)** **(i)** $CaCO_3$ **[1]**

   (ii) Any two from: coal **[1]**; crude oil **[1]**; natural gas **[1]**

   (b) The amount of carbon dioxide decreased **[1]** because carbon dissolved in the water. **[1]**

   (c) Little or no oxygen **[1]**; a large amount of carbon dioxide **[1]**; water vapour **[1]**; small amounts of other gases. **[1]**

Page 159 Gases in the atmosphere

Quick quiz

(a) nitrogen

(b) oxygen

(c) carbon dioxide/water vapour

1. **(a)** 80/100 = 4/5 **[1]**

   (b) Bar chart with oxygen at 20% **[1]**, nitrogen at 80% **[1]**, other gases at <1%. **[1]**

2. **(a)** carbon dioxide : argon = 0.04 : 0.96 **[1]** = 1 : 24 **[1]**

   (b) water : carbon dioxide = 0.5 : 0.04 **[1]** = 25 : 2 (or 12.5 : 1) **[1]**

3. Difference: 95% – 0.04% = 94.96% **[1]**. Percentage change: 94.96/95 × 100% **[1]** = 99.96% decrease in CO_2 **[1]**

4. Any one from: seasonal changes **[1]**; the effect of human activities **[1]**

Page 160 Greenhouse gases

Quick quiz

carbon dioxide; greenhouse gases; infrared radiation; re-emitted; warming

1. methane CH_4 **[1]**, water vapour H_2O **[1]**

2. Short-wavelength radiation/solar radiation from the Sun enters the Earth's atmosphere and passes through to the Earth's surface. **[1]**

   Some of the energy is absorbed by the surface and some is radiated away at different wavelengths. **[1]**

   Greenhouse gases absorb long-wavelength/infrared radiation. **[1]**

   And re-radiate it back to Earth, warming its surface. **[1]**

3. **(a)** Use of fossil fuels – industry/motor vehicles **[1]**

   (b) Carbon dioxide is a greenhouse gas **[1]** which prevents infrared radiation escaping the Earth. **[1]** An increase in carbon dioxide level therefore causes the atmosphere of the Earth to warm up. **[1]** This causes climate change which may have negative effects on the environment e.g. extreme weather, decrease in biodiversity and a rise in sea levels/flooding. **[1]**

Page 161 Human contribution to greenhouse gases

Quick quiz

butane + oxygen $\rightarrow$ carbon dioxide + water (both products circled)

$2C_4H_{10} + 13O_2 \rightarrow 8CO_2 + 10H_2O$

1. **(a)** The increasing number of farm animals **[1]** leads to production of more methane as they digest their food. **[1]** Burning fossil fuels and dumping waste in landfills **[1]** releases carbon dioxide and methane. **[1]** (Also, e.g. agriculture such as rice-growing; thawing tundra owing to global warming).

   (b) Deforestation – the destruction of the rainforests means there are fewer trees photosynthesising and removing carbon dioxide from the air. **[1]**

   Combustion of fossil fuels – releases carbon dioxide as a waste product. **[1]**

   Population increase – an increase in people respiring, burning fuel and consuming more resources increases carbon dioxide levels. **[1]**

   Increased use of landfill – as microorganisms decompose waste, they respire releasing carbon dioxide. **[1]**

2. In peer review, scientists check other scientists' experimental results and explanations to ensure that they are accurate. **[1]** This can be done by repeating experiments for reproducibility or by analysing data. **[1]** If the findings are accepted, they are published, if not they are rejected. **[1]**

3. (405 – 308)/308 × 100 **[1]** = 31.5% **[1]**

4. One from: Biofuels still produce carbon dioxide when they burn **[1]** fossil fuels are burnt by harvest machinery releasing carbon dioxide. **[1]**

Page 162 Global climate change

True, True, False, False

1. **(a)** Environmental – as sea levels rise habitats will be lost **[1]** causing species of plants and animals to die out/decreasing food sources. **[1]**

   (b) Social – rising sea levels will cause erosion of coast lines **[1]** damaging habitats/damaging natural beauty of the areas/putting homes at risk. **[1]**

   (c) Economic – coastal areas will no longer be attractive to the tourist industry **[1]** thus reducing the revenue of businesses in the area, land and business premises will be put at risk. **[1]**

2. **(a)** Answer in the range of 13.85–13.88 °C (accept ±0.02) **[1]**

   (b) (i) 13.87–13.65 = 0.22 °C (accept ±0.02) **[1]**

   (ii) 14.62–13.87 = 0.75 °C (accept ±0.02) **[1]**

   (c) 0.75/0.22 = 3.4 **[1]**

   (d) The trend in temperature is rising **[1]** and the increase is getting faster/rate is accelerating. **[1]**

   (e) Any two from: more intense storms **[1]**; more storms/hurricanes **[1]**; higher summer temperatures **[1]**; lower/ higher precipitation **[1]**; warmer winters **[1]**; unpredictable weather patterns **[1]**; flooding. **[1]**

Page 163 Reducing the use of resources

Quick quiz

False, True, True, True

Only non-renewable resources need to be recycled or reused to sustain them.

1. Any two from: We need to save our resources for future generations **[1]**; using raw materials to make products needs energy which can cause greenhouse gases to be produced **[1]**; to protect the environment and prevent visual pollution. **[1]**

2. Any two from: to conserve our supply of metal ores **[1]**; saves landfill space **[1]**; less energy is required to recycle **[1]**; less noise or dust pollution. **[1]**

3. Valuable resources are not wasted/can be recycled/land is not used up for landfill. **[1]** Resources dumped in landfill could release greenhouse gases on decomposition. **[1]**

4. **(a)** Any two from: burning/(complete) combustion of carbon **[1]**; compounds/(fossil)fuels/wood/ rubbish/plastic **[1]**; respiration from plants/animals/organisms **[1]**; eruption from volcanoes. **[1]**

   (b) Carbon capture and storage. **[1]** Planting more trees. **[1]**

5. **(a)** Reducing the human contribution to greenhouse gases. **[1]**

   (b) Any two from: reducing the use of fossil fuels **[1]**; using alternative low-carbon energy sources **[1]**; carbon dioxide could be removed from Earth's atmosphere using carbon capture and storage **[1]**; planting more trees **[1]**; using improved building materials such as insulation. **[1]**

Page 164 Key concepts in Physics

Quantities and their units

metre: distance; kilogram: mass; second: time; ampere: current; metre cubed: volume; volt: potential difference; coulomb: charge

Prefixes

Conversion: milli: $\times 10^{-3}$; mega: $\times 10^{6}$; nano: $\times 10^{-9}$; micro: $\times 10^{-6}$; giga: $\times 10^{9}$; kilo: $\times 10^{3}$; centi: $\times 10^{-2}$

Abbreviation: giga: G; mega: M; kilo: k; centi: c; milli: m; micro: μ; nano: n

Conversions

1. 0.000 000 0023 m
2. 4.8 g
3. 400 000 000 V
4. 0.15 MJ
5. 2.7 mA
6. 40 μs
7. 1.8 m

Time

False, False, True, True

Calculations

1. mass in kg = 160/2.205 = 72.56 = 73 kg to 2 significant figures

2. diameter = 6370 × 2 = 12 740 km; 1.274 km = 1.274×10^{4} km = 1.274×10^{7} m

3. speed of light = 300 000 km/s = 300 000 000 m/s = 3.0×10^{8} m/s

4. circumference = 4 400 000 km = 4.4×10^{6} km; = 4.4×10^{9} m; radius = $4.4 \times 10^{9} / 2\pi = 7.0028 \times 10^{8}$ m = 7×10^{8} m to 1 significant figure

Page 165 Scalar and vector quantities

Quick quiz

distance – scalar; momentum – vector; efficiency – scalar; speed – scalar; acceleration – vector; weight – vector; force – vector; temperature – scalar

1. **(a)** Arrow pointing in the same direction that is twice as long as the one given. **[1]**

   (b) 300 + 150 = 450 N **[1]**

2.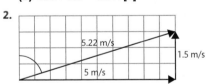

   Correctly drawn scale diagram **[1]**; 5.22 m/s **[1]**; 73.3° (east of north) **[1]**

3. **(a)** Speed is a scalar quantity whereas velocity is a vector OR speed only has magnitude whereas velocity has magnitude and direction. **[1]**

   (b)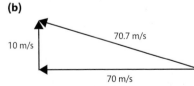

   Correctly drawn scale diagram **[1]**; resultant velocity = 70.7 m/s **[1]**; 81.9° (west of north) **[1]**

Page 166 Distance and speed

Quick quiz

True, False, False, True

1. **(a)** 20 miles **[1]**

   (b) Zero (as she ends at the place she began). **[1]**

2.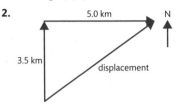

   Correct scale drawing **[1]**; magnitude = 6.1 km **[1]**; direction = 55° (east of north) **[1]**

3. **(a)** 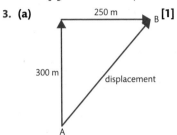 **[1]**

   (b) 300 + 250 = 550 m **[1]**

   (c) Resultant displacement = 391 m **[1]**; direction = 39.8° (east of north) **[1]**

Page 167 Speed and velocity

Quick quiz

speed, direction, distance, time

1. 100 km = 100 000 m; 2 hours = 7200 s average speed = distance/time = 100 000/7200 **[1]** = 13.9 m/s **[1]**

2. distance = 3000 m; time = 1800 s average velocity = distance/time = 3000 m/1800 s **[1]** = 1.7 m/s north **[1]**

3. **(a)** 3 m/s **[1]**

   (b) 6 m/s **[1]**

4. **(a)** velocity = distance/time = 50 000 m/ 5400 s **[1]** = 9.26 m/s west **[1]**

   (b) The speed will not have been constant throughout the journey. **[1]**

   (c) distance of second bus = 100 km; average velocity = 100 000 m/5400 s = 18.52 m/s west **[1]** (twice the velocity of the first bus: accept 2 × 9.26 m/s = 18.52 m/s)

Page 168 Distance–time graphs

Quick quiz

the gradient of the line increases – this means the object is accelerating

the gradient of the line decreases – this means the object is decelerating

the gradient of the line is zero – this means the object is stationary

1. A–B: The cyclist travels 30 km in 3 hours. The speed of the cyclist is 10 km/h. **[1]**

   B–C: The cyclist is stationary for 5 hours. **[1]**

C–D: The cyclist travels a further 90 km in 4 hours. The speed is 22.5 km/h. **[1]**

2. **(a)** 250 m **[1]**
   (b) Constant speed (of 5 m/s). **[1]**
   (c) Tangent drawn at t = 50 s **[1]**; speed = gradient of the tangent / dy/dx **[1]**; s = 5 m/s **[1]**

3. Distance on the y-axis and time on the x-axis **[1]**; a curved line drawn with increasing gradient. **[1]**

Page 169 Uniform acceleration

Quick quiz

x – displacement – m; u – initial velocity – m/s; v – final velocity – m/s; a – acceleration – m/s^2; t – time – s

1. **(a)** $v = u + at$ **[1]**; $v = 0 + (3 \times 6)$ **[1]** = 18 m/s **[1]**
   (b) $x = (v^2 - u^2)/2a$ **[1]** = $(18^2 - 0)/(2 \times 3)$ **[1]** = 54 m **[1]**

2. **(a)** $x = (v^2 - u^2)/2a$ **[1]** = $(0^2 - 10^2)/2 \times -9.8$ **[1]** = 5.10 m **[1]**
   (b) $a = (v - u)/t$ so $t = (v - u)/a$ **[1]** = $(0 - 10)/-9.8$ **[1]** = 1.02 s **[1]**

3. **(a)** $v = u + at = 0 + (15 \times 5)$ **[1]** = 75 m/s **[1]**
   (b) $x = (v^2 - u^2)/2a$ **[1]** = $(75^2 - 0^2)/(2 \times 15)$ **[1]** = 187.5 m **[1]**

4. $v^2 = u^2 + 2ax$; $x = (v^2 - u^2)/2a$ **[1]** = $(10^2 - 8^2)/(2 \times 2)$ **[1]** = 9 m **[1]**

Page 170 Velocity-time graphs

Quick quiz

gradient of the line – acceleration; area under the line – distance travelled; a horizontal line – constant speed

1. **(a)** speed **[1]**
   (b) acceleration **[1]**
   (c) distance **[1]**

2. **(a)** velocity / speed on y-axis, time on x-axis **[1]**; diagonal line from 0 to 8 m/s over 10 seconds **[1]**; horizontal line at 8 m/s from 10 to 70 seconds **[1]**; diagonal line from 8 to 0 m/s from 70 to 90 seconds **[1]**
   (b) distance = 8 × 60 **[1]** = 480 m **[1]**

3. **(a)** velocity / speed on y-axis; time on x-axis **[1]**; diagonal line from 0 to 10 m/s over 20 seconds **[1]**; horizontal line from 20 to 50 seconds **[1]**; diagonal line from 10 to 0 m/s over final 10 seconds **[1]**
   (b) acceleration = 10/20 **[1]** = 0.5 m/s^2 **[1]**
   (c) distance = (10 × 20)/2 + 10 × 30 + (10 × 10)/2 **[1]** = 100 + 300 + 50 **[1]** = 450 m **[1]**

Page 171 Gravity

Quick quiz

mass – the amount of matter in an object – kg; weight – the force acting on an object due to gravity – N; gravitational field strength – the strength of gravity at any one point – N/kg

1. **(a)** mass = weight/gravitational field strength **[1]** = 25/9.8 = 2.55 kg **[1]**
   (b) g = weight/mass = 4.1 / 2.55 **[1]** = 1.6 N/kg **[1]**

2. **(a)** $W = mg$, so $m = W/g$ **[1]** = 1.6 × 10^5 N/9.8 N/kg **[1]** = 16 327 kg **[1]**
   (b) **(i)** mass = 16 327 kg **[1]** (same as mass on Earth)
   (ii) $W = mg$ = 16 327 kg × 1.6 N/kg **[1]** = 26 123 N **[1]**

3. **(a)** W on Earth = mg = 55 × 9.8 **[1]** = 539 N **[1]**
   (b) W on Moon = 55 × 1.6 = 88 N **[1]**; difference in weight = 539 – 88 **[1]** = 451 N **[1]**

Page 172 Newton's laws of motion

Quick quiz

Newton's first law – An object will continue to move in the same direction at the same speed unless acted upon by a resultant force.

Newton's second law – The acceleration of an object is proportional to the resultant force and inversely proportional to the mass of the object.

Newton's third law – When two objects interact, they exert an equal and opposite force on each other.

1. The racing bikes have low mass because the lower the mass, the greater the acceleration for the same accelerating force. **[2]**

2. 1 The forces are the same size. **[1]**
   2 The forces act in opposite directions. **[1]**
   3 The forces act on different objects. **[1]**

3. There are forces of friction and air resistance acting on the moving ball, **[1]** so the resultant force on the ball is in the opposite direction to its motion, **[1]** causing it to slow down. **[1]**

4. **(a)** Moving in a straight line, **[1]** at constant speed. **[1]**
   (b) $F = ma$ **[1]** so reducing the mass **[1]** or increasing the maximum force from the engine would increase the maximum acceleration. **[1]**

Page 173 Newton's second law

Quick quiz

True, True, True, False

1. Resultant force = 1200 N – 600 N = 600 N in the forwards direction/to the right **[1]**; acceleration = force/mass = 600 N/1500 kg **[1]** = 0.4 m/s^2 forwards **[1]**

2. Resultant force = 150 N – 30 N = 120 N **[1]**; mass = force/acceleration = 120 N/2 m/s^2 **[1]** = 60 kg **[1]**

3. Acceleration = force/mass = 12 000/15 000 **[1]** = 0.8 m/s^2 **[1]**

4. Inertial mass × acceleration = force needed to stop. **[1]** More massive objects have greater inertial mass, resulting in a larger force for the same acceleration. **[1]**

Page 174 Centripetal force

Quick quiz

True, True, True, False

1. An object travelling in a circular path is changing direction so it must be changing velocity **[1]** so it is accelerating. **[1]** If an object is accelerating there must be a resultant force acting on it. **[1]**

2. **(a)** Tension (pull) in the string. **[1]**
   (b) The conker will no longer move in a circle **[1]** since the centripetal force is gone. It will act as a projectile moving freely under gravity. **[1]**

3. **(a)** Arrow labelled A, from Earth towards the centre of the Sun. **[1]**
   (b) Arrow labelled R, from Earth towards the centre of the Sun. **[1]**
   (c) The resultant force on the Earth would increase, **[1]** so Earth would move closer to the Sun, **[1]** so the radius of the orbit would be smaller. **[1]**

Page 175 Practical: Investigating acceleration

Quick quiz

speed – m/s; mass – kg; acceleration – m/s^2; force – N

1. **(a)** **(i)** The independent variable is the one that is changed deliberately in the experiment, **[1]** and so is force. **[1]**
   (ii) The dependent variable is the one that is measured in the experiment, **[1]** and so is acceleration. **[1]**
   (b) gradient = 1/mass of trolley **[1]**

2. **(a)** Force applied (i.e. the number of masses on the mass holder pulling the trolley through the light gate), **[1]** OR distance between trolley and light gate.
   (b) Attach masses on a mass holder to the first trolley. **[1]** Measure acceleration of the trolley through the light gate. **[1]** Change the trolley and measure the acceleration, **[1]** (continue with other trolleys). Plot a graph of mass against acceleration. **[1]**

Page 176 Momentum

Quick quiz

False, False, True, True

1. **(a)** momentum = mass × velocity = 1000 × 25 **[1]** = 25 000 **[1]** kg m/s **[1]**
   (b) If the velocity halves, momentum will also halve. **[1]**
   (c)

(d) straight line **[1]**; through the origin / through (0,0) **[1]**

(e) gradient = mass **[1]**

2. Initial momentum = 15 000 × 200 **[1]** = 3 × 10⁶ kg m/s **[1]**; final momentum = 14 000 × 210 = 2.94 × 10⁶ kg m/s **[1]**; change in momentum = 60 000 kg m/s **[1]**

Page 177 Conservation of momentum

Quick quiz

collide, conserved, after, external, system, closed, law, momentum

1. momentum before = (5 × 4) + (7 × 2) **[1]** = 34 kg m/s **[1]**; momentum after = momentum before; velocity = 34 kg m/s/12 kg **[1]** = 2.83 m/s **[1]**

2. (a) p = 15 000 × 8 **[1]** = 120 000 kg m/s **[1]**

(b) p = 120 000 kg m/s **[1]**

(c) velocity = 120 000 kg m/s/16 000 kg **[1]** = 7.5 m/s **[1]**

(d) driver momentum before = 75 × 8 = 600 kg m/s **[1]**; driver momentum after = 75 × 7.5 = 562.5 kg m/s **[1]**; change in momentum = 600 − 562.5 = 37.5 kg m/s **[1]**

Page 178 Stopping distance

Quick quiz

False, False, True, False

1. (a) distance = speed × time = 13 × 1.3 **[1]** = 17 m **[1]**

(b) Being tired increases thinking distance, **[1]** because her reaction time will be greater. **[1]**

2. (a) As speed increases, so do thinking and braking distance. **[1]** Thinking distance is directly proportional to speed OR increases by 3 metres for every 10 mph increase in speed. **[1]** Braking distance increases much more than thinking distance as speed increases. **[1]**

(b) (i) no change **[1]**

(ii) increases **[1]**

Page 179 Factors affecting braking distance

Quick quiz

braking, thinking, stopping

1. Anything that reduces the frictional force between the tyres and the road will increase the time for which the brakes must be applied, **[1]** increasing the braking distance. **[1]** Wet/icy/muddy roads will reduce the frictional force. **[1]**

2. There is a maximum frictional force that the brakes can apply **[1]** so the greater the speed of the vehicle the longer the force will need to act for. **[1]** Therefore, the braking distance will be greater if the car has a greater speed. **[1]**

3. Friction causes the brakes to heat up. **[1]** As they get hotter, they apply less friction **[1]** (and so are not as efficient).

4. 12 kN = 12 000 N **[1]**; 12 000 = 1000 × u/2.4 **[1]**; u = 12 000 × 2.4 /1000 **[1]** = 29 m/s to 2 significant figures **[1]**

Page 180 Gravitational potential energy

Quick quiz

$\Delta h = \dfrac{\Delta GPE}{m \times g}$ and $g = \dfrac{\Delta GPE}{M \times \Delta h}$

1. height = 1.09 km = 1090 m **[1]**; ΔGPE = 65 × 10 × 1090 **[1]** = 708 500 J **[1]**

2. (a) ΔGPE = 60 × 10 × 300 **[1]** = 180 000 J **[1]**

(b) 223 000 = 60 × 10 × Δh **[1]**; Δh = 223 000 / (60 × 10) **[1]** = 370 m **[1]**

3. 63 700 = m × 10 × 98 **[1]**; m = 63 700 / (10 × 98) **[1]** = 65 kg **[1]**

Page 181 Kinetic energy

Quick quiz

mass = $2E_k/v^2$; speed = $\sqrt{\dfrac{2E_k}{m}}$

1. (a) $E_k = \frac{1}{2} \times m \times v^2$ **[1]** = $\frac{1}{2}$ × 10 000 × 10² = 500 000 J **[1]**

(b) 500 000 J

(c) An increase in the number of passengers means an increase in mass. **[1]** If mass increases, so does the kinetic energy. **[1]**

2. The kinetic energy increases by a factor of 4, **[1]** because the speed has doubled and the kinetic energy depends on speed squared. **[1]**

3. E_k (initial) = $\frac{1}{2}$ × 1200 × 10² = 60 000 J **[1]**; E_k (final) = $\frac{1}{2}$ × 1200 × 15² = 135 000 J **[1]**; Increase in E_k = 135 000 − 60 000 = 75 000 J **[1]**

4. 21 = 0.5 × 12 × v^2 **[1]**; $v = \sqrt{2 \times 21 \div 12}$ **[1]** = 1.9 m/s **[1]**

Page 182 Conservation of energy

Quick quiz

True, False, False, True, True

1. (a) Energy transferred by heating, light and sound. **[1]**

(b) Transfers by light and sound. **[1]**

(c) Transfer by heating. **[1]**

2. (a) heating **[1]**

(b) lubrication **[1]**

(c) It is dissipated to the surroundings. **[1]**

3. Before the ball is dropped, it has gravitational potential energy. **[1]** As the ball falls, the GPE decreases and is transferred to kinetic energy. **[1]** After the ball bounces, the kinetic energy decreases and is transferred to GPE. **[1]**

4. The kinetic energy of the car **[1]** is transferred by friction to thermal energy in the brakes and the surroundings. **[1]**

Page 183 Efficiency

Quick quiz

The closer to 1 (or 100%), the more efficient the device; If a device is 40% efficient, 40% of the energy is usefully transferred and 60% is wasted.

1. Efficiency = useful energy transferred/total energy supplied. **[1]** If both lamps have the same useful energy output each second, then the one with the greater energy input each second must be wasting more energy. **[1]** Lamp B is more efficient. **[1]**

2. (a) 2000 − 1800 = 200 J **[1]**

(b) 1800/2000 **[1]** = 0.9 **[1]**

(c) Energy is usefully transferred to kinetic energy in the motor **[1]** and thermal energy in the heating element. **[1]**

(d) Wasted energy transfers are by heating to the case of the hairdryer **[1]** and by sound to the thermal energy store of the surroundings. **[1]**

3. 0.4 = useful energy transferred / 30 **[1]**; useful energy transferred = 0.4 × 30 **[1]** = 12 MJ **[1]**; energy wasted = 30 − 12 = 18 MJ **[1]**

Page 184 Renewable energy resources

Quick quiz

Sun – energy transferred by light is used to generate electricity using solar panels

wind – wind forces turbines to rotate, generating electricity

tides – daily movement of the ocean is used to generate electricity

1. **Advantages:** can be placed in isolated locations, **[1]** no fuel costs. **[1]**

Disadvantages: Any two from: some people think they spoil the landscape; some maintenance costs **[1]** danger to birds **[1]** noisy **[1]** only work when windy **[1]** cannot be used in storms. **[1]**

2. **Tidal barrage:**

Advantage: Any one from: free energy **[1]** low maintenance costs once built **[1]** predictable energy output **[1]** tides store a large amount of energy. **[1]**

Disadvantage: Any one from: change movement of water in estuaries so can disrupt wildlife; **[1]** costly to build **[1]** limited location **[1]** low power output. **[1]**

Hydroelectric dam

Advantage: Any one from: reliable **[1]** high power output **[1]** small wheels work in isolated locations **[1]** free energy. **[1]**

Disadvantage: Any one from: some maintenance costs **[1]** dams flood valleys, destroying habitats. **[1]**

3. It is not realistic because it is not always sunny / the panels do not produce electricity at night. **[1]** A town would require greater amounts of power than could be delivered by solar panels alone. **[1]**

Page 185 Non-renewable energy resources

Quick quiz

coal, oil and natural gas

1. **Advantages:** Steam is the only gas emitted – nuclear power has no effect on global warming. **[1]** Small amounts of fuel produce large amounts of energy. **[1]**

   Disadvantages: Transport of radioactive fuel and waste is dangerous and expensive. **[1]** Nuclear power plants are expensive to decommission. **[1]**

   (Other possible disadvantages include the fact that nuclear waste stays radioactive for thousands of years, accidents can release radioactive substances into the environment, and nuclear power stations take a long time to start up and shut down.)

2. Non-renewable resources are in short supply/Oil has many other uses (making plastics, for example) – if oil runs out, alternatives will need to be found **[1]** As resources become scarcer, they will become more expensive **[1]** Burning fossil fuels produces carbon dioxide, which contributes to global warming, so we need to find alternatives to fossil fuels. **[1]**

3. Any two from: Easy to obtain, cheap, other vehicles (e.g. electric vehicles) do not have the range and convenience of petrol and diesel vehicles, much easier and quicker to refuel. **[2]**

4. Any two explanations with named substances: Carbon dioxide is produced, which contributes to global warming **[2]** Smoke and sulfur dioxide can cause breathing problems **[2]** Coal is bulky and heavy, so needs a lot of energy to transport. **[2]**

Page 186 Types of wave

Quick quiz

longitudinal; transverse; transverse; longitudinal; longitudinal

1. speed = distance travelled/time. distance = 25 × 2 = 50 m **[1]**; speed = 50/0.15 **[1]** = 333 m/s **[1]**

2. $v = x/t$, so $t = x/v$ **[1]**; time to reach station, through air = 495/330 = 1.5 s **[1]**; through steel rail = 495/5800 = 0.085 s **[1]**; difference in time = 1.5 − 0.085 = 1.415 s **[1]**

3. **(a)** wave speed = frequency × wavelength **[1]**

   (b) 330 = 11 000 × λ **[1]**; λ = 330 / 11 000 **[1]** = 0.030 m **[1]**

Page 187 Properties of waves

Quick quiz

amplitude – the maximum displacement of a point on a wave away from its undisturbed position

crest – the top of a wave

frequency – the number of waves passing a point each second

trough – the bottom of a wave

wavelength – the number of waves passing a point each second

time period – the time taken to complete one full cycle or wave

1. **(a)** 340 = f × 1.7 **[1]**; f = 340/1.7 **[1]** = 200 Hz **[1]**

   (b) $v = f \times \lambda$ and $v = \frac{x}{t}$ so $f \times \lambda = \frac{x}{t}$ **[1]** and $x = t \times f \times \lambda$ **[1]** = 20 × 50 × 6.8 **[1]** = 6800 m **[1]**

2. **(a)** 0.5 = f × 0.1 **[1]** so f = 0.5/0.1 **[1]** = 5 Hz **[1]**

   (b) $f \times \lambda = \frac{x}{t}$ **[1]** so $t = \frac{x}{f \times \lambda}$ **[1]** = 50/(0.2 × 2) **[1]** = 125 s **[1]**

3. To reduce timing error **[1]** because any error he makes in timing will be spread out over the total number of waves **[1]** / because there may be less than one wave every second **[1]** so he needs to time over a longer period. **[1]**

4. 1500 = 500/t **[1]** so t = 500/1500 **[1]** = 0.33 s **[1]**

Page 188 Practical: Investigating waves

Quick quiz

2, 6, 1, 3, 4, 5

1. **(a)** half the wavelength **[1]**

   (b) Determine the wavelength by measuring length L and doubling it. **[1]** Use the frequency from the frequency generator. **[1]** Calculate the speed using the equation speed = frequency × wavelength. **[1]**

2. **(a)** Same frequency of oscillation, **[1]** same tension / weight on the string. **[1]**

   (b) Measure from the point of attachment on the oscillator to where the string touches the pulley **[1]** using a metre rule **[1]** placed close to the string. **[1]**

Page 189 Types of electromagnetic waves

Quick quiz

microwaves, infrared, ultraviolet, X-rays, gamma rays

1. **(a)** $f = v/\lambda = 3.0 \times 10^8 / 3.5 \times 10^{-7}$ **[1]** = 8.6×10^{14} Hz **[1]**

   (b) causes premature skin ageing **[1]**; can cause skin cancer **[1]**

2. **(a)** They pass through soft tissue but are absorbed by bones, **[1]** so the different types of tissue will show up on a photograph. **[1]**

   (b) X-rays are ionising, **[1]** so they can mutate cells/genes, causing cancer. **[1]**

   (c) The benefits of making an X-ray image to find out what is wrong **[1]** outweigh the risks from the X-rays. **[1]**

Page 190 Properties of electromagnetic waves

Quick quiz

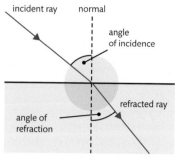

1. Grass absorbs all the wavelengths in visible light except green light. **[1]** The grass reflects green light and so appears to be green. **[1]**

2.

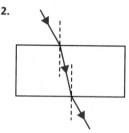

Angle of refraction is greater than angle of incidence where the light leaves the block, **[1]** final refracted ray is parallel to original incident ray. **[1]**

3. **(a)** An electromagnetic wave 'bouncing back' from a surface. **[1]**

   (b) Any two from: refraction, transmission, absorption.

4.

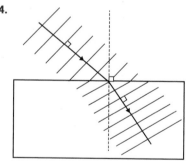

Page 191 Practical: Investigating refraction

Quick quiz

False, False, True

1. Refraction is the change in direction **[1]** of a ray of light due to a change in speed **[1]** as it passes from one material into another. **[1]**

2. **(a)** The angles are measured to 0.1° **[1]** and an ordinary protractor measures to the nearest degree. **[1]**

   (b) y-axis labelled Angle of refraction in degrees **[1]**; x-axis labelled Concentration of sugar solution (%) **[1]**; five points plotted correctly **[1]**; line of best fit drawn correctly **[1]**

   (c) As the concentration of sugar solution increases, the angle of refraction decreases **[1]** linearly **[1]**

(d) 40% **[1]**

(e) Line extrapolated to 0 concentration **[1]**; angle of refraction is 40.7° **[1]**

Page 192 Applications of EM waves

Quick quiz

radio waves – TV and communications; infrared – thermal imaging; visible – lasers; ultraviolet – tanning; X-rays – medical imaging

1. **(a)** The microwaves are absorbed by the water in the food **[1]** and transfer energy to the food. **[1]**

   (b) Microwaves penetrate food by about 1 cm, **[1]** so they cook food faster than infrared which only heats from the surface. **[1]**

2. high energy **[1]** kill bacteria easily **[1]**

3. **(a)** radio waves **[1]**

   (b) They are able to penetrate soft tissue in the body, **[1]** but are absorbed by bones. **[1]**

   (c) They can kill cancerous cells in the body. **[1]**

Page 193 The structure of an atom

Quick quiz

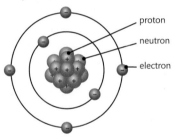

carbon atom

1. Electrons orbit the nucleus. An electron is negatively charged. **[1]** Protons are found in the nucleus. A proton is positively charged. **[1]** Neutrons are found in the nucleus. A neutron is neutral. **[1]**

2. $(1.45 \times 10^{-10})/(1 \times 10^{-15})$ **[1]** $= 145\,000$ times larger **[1]**

3. They both have a relative mass of 1 **[1]**; protons have a relative charge of +1 **[1]**; whereas neutrons have a relative charge of 0. **[1]**

4. An electron in an atom absorbs electromagnetic radiation. **[1]** This promotes the electron to a higher energy level. **[1]** When the electron drops back to a lower energy level, electromagnetic radiation is emitted (with wavelength or frequency in the visible part of the spectrum). **[1]**

Page 194 Mass number, atomic number and isotopes

Quick quiz

False, True, True, False

1. **(a)** Isotopes are atoms with the same atomic number **[1]** but a different mass number/number of neutrons. **[1]**

(b) (i) Both isotopes of carbon have 6 protons **[1]** and 6 electrons. **[1]**

   (ii) Carbon-14 has 2 extra neutrons. **[1]**

2. **(a)** 92 protons **[1]**; 92 electrons **[1]**; 146 neutrons. **[1]**

   (b) same number of protons **[1]**; same number of electrons **[1]**; uranium 238 has 3 more neutrons than uranium-235. **[1]**

3. **(a)** ion **[1]**; **(b)** 2+ **[1]**

Page 195 Development of the atomic model

Quick quiz

Plum pudding model; In the nucleus of the atom.

1. Bohr predicted that electrons travel in circular orbits around the nucleus, **[1]** which contains positively charged protons. **[1]** Later, evidence was found for the existence of uncharged particles called neutrons in the nucleus. **[1]**

2. The plum pudding model has electrons randomly distributed throughout the atom, but the nuclear model has electrons orbiting the nucleus. **[1]** The plum pudding model has the mass evenly distributed throughout the atom, but the nuclear model has most of the mass in a small nucleus with a positive charge. **[1]**

3. Positive alpha particles were fired at gold foil and most passed straight through without being deflected. **[1]** This suggested that the atom was mostly empty space. **[1]** Some particles were deflected. **[1]** This suggested that the mass was concentrated at the centre of the atom. **[1]** It also showed that the centre of the atom was positively charged. **[1]**

Page 196 Ionising radiation

Quick quiz

False, True, False, True

1. A random process means that there is no way to predict which atom will decay next, **[1]** and there is no way to predict when a particular atom will decay. **[1]** The process is not affected by external conditions such as temperature or pressure. **[1]**

2. 2 protons and 2 neutrons **[1]**

3. One high-speed electron from the nucleus **[1]**

4. The radiation emitted by radioactive substances may knock electrons off the atoms in the materials it travels through. **[1]** This process is called ionisation and leaves the atoms positively charged because they lose electrons. **[1]** Ionisation in a living cell in the human body may damage the DNA **[1]** causing cancer. **[1]**

5. When radiation passes through the air it collides with air particles, ionising them. **[1]** Alpha particles are large particles with a charge of +2, so they are much more

likely to collide with air particles and so do not travel far through the air. **[1]** Beta particles are much smaller than alpha particles and have a charge of –1 so they are much less likely to collide with air particles and so travel further through the air. **[1]** Gamma rays are electromagnetic radiation and have very few collisions with air particles so their range through the air is much further than either alpha or beta particles. **[1]**

Page 197 Background radiation

Quick quiz

False, True, False, True

1. The activity from a radioactive source is the rate at which nuclei in the source decay. **[1]** The count rate from the source is the number of decays each second recorded by a detector. **[1]**

2. Alpha radiation only travels a few centimetres in air, **[1]** so the G-M tube must be placed very close to the source. **[1]** Radiation enters the G-M tube through a window at one end and may be absorbed in the end of the tube. **[1]**

3. **(a)** Rocks contain radioactive isotopes. **[1]** The number of radioactive isotopes varies according to the type of rock in a location. **[1]** A person in an area with rocks which contain higher levels of radioactive isotopes will be exposed to a higher level of background radiation than a person in an area where the rocks have lower levels of radioactive isotopes. **[1]**

   (b) Any two of: taking a flight at high altitude **[1]** medical X-rays **[1]** going down a mine **[1]** being in a house with radon gas. **[1]**

4. Measure the background count rate, with no source in place. **[1]** Measure the count rate with the source in place. **[1]** Subtract the background count rate from the count rate with the source to give the count rate from the source alone. **[1]**

Page 198 Beta decay

Quick quiz

β– particle, β+ particle, β+ particle, β– particle, both

1. When an unstable nucleus decays by β– emission, a neutron changes to a proton and an electron, **[1]** which is immediately emitted from the nucleus. The proton remains in the nucleus, so the atomic number increases by one, **[1]** forming a new element.

2. Both β+ particles and β– particles are emitted from the nuclei of unstable atoms, **[1]** have negligible mass **[1]** and are moderately ionising and moderately penetrating. **[1]**

   A β+ particle has a mass of +1.
   A β– particle has a mass of –1. **[1]**

   A β+ particle is formed when a proton changes to a neutron, so the atomic number of the nucleus decreases by 1, but when a β– particle is formed, a neutron changes to a proton, so the atomic number of the nucleus increases by 1. **[1]**

3. The particles pass through the air in a straight line until they enter the area between the plates. **[1]** β– particles have a negative charge **[1]**, so they are attracted towards the positively charged plate and the path curves upwards. **[1]** When the particles leave the region between the plates there is no force acting on them from the plates, so they continue in a straight line. **[1]**

Page 199 Nuclear decay

Quick quiz

$$^{226}_{88}\text{Ra} \rightarrow {}^{222}_{86}\text{Rn} + {}^{4}_{2}\text{He}$$

$$^{14}_{6}\text{C} \rightarrow {}^{14}_{7}\text{N} + {}^{0}_{-1}\text{e}$$

$$^{24}_{11}\text{Na} \rightarrow {}^{24}_{12}\text{Mg} + {}^{0}_{-1}\text{He}$$

$$^{219}_{86}\text{Rn} \rightarrow {}^{215}_{84}\text{Po} + {}^{4}_{2}\text{He}$$

1. When an unstable nucleus decays by emitting an alpha particle, it loses two protons and two neutrons, **[1]** so the atomic number goes down by two, forming a new element. **[1]**

2. There is an electric field between the plates. **[1]** Alpha particles are positively charged **[1]** so in the electric field the path of the particles will curve towards the negative plate. **[1]** On leaving the field, the path becomes a straight line. **[1]**

3. (a) When a nucleus emits an alpha particle, a β– particle or a β+ particle, it may be left in an unstable state. **[1]** To make the nucleus more stable, some energy is emitted in the form of a gamma ray. **[1]**

   (b) A gamma ray is an electromagnetic wave. **[1]** It has no charge so the atomic number does not change. **[1]** It has no mass so the mass number does not change. **[1]**

4. In neutron decay, a neutron is emitted from the nucleus so the mass number decreases by one. **[1]** The atomic number does not change, **[1]** so another isotope of the same element is formed. **[1]**

Page 200 Half-lives

Quick quiz

half, time, rate, half, time, nuclei

1.

Activity (Bq)	1500	750	375	187.5	93.75	46.88
Time (years)	0	30	60	90	120	150

The sample is approximately 150 years old. [1 mark for correct calculations, 1 mark for correct half-life.]

2. (a)

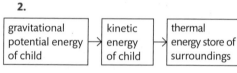

Axes correct way around **[1]**; points accurately plotted **[1]**; smooth line of best fit drawn **[1]**

   (b) horizontal line drawn from 500 nuclei to meet line of best fit **[1]**; vertical line drawn down from this point to meet x-axis **[1]**; half-life between 6 and 8 minutes **[1]**

Page 201 Dangers of radioactivity

Quick quiz

False, False, False, True

1. Ionising radiation may cause direct damage to body tissue if the radiation collides with cells. **[1]** Indirect damage can occur if the radiation causes ions to be produced. **[1]** These ions can destroy cells in our body or they can mutate the genes within the cells. **[1]**

2. (a) It takes time for the gamma emitter to travel around her body. **[1]**

   (b) Alpha particles could not pass through the skin **[1]** so would not be detected outside the body **[1]**, but gamma rays can pass through the body and so be detected. **[1]**

   (c) This reduces their exposure to gamma radiation **[1]** as the radiation cannot pass through the lead. **[1]**

   (d) Radiation exposes the film in the badge **[1]** so the amount of radiation the staff are exposed to over time is monitored. **[1]**

   (e) So gamma rays can be detected in all directions **[1]** producing a more accurate picture of her spine. **[1]**

Page 202 Radioactive contamination and irradiation

Quick quiz

X-rays, damaging, radioactive, precautions, dose

1. (a) Any two from: increased exposure time **[1]** higher activity of radioactive source **[1]** being closer to the source. **[1]**

   (b) Irradiation is the process of exposing an object to radiation. **[1]**

   Contamination is the unwanted presence of materials containing radioactive atoms. **[1]**

2. (a) Peer review is when scientific research is checked and evaluated by other scientists. **[1]**

   (b) It makes scientists more confident about each other's findings. **[1]**

3. (a) To prevent contamination of her hands. **[1]**

   (b) One from: wear protective clothing **[1]**; stay behind a screen **[1]**; handle the source with long tongs **[1]**; point the source away from her body. **[1]**

   (c) The dose is very small/the activity of the source is low. **[1]**

Page 203 Revising energy transfers

Quick quiz

False, False, True, True, False

1. (a) energy transferred by sound = 10% **[1]**

   (b)

   energy transferred by electricity 100%

   thermal energy 50%

   kinetic energy 40%

   energy transferred by sound 10%

   Arrow for kinetic energy correct **[1]**

   Arrow for sound correct **[1]**

2.

gravitational potential energy of child	→	kinetic energy of child	→	thermal energy store of surroundings

   [1 mark for each store]

3. 108 kJ = 108 000 J **[1]**

   $108\,000 = 0.5 \times m \times 12^2$ **[1]**

   $m = 108\,000/(0.5 \times 144)$ **[1]** = 1500 kg **[1]**

Page 204 Work done and energy transfer

Quick quiz

False, True, False, False, True

1. (a) 30 000 J **[1]**

   (b) Work done = 2500 N **[1]**

   $E = F \times s$ so $s = W/F$ **[1]** = 30 000/2500 **[1]** = 12 m **[1]**

2. (a) work done = force × distance moved in the direction of the force **[1]**

   (b) 750 kJ = 750 000 J **[1]**; 750 000 = $F \times 75$ **[1]**; $F = 750\,000 / 75$ **[1]** = 10 000 N **[1]**

3. $W = F \times s = 600 \times 2.5$ **[1]** = 1500 N **[1]**

Page 205 Power

Quick quiz

energy transferred = power × time; power = work done/time; work done = power × time

1. 2.5 kW = 2500 W, 2 minutes = 120 s **[1]**; $E = 2500\,\text{W} \times 120\,\text{s}$ **[1]** = 300 000 J **[1]**

2. (a) $E = 800 \times 7.5$ **[1]** = 6000 J **[1]**

   (b) $P = 6000/15$ **[1]** = 400 W **[1]**

3. 3 kW = 3000 W **[1]**; 30 minutes = 30 × 60 = 1800 s **[1]**; $E = P \times t = 3000 \times 1800$ **[1]** = 5.4×10^6 J **[1]**

4. $P = E/t$ so $t = E/P = 240\,000/800$ **[1]** = 300 seconds **[1]** = 5 minutes **[1]**

Page 206 Forces

Quick quiz

Contact forces: tension, friction

Non-contact forces: weight, magnetic, electrostatic, gravitational force

1. (a)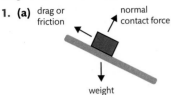

   Three arrows drawn and labelled as shown. [1 mark for each correct arrow and its label.]

   (b)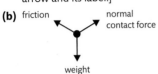

   Three arrows drawn and labelled as shown. [1 mark for each correct arrow and its label]

2. Air resistance labelled opposing direction of motion, **[1]** lift labelled upwards, **[1]** weight labelled downwards, **[1]** thrust labelled in direction of motion. **[1]**

3. Raise one end of the runway **[1]** until the trolley just starts to move **[1]** so the gravitational force on the trolley balances the frictional forces on the trolley. **[1]**

Page 207 Resultant forces

Quick quiz

2,3,1

1. resultant force = $m \times a$ = 1000 × 1.5 **[1]** = 1500 N **[1]**; force from engine = 500 + 1500 = 2000 N **[1]**

2.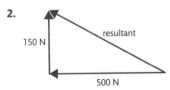

   500 N force and 150 N force drawn at right angles and labelled, **[1]** suitable scale e.g. 100 N : 1 cm, **[1]** resultant correctly drawn with arrow, **[1]** resultant force of 522 N **[1]** (or 520 N to 2 s.f.)

3. (a) The maximum speed a free falling object reaches when the resultant force is zero. **[1]**

   (b) The weight acts vertically downwards **[1]** so the skydiver accelerates downwards. **[1]** The air resistance force increases as the skydiver's speed increases **[1]** until the resultant force = 0 and the skydiver moves at a constant speed. **[1]**

   (c) Opening the parachute increases air resistance **[1]** so there is a resultant force upwards **[1]** so the skydiver decelerates. **[1]** As speed decreases air resistance decreases until the resultant force is zero again. **[1]**

Page 208 Circuit diagrams

Quick quiz

Component	Circuit symbol
thermistor	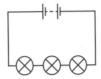
lamp	⊗
ammeter	—(A)—

1. (a) correct symbols **[1]**; correct circuit **[1]**

   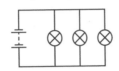

   (b) correct symbols **[1]**; correct circuit **[1]**

   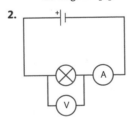

   (c) The lamps in the parallel circuit would be brighter. **[1]**

2.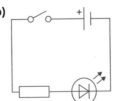

   All symbols drawn correctly **[1]**; ammeter shown connected in series with the lamp **[1]**; voltmeter connected in parallel with the lamp. **[1]**

3. (a) An LED lights up when the current in it is in one direction but not when the current is in the other direction. **[1]**

   (b)

   all symbols drawn correctly **[1]**; LED in correct orientation **[1]**

Page 209 Current, resistance and potential difference

Quick quiz

current – the flow of charge, measured in amps (A)

potential difference – the energy given to each unit of charge, measured in volts (V)

resistance – opposition to the flow of charge, measured in ohms (Ω)

1. (a) The reading will be 2 V **[1]** because the pd supplied by the cell is divided equally between the resistors. **[1]**

   (b) total resistance of circuit = 3 × 10 W = 30 W **[1]**; $I = V/R$ = 6/30 **[1]** = 0.2 A **[1]**

   (c) It will halve **[1]** as current is proportional to potential difference. **[1]**

2. 12 = 5 × R **[1]**; R = 12/5 **[1]** = 2.4 Ω **[1]**

3. 230 = 10 × R **[1]**; R = 230/10 **[1]** = 23 Ω **[1]**

4. 30 mΩ = 0.03 W **[1]**; 4.5 = I × 0.03 **[1]**; I = 4.5/0.03 **[1]** = 150 A **[1]**

Page 210 Charge, current and energy

Quick quiz

False, False, True

1. (a) 30 minutes = 30 × 60 = 1800 s **[1]**; charge = current × time = 10 × 1800 **[1]** = 18 000 C **[1]**

   (b) energy transferred = charge flow × potential difference = 18 000 × 230 **[1]** = 4 140 000 J **[1]**

2. (a) The reading would remain at 0.75 A **[1]** because the current is the same at all points in a series circuit. **[1]**

   (b) $Q = I \times t$ = 0.75 × 120 **[1]** = 90 C **[1]**

3. (a) 50 = 0.5 × t **[1]**; t = 50/0.5 **[1]** = 100 s **[1]**

   (b) $E = Q \times V$ = 50 × 12 **[1]** = 600 J **[1]**

Page 211 Series and parallel circuits

Quick quiz

series; parallel; parallel; series; parallel

1. (a) 10 + 3 = 13 Ω **[1]**

   (b) Total resistance will be less than 3 Ω. **[1]**

2. (a) 12 – 7 = 5 V **[1]**

   (b) 10 + 14 = 24 Ω **[1]**

   (c) It will be less than before **[1]** because the current has more than one route around the circuit. **[1]**

3. (a)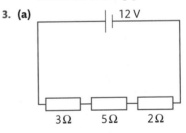

   12 V supply connected in series with three resistors correctly labelled **[1]**; correct circuit symbol for resistor shown **[1]**

   (b) 3 + 5 + 2 = 10 Ω **[1]**

   (c) Total resistance of the resistors would be less than the resistance of the smallest resistor, so less than 2 Ω. **[1]**

Page 212 Practical: Resistance

Quick quiz

The opposition to the flow of electrical charge in a circuit.

1. (a) The wire needed to be cleaned to remove dirt/oxide **[1]** that would increase the resistance. **[1]**

   (b) Use longer lengths of wire **[1]**; keep the current low. **[1]**

2. Marks awarded for coherent explanation and ordering of ideas as well as scientific knowledge – Level 3 answer **[5–6]**, Level 2 answer **[3–4]**, Level 1 answer **[1–2]**.

Indicative content:

- Connect the thermistor in a series circuit with a power supply and ammeter
- Place a voltmeter in parallel with the thermistor
- Put the thermistor in a beaker of hot water
- Avoid contact of the other electrical equipment with water
- Measure the temperature of the water with a thermometer
- Measure the potential difference across the thermistor with the voltmeter
- Measure the current through the thermistor with the ammeter
- Calculate the resistance of the thermistor using $R = V/I$
- Repeat for different temperatures as the water cools
- Plot a graph of temperature against resistance
- As temperature decreases, the resistance of the thermistor increases

3. As the resistance of the variable resistor increases, the total resistance of the circuit increases **[1]**. The potential difference of the supply does not change **[1]** and $I = V/R$ so the current in the circuit decreases. **[1]** The current is the same in all parts of a series circuit, so the current in the fixed resistor decreases. **[1]**

Page 213 Resistors

Quick quiz

A = diode; B = fixed resistor; C = filament lamp

1. (a) For a resistor, the gradient of an I–V graph is equal to 1/resistance. **[1]** The steeper the line, the lower the resistance. **[1]**.

(b) A straight line **[1]** through the origin. **[1]**

(c) A current flowing through the filament causes heating. **[1]** The increased current at higher potential differences increases the temperature of the filament, and so increases its resistance. **[1]** As the resistance is not constant, **[1]** the gradient of the I–V graph (which is 1/resistance) will not be constant. **[1]**

2. (a)

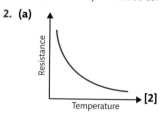

[2]

(b)

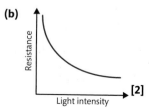

[2]

Page 214 Practical: I–V characteristics

Quick quiz

5, 4, 2, 1, 3

1. (a)

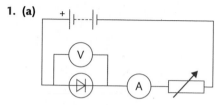

ammeter in series with diode **[1]**; voltmeter in parallel with diode **[1]**; variable resistor and power supply in series with diode **[1]**

(b)

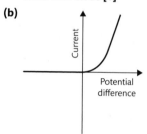

shape of curve for positive pd **[1]**; shape of curve for negative pd **[1]**

2. (a) So the current in the circuit could be varied. **[1]**

(b) Straight line passing through the origin. **[1]**

(c) A straight line through the origin / through (0,0) **[1]** shows that current is proportional to potential difference. **[1]**

(d) Turning the circuit off allows the temperature of the wire to remain constant. **[1]** If the temperature of the wire increased it would affect the values of current and potential difference. **[1]**

Page 215 Energy transfer in circuits

Quick quiz

current, heats, electrons, ions

1. When the appliance is switched on, an electric current does work **[1]** against electrical resistance. **[1]** Energy is transferred as thermal energy, heating the appliance, and this energy is then dissipated to the surroundings. **[1]**

2. (a) Any suitable suggestion, such as: heating water in an electric kettle/ coffee machine **[1]**; heating in a toaster or other heating device **[1]**; heating the filament in a light bulb till it glows **[1]**; melting the fuse in a circuit when the current is too high. **[1]**

(b) Any suitable suggestion, such as: energy is wasted heating power transmission cables **[1]**; electric motors become warm when used for a long time **[1]**; devices such as laptops require cooling fans to prevent overheating. **[1]**

3. (a) 2 minutes = 2 × 60 = 120 s; 750 mA = 0.75 A **[1]**; $E = V \times I \times t$; 810 = V × 0.75 × 120 **[1]**; V = 810 / (0.75 × 120) **[1]** = 9 V **[1]**

(b) The filament has electrical resistance. **[1]** When the torch is switched on the current in the filament does work against the resistance, **[1]** and energy is transferred to thermal energy, heating the filament. **[1]**

Page 216 Electrical power

Quick quiz

power – watts (W); energy – joules (J); time – seconds (s); current – amps (A); potential difference – volts (V); resistance – ohms (Ω)

1. 200 kJ = 200 000 J, 3 minutes = 3 × 60 = 180 s **[1]**; $P = E / t$ = 200 000 / 180 **[1]** = 1111 W (1.1 kW) **[1]**

2. $P = I \times V$ = 230 × 5 **[1]** = 1150 W **[1]**

3. (a) $P = I \times V$; 2000 = 230 × I **[1]**; I = 2000/230 **[1]** = 8.7 A **[1]**

(b) $P = I^2 \times R$; 2000 = 8.7² × R **[1]**; R = 2000/8.7² **[1]** = 26.4 Ω **[1]**; **OR** $V = I \times R$; 230 = 8.7 × R **[1]**; R = 230/8.7 **[1]** = 26.4 Ω **[1]**

4. (a) $P = I \times V$; 800 = 230 × I **[1]**; I = 800/230 **[1]** = 3.5 A **[1]**

(b) t = 5 × 60 = 300 s **[1]**; $E = P \times t$ = 800 × 300 **[1]** = 240 000 J (240 kJ) **[1]**

Page 217 Mains electricity

Quick quiz

False, True, True, False

1. (a) Touching the live wire is dangerous because you complete a new circuit **[1]** between the live wire and the ground. **[1]**

(b) An earth wire (from the three-core cable) is connected to the metal casing of the appliance to stop the case becoming live. **[1]**

2. live wire **[1]**

3. (a) Supply from a battery is direct current and supply from the mains is alternating current. **[1]** Direct current travels in one direction only and alternating current continually changes direction. **[1]**

(b) 50 Hz or hertz **[1]**

4.

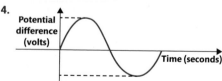

Correctly drawn axes **[1]**, correctly shaped graph with line crossing x-axis at equal time intervals **[1]** and equal potential difference above and below x-axis. **[1]**

Page 218 Energy transfers in appliances

Quick quiz

useful, wasted, wasted, wasted

1.

Device	Energy source or store	Useful energy transfers	Wasted energy transfers
Hair dryer	transfer by electricity	kinetic, thermal	transfer by sound
Electric drill	transfer by electricity	kinetic	thermal, transfer by sound
Mobile phone	chemical energy	transfers by sound and light	thermal

1 mark for each correct row.

2. (a) transfer by sound, light and heating **[1]**

(b) useful: transfer by sound and light **[1]**; wasted: transfer by heating (to thermal store of the environment) **[1]**

(c) 500 J **[1]**

(d) Heats up the surrounding environment. **[1]**

Page 219 Magnetic fields

Quick quiz

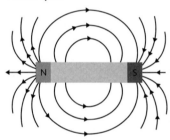

1. An object that becomes magnetic when placed in a magnetic field **[1]**; always attracted to a permanent magnet. **[1]**

2. A plotting compass will point toward south (and away from north). **[1] OR** It will repel a known south pole / attract a known north pole. **[1]**

3. The closer the field lines, the stronger the field. **[1]**

4. Any 4 from the following: Place a plotting compass at the north pole of a bar magnet and draw a dot where it points. **[1]** Move the compass so that the back of the needle is on the dot. **[1]** Draw a second dot where the compass points. **[1]** Repeat until the compass reaches the other side of the magnet. **[1]** Join the dots together and add arrows on the line showing the direction of the field, north to south. **[1]** Repeat this for other starting points near the north pole of the magnet. **[1]**

Page 220 Electromagnetism

Quick quiz

D, A, A, D

1. (a) A coil of wire **[1]** carrying a current that generates a magnetic field. **[1]**

(b) adding an iron core **[1]**

2. (a)

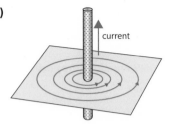

circles around wire **[1]**, direction **[1]**

(b) distance of the point from the wire **[1]**, current in the wire **[1]**

3. (a) using the right-hand grip rule, the thumb points in the direction of the current **[1]**

(b) using the right-hand grip rule, the direction of the fingers represents the direction of the magnetic field **[1]**

Page 221 The motor effect

Quick quiz

thumb – motion / direction of force; first finger – magnetic field; second finger – current

1. Increasing the magnetic flux density of the magnetic field, **[1]** increasing the current in the wire, **[1]** increasing the length of the wire in the magnetic field. **[1]**

2. (a) Arrow pointing downwards from the wire. **[1]**

(b) 10 cm = 0.1 m **[1]**; $F = B \times I \times l = 0.5 \times 5 \times 0.1$ **[1]** = 0.25 N **[1]**

3. $0.5 = B \times 10 \times 0.45$ **[1]**; $B = 0.50/(10.0 \times 0.45)$ **[1]** = 0.11 T **[1]**

4. $F = 7 \times 10 \times 0.1$ **[1]** = 7 N **[1]**

Page 222 Transformers

Quick quiz

True, True, False, False

1. A transformer consists of two coils **[1]** of insulated wire **[1]** wound onto an iron core. **[1]**

2. (a) Iron is easily magnetised. **[1]**

(b) The coils are insulated so the current does not short across adjacent turns of wire **[1]** or the iron core. **[1]**

(c) If the current in the primary coil was dc, a magnetic field would be produced in the core, but this field would not change **[1]** so it would not induce a potential difference across the secondary coil. **[1]**

3. When there is an alternating current in the primary coil **[1]** an alternating magnetic field is produced in the iron core. **[1]** The magnetic field passes through the core to the secondary coil **[1]** and induces an alternating potential difference across its ends. **[1]**

4. size of the current in the primary coil **[1]**; size of the potential difference across the primary coil **[1]**; number of turns on the primary coil **[1]**; number of turns on the secondary coil **[1]**

Page 223 Transformers and the National Grid

True, True, False, False

1. (a) Step-down, as potential difference has decreased. **[1]**

(b) $V_p \times I_p = V_s \times I_s$; $230 \times 0.5 = 10 \times I_s$ **[1]**; $I_s = (230 \times 0.5)/10$ **[1]** = 11.5 A **[1]**

2. (a) Increasing the potential difference decreases the current. **[1]** This means less energy is wasted. **[1]**

(b) To make it safe for use in homes/industry. **[1]**

3. (a) step-up as the potential difference has increased **[1]**

(b) $330 \times 3 = 15\,000 \times I_s$ **[1]**; $I_s = (330 \times 3)/15\,000$ **[1]** = 0.066 A **[1]**

Page 224 Changes of state

Quick quiz

True, True, True, False

1. The energy supplied to the ethanol increases the kinetic energy of the particles, **[1]** so the temperature of the ethanol sample increases. **[1]** When the ethanol reaches its boiling point, the energy supplied is used to break bonds between the particles of the liquid **[1]** so it changes state and becomes a gas. **[1]** During the change of state there is no increase in the kinetic energy of the particles so the temperature remains constant. **[1]**

2. (a)

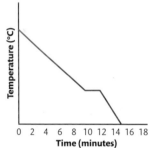

Correct shape **[1]**; correct values for time, line flat at 10–12 minutes, graph stops at 15 minutes. **[1]**

(b) Between 10 and 12 minutes there is no change in the kinetic energy of the particles so no change in the temperature of the stearic acid. **[1]** The energy released comes from the potential energy stores in the bonds between the particles. **[1]**

Page 225 Density

Quick quiz

mass – kg; volume – m^3; density – kg/m^3 length – m

1. (a) volume = $0.10 \times 0.15 \times 0.050$ **[1]** = $7.5 \times 10^{-4}\,m^3$ **[1]** Max 1 mark if not in standard form.

(b) density = mass/volume = $2.0/7.5 \times 10^{-4}$ **[1]** = $2666\,kg/m^3$ **[1]** = $2700\,kg/m^3$ to 2 significant figures. **[1]**

(c) volume = mass/density **[1]** = 10.50/2700 **[1]** = $3.9 \times 10^{-3}\,m^3$ **[1]**

2. (a) volume = 10 / 1 000 000 **[1]** = $1 \times 10^{-5}\,m^3$ **[1]**

   (b) 915 = $m/(1 \times 10^{-5})$ **[1]**; $m = 915 \times (1 \times 10^{-5})$ **[1]** = $9.15 \times 10^{-3}\,kg$ **[1]**

3. 2.5 cm = 0.025 m **[1]**; 2400 = 30 / (0.025 × area) **[1]**; area = 30 /(2400 × 0.025) **[1]** = $0.5\,m^2$ **[1]**

Page 226 Practical: Density of materials

Quick quiz

True, False, False, False, True

1. Measure the mass of the object using a top pan balance. **[1]** Put some water in a measuring cylinder and record the initial level of the water. **[1]** Lower the object into the measuring cylinder. Record the final level of the water. **[1]** Subtract the initial level from the final level to give the volume of the object. **[1]** Use the equation density = mass/volume to calculate the density of the object. **[1]**

2. Measure the mass of an empty container on a balance. **[1]** Fill the container with milk and measure the new mass. **[1]** Subtract the mass of the container to give the mass of the milk. **[1]** Measure the volume of milk by pouring it into a clean, dry measuring cylinder. **[1]** Determine the density by dividing the mass by the volume. **[1]**

3. 0.5 kg = 500 g **[1]**; volume of cuboid = $10 \times 5 \times 3 = 150\,cm^3$ **[1]**; density = mass/volume = 500/150 **[1]** = $3.33\,g/cm^3$ **[1]**

4. To avoid making a splash, suspend the rock from a piece of string and lower it carefully into the water. **[1]** To ensure accurate reading of the volume, stand the measuring cylinder on a flat surface. **[1]** The water will create a meniscus at the edge. This should be ignored. **[1]**

Page 227 Specific heat capacity

Quick quiz

$m = \Delta Q/c\Delta\theta$; $c = \Delta Q/m\Delta\theta$; $\Delta\theta = \Delta Q/mc$

1. 1500 g = 1.5 kg **[1]**; $\Delta Q = 1.5 \times 4200 \times 80$ **[1]** = 504 000 J **[1]**

2. (a) the amount of energy needed to raise the temperature of 1 kg of a material by 1 °C **[1]**

   (b) 400 000 = 20 × c × 25 **[1]**; c = 400 000/(20 × 25) **[1]** = 800 J/kg °C **[1]**

3. $\Delta Q = 1 \times 900 \times 12$ **[1]** = 10 800 J (10.8 kJ) **[1]**

Page 228 Specific latent heat

Quick quiz

False, True, True, False

1. Q = 1 680 000 J **[1]**; L = 1 680 000/5 **[1]** = 336 000 J/kg **[1]**

2. (a) The energy required to change 1 kg of a solid into 1 kg of a liquid **[1]** without changing the temperature. **[1]**

   (b) Q = 0.03 × 336 000 **[1]** = 10 080 J **[1]**

3. 112 000 = $5 \times 10^{-2} \times L$ **[1]**; L = 112 000/0.05 **[1]** = 2 240 000 J/kg **[1]** = 2.24×10^6 J/kg **[1]**

Page 229 Practical: Properties of water

Quick quiz

higher, higher, high

1. 1: Measure the start temperature of the aluminium block using the thermometer. **[1]**

   2: Heat the block using the electric heater for 5 minutes measured using the stopwatch. **[1]**

   3: Measure the highest temperature reached after switching off the heater. **[1]**

   4: Calculate the energy input using the power rating of the heater multiplied by the time in seconds. **[1]**

   5: Calculate the specific heat capacity using $c = \Delta Q/m\Delta\theta$. **[1]**

2. Any three from: measure the temperature of the water in the middle rather than at the top **[1]** insulate the beaker of water **[1]** reduce the initial temperature of the block **[1]** repeat the experiment several times and calculate a mean. **[1]**

3. (a) Substance Y. **[1]** It has the higher specific heat capacity so it takes more energy to warm up the same mass. **[1]**

   (b) $\Delta Q = 2 \times 2200 \times 40$ **[1]** = 176 000 J (or 176 kJ) **[1]**

Page 230 Particle motion in gases

Quick quiz

False, True, False, True, False

1. Absolute zero is the lowest temperature theoretically possible, **[1]** at which the particles in a substance stop vibrating. **[1]** At absolute zero the pressure and volume of a gas are both zero. **[1]**

2. If the gas is heated, the kinetic energy of the particles increases. **[1]** This causes the particles to move faster and spread out. **[1]** As the gas bottle is sealed it has a fixed volume **[1]** so the pressure inside the container will increase as the particles collide with the walls of the container more often. **[1]**

3. (a) 0 + 273 **[1]** = 273 K **[1]**

   (b) 298 – 273 **[1]** = 25 °C **[1]**

   (c) The container is sealed so no gas can enter or leave **[1]** so the mass remains constant. **[1]** The kinetic energy of the gas increases as it is heated **[1]** so the rate of collisions with the container walls increases and the pressure increases. **[1]**

Page 231 Forces and elasticity

Quick quiz

False, False, True, True

1. (a) weight = 0.2 × 10 **[1]** = 2 N **[1]**

   (b) 2 = k × 0.1 **[1]**; k = 2/0.1 **[1]** = 20 N/m **[1]**

   (c) $E = 0.5 \times 20 \times 0.1^2$ **[1]** = 0.1 J **[1]**

2. (a)

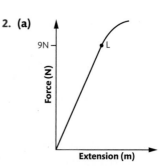

   axes correctly labelled **[1]**; straight line up to limit of linear behaviour **[1]**; curved line beyond limit of linear behaviour **[1]**

   (b) on the graph above, labelled L **[1]**

   (c) spring constant = the gradient of the line **[1]**

Page 232 Practical: Force and extension

Quick quiz

False, True, True

1. (a) Measure the length of the spring from the same point on the spring each time. **[1]**

   (b) The graph will be a straight line **[1]** that passes through the origin. **[1]**

   (c) spring constant = gradient of the graph **[1]**

   (d) 4 cm = 0.04 m **[1]**; $E = \frac{1}{2} \times 49 \times 0.04^2$ **[1]** = 0.0392 J **[1]**

2. (a)

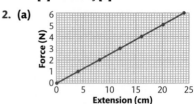

   suitable scale on x-axis and suitable scale on y-axis **[1]**; 7 points accurately plotted **[2]** (only 1 mark if 6 points plotted accurately); line drawn correctly **[1]**

   (b) gradient = 6/24 **[1]**; spring constant = gradient = 0.25 **[1]** N/cm **[1]**

   (c) Force applied is directly proportional to extension of the spring. **[1]**

Practice paper: Biology answers

1. (a) The guard cells change shape to open the stoma during the day and close it at night. **[1]**

   The stoma allows gases/carbon dioxide and oxygen to be exchanged between the leaf and the air. **[1]**

   (b) image diameter = 1.2 cm (allow ± 0.1 cm) **[1]**

   real diameter = $\frac{1.2}{200}$ = 0.006 **[1]**

   (conversion to) 60 (μm) **[1]**

   Allow 60 (μm) with no working shown for 3 marks.

   (c) site of photosynthesis in the guard cell **[1]**

   (d) Magnification of light microscope not high enough to see detail. **[1]**

Electron microscope produces much higher magnification than light microscope. **[1]**

(e) Any one from: mitochondrion **[1]** nucleus **[1]** ribosome. **[1]**

(f) Any one from: nucleus **[1]** mitochondrion **[1]** choloroplast **[1]** vacuole. **[1]**

2. (a) Suggestions that makes reference to at least four of the following points:
   - wipe chips dry with paper towel before measuring mass, both before and after immersion
   - use accurate balance, e.g. measures to 0.05 g or less
   - make sure each chip is fully covered by solution in beaker
   - use wider range of concentrations with smaller differences between them
   - use several chips in each beaker and calculate mean for each beaker
   - control for temperature, e.g. using a water bath
   - repeat the investigation several times
   - one valid aspect relating to the potato, e.g. same variety, same age **[4]**

   (b) $\frac{(4.28 - 5.04)}{5.04} \times 100 = -15.07936$ **[1]**
   = −15.08 (%) **[1]**
   (allow total of 1 mark if minus sign missing)

   (c) Water enters the potato cells by osmosis when the sugar concentration inside the cells/ cytoplasm is greater than that of the solution (0% solution). **[1]**
   Water leaves the potato cells by osmosis when the sugar solution concentration is greater than the concentration inside the cells/ cytoplasm (30% solution). **[1]**

3. (a) The cells containing the modified gene divide by mitosis. **[1]**
   So all the cells of the mosquito will contain the gene. **[1]**

   (b) Any one suitable such as: spraying water with insecticide to kill young mosquitoes **[1]** spraying doorways and windows with insecticide to kill resting mosquito adults **[1]** using mosquito nets while sleeping to prevent mosquitoes getting to skin to bite. **[1]**

   (c) Flying adult mosquitoes suck blood from infected people that contains the protist that causes malaria. **[1]** This protist enters another person's blood when the mosquito bites them. **[1]**
   Killing mosquitoes before they develop into flying adults prevents the protist being spread from person to person. **[1]**

(d) Difficult to predict impact on other organisms in area, **[1]** need to check no harm caused before release on a large scale. **[1]**

4. (a) Water is transported through the plant in xylem, **[1]** from roots to leaves. **[1]**

   (b) 27/5 = 5.4 (mm/min) **[1]**

   (c) Temperature, because rate of transpiration is faster as temperature increases air movement **[1]** light intensity because rate of transpiration increases as light intensity increases up to a particular level (when all stomata are open). **[1]**

   (d) Plant A/upper surface covered **[1]** because most stomata, where water loss occurs, are on the lower side of the leaf. **[1]**

5. (a) A method that makes reference to the following points: samples of plant number and soil moisture taken using quadrats **[1]** placed at regular distances along a line/tape measure from top to bottom of slope. **[1]**

   (b) Bulbous buttercups are more common where the ground is drier, **[1]** creeping buttercups are more common where the ground is wetter/ more moist. **[1]**

   (c) Competition between the buttercup species so the less competitive is only found where the other doesn't grow well. **[1]**

6. (a) Pathogens are trapped in the runny mucus **[1]** and the mucus is moved out of the trachea and bronchi (by ciliated cells) to the back of the mouth where it is swallowed. **[1]**

   (b) Ff **[1]**

   (c) B must have one allele for CF because D has inherited it. **[1]** They cannot have two alleles for CF as they do not have the disorder. **[1]**

   (d)

		father's (D) alleles	
		f	f
mother's	F	Ff	Ff
(E) alleles	f	ff	ff

   father's alleles correct **[1]**; offspring genotypes correct **[1]**

   Person G has a 50% / 1 in 2 chance of having CF. **[1]**

   (e) Any four clearly made points about the set-up and results of the trial, such as: a placebo would have looked, and been used, exactly like the medication but did not contain the replacement allele **[1]** double-blind trial means neither the people carrying out the trial nor the patients know who gets the allele or the placebo **[1]** using placebo and double-blind trial reduces risk of bias in results **[1]** results show a far smaller loss of lung function in group with allele than placebo **[1]** allele group still suffered some loss of lung function, so this isn't a cure **[1]**

only 140 people in trial – needs larger clinical trials to avoid effects of random variation in test groups. **[1]**

7. (a) Answer should indicate the strong relationship between weight and type 2 diabetes, such as: there is a strong positive correlation between weight and type 2 diabetes. / A much higher proportion of obese people have type 2 diabetes than people with lower weight. / As weight/mass increases, the percentage of people with type 2 diabetes increases. **[1]**

   (b) Exercise more to reduce mass/weight, **[1]** eat a carbohydrate-controlled/ healthy diet to reduce mass/weight. **[1]**

   (c) Any suitable reason that explains why people do not take advice, such as: obese people can find it difficult to lose weight/exercise more. **[1]**

   (d) Marks awarded for coherent explanation and ordering of ideas as well as scientific knowledge – Level 3 answer **[5–6]**, Level 2 answer **[3–4]**, Level 1 answer **[1–2]**.

   Indicative content:
   - cause of type 1 diabetes is faulty pancreas cells that do not produce insulin
   - blood glucose concentration can rise very high after a meal
   - high blood glucose concentration is damaging to cells
   - rise in blood glucose concentration needs to be limited to prevent harm
   - control of blood glucose concentration by injections of insulin
   - correct amount of insulin needs to be injected to prevent blood glucose going too high or too low
   - monitoring checks blood glucose concentration to identify correct insulin dose
   - wearable monitor makes it much easier to check blood glucose concentration more often than using finger-prick blood test
   - this should make it easier to identify correct dose and timing of injections
   - better control of blood glucose concentration should reduce risk of damage

Practice paper: Chemistry answers

1. (a) ionic bonding **[1]**

   (b) Metals contain delocalised electrons. **[1]** As the electrons move, they carry charge/electricity through the metal. **[1]**

   (c) A covalent bond is formed when a pair of electrons is shared between atoms. **[1]**

   (d) In graphene, each carbon atom forms three covalent bonds with other carbon atoms **[1]** in a single layer of hexagonal rings. **[1]**

(e) [1 mark for each correct row]

Ion	Atomic number	Mass number	Number of protons	Number of electrons	Number of neutrons
Mg^{2+}	12	24	12	10	12
O^{2-}	8	16	8	10	8
K^+	19	39	19	18	20

(f) simple molecular (covalent) **[1]**

2. (a) B **[1]** and C **[1]**

(b) fractional distillation **[1]**

(c) As the chain length increases:
- boiling points increase **[1]**
- they become more viscous/thicker/less easy to pour **[1]**
- they become less flammable **[1]**

3. (a) Pass the gas through limewater, **[1]** if carbon dioxide is present, it will turn cloudy/milky. **[1]**

(b)

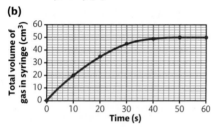

All points plotted correctly ± 0.5 square **[1]** (1 mark if 6 points correct) line of best fit **[1]**

(c) $\frac{35 - 0}{20 - 0} = 1.75$ **[1]** cm^3/s **[1]**

(d) Steeper line, levelling off sooner **[1]** and finishing at same level. **[1]**

(e) $50\,cm^3 = 50/1000 = 0.05\,dm^3$; $7.3/0.05 = 146\,g/dm^3$ **[1]**

4. (a) The reactions still happen; **[1]** the rate of the forward reaction is equal to/the same as the rate of the reverse reaction. **[1]**

(b) As temperature increases, the percentage yield of ethene at equilibrium decreases. **[1]**

As pressure increases, the percentage yield of ethene at equilibrium increases. **[1]**

[Accept reverse statements]

(c) Low temperature and high pressure/ temperature at or below 200 °C and pressure of 50 atmospheres or greater. **[1]**

5. (a) $M_r = 12.0 + (3 \times 19.0) + 35.5 = 104.5$ **[1]**

(b) number of moles $= \frac{1.65 \times 10^{-3}}{104.5}$ mol **[1]**
$= 1.58 \times 10^{-5}$ **[1]** [1 mark for correct answer without working]

(c) number of molecules = number of moles × Avogadro constant

number of molecules $= 1.58 \times 10^{-5} \times 6.02 \times 10^{23}$ **[1]** $= 9.51 \times 10^{18}$ (3 significant figures) **[1]**

6. (a)

Gas	% composition
carbon dioxide and other trace gases	<1
nitrogen **[1]**	80
oxygen	20 **[1]**

(b) water vapour in the atmosphere condensed, forming the oceans, **[1]** carbon dioxide gas dissolved into the oceans/carbon dioxide formed carbonate rocks/shells of sea creatures, **[1]** photosynthesis by primitive plants/algae reduced the amount of carbon dioxide **[1]** and released oxygen. **[1]**

7. (a) lead oxide + nitric acid **[1]** → lead nitrate + water **[1]**

(b)
- Place ($25\,cm^3$) of nitric acid in a beaker. **[1]**
- Warm the acid using a Bunsen burner/electric heater/ suitable apparatus. **[1]**
- Add spatulas of lead oxide to nitric acid until the oxide is in excess/no more will dissolve. **[1]**
- Use a filter funnel and filter paper to separate the excess lead oxide from the salt solution. **[1]**

(c)
- Gently heat the salt solution with a Bunsen burner/water bath/electric heater/suitable apparatus to remove about 1/3 of the waste. **[1]**
- Leave the solution to cool – crystals should form. **[1]**
- Crystals can be filtered and dried to produce a pure dry sample of lead nitrate. **[1]**

8. (a) They all have one electron in their outermost (electron) shell **[1]** which gives them similar chemical properties **[1]**.

(b) $2K + 2H_2O \rightarrow 2KOH + H_2$ **[1]**

(c) At least one similarity and one difference must be given to gain full marks.

Marks awarded for coherent explanation and ordering of ideas as well as scientific knowledge – Level 3 answer **[5–6]**, Level 2 answer **[3–4]**, Level 1 answer **[1–2]**.

Indicative content:
- In Group 1 reactivity increases down the group, whereas in Group 7 reactivity decreases down the group.
- Reactivity is linked to an atom's ability to gain or lose electrons to acquire a full outer electron shell.
- Atoms of Group 1 elements have 1 electron in the outer electron shell, so they need to lose this electron to gain a stable full outer electron shell.
- Atoms of Group 7 elements have 7 electrons in their outer shell so they need to gain an electron to gain a stable full outer electron shell.
- (In atoms of elements) further down each group, the outer electron(s) is/are further from the nucleus, so the attraction between the nucleus and the outer electrons decreases.
- In Group 1 elements, this means the outer electron is more easily lost and so reactivity increases.
- In Group 7 elements, atoms gain an extra electron less easily and so reactivity decreases.

Practice paper: Physics answers

1. (a) The amount of energy required to raise the temperature of 1 kg of a material by 1 °C. **[1]**

(b) $0.5 \times 4200 \times (80 - 20)$ **[1]** $= 126\,000\,J$ (or 126 kJ) **[1]**

(c) (i) Reading at 90 seconds/58 °C is anomalous **[1]** because it does not fit the pattern of increases in temperature with time. **[1]** (Note that the measurements at 240 and 270 seconds are NOT anomalous.)

(ii) Any one from: take more readings **[1]** at shorter intervals **[1]**

(iii) Water is boiling **[1]**

2. (a) Kinetic energy increases, gravitational potential energy decreases **[1]**

(b) 0.030 kg **[1]**

(c) (i) $0.45 = 0.03 \times 9.8 \times h$ **[1]** height $h = 0.45/(0.03 \times 9.8)$ **[1]** $= 1.53\,m$ **[1]** (allow 1.53 (m) without working shown for 3 marks)

(ii) kinetic energy = 0.45 J **[1]** because energy is conserved/ energy transferred = change in gravitational potential energy **[1]**

(d) $0.45 = \frac{1}{2} \times 0.030 \times v^2$ **[1]**; $v = \sqrt{\frac{2 \times 0.45}{0.030}}$ or $\sqrt{\frac{0.45}{0.5 \times 0.030}}$ **[1]** $= 5.5\,m/s$ **[1]** (allow 5.5(m/s) without working shown for 3 marks)

3. (a) Energy transferred per unit charge between two points in a circuit. **[1]**

(b) $2000 = 230 \times I$; $I = 2000/230 = 8.6956$ **[1]** $= 8.70$ to 3 s.f. **[1]** A **[1]**

(c) (i) It shows a filament lamp. **[1]** The graph of current against potential difference for a filament lamp is not a straight line at all values/ current is not proportional to potential difference **[1]** and this component has a potential difference that does not change proportionally to current. **[1]**

(ii) Energy supplied by electricity is transferred to the surroundings by light **[1]** and transferred to/ dissipated to the surroundings by heating of the filament. **[1]**

4. (a) The forces between the particles are very small. **[1]**

(b) In the solid the particles are packed more closely than in the liquid **[1]**

which means there is more mass in the same volume, **[1]** so the density is higher in the solid. **[1]**

(c) density = $1.5/5.0 \times 10^{-4}$ **[1]** = $3000\,\text{kg/m}^3$ **[1]**

(d) Measure the mass of the rock using a balance. **[1]**

Determine the volume of the rock by displacement of water from a displacement can into a measuring cylinder. **[1]**

Measure the volume of water in the measuring cylinder. **[1]**

Density = mass/volume. **[1]**

5. (a) Atoms have the same number of protons **[1]** but different number of neutrons. **[1]**

(b) (i) $^{14}_{6}\text{C} \rightarrow {}^{14}_{7}\text{N} + {}^{0}_{-1}\text{e}$

[correctly placed 0 **[1]**, correctly placed –1 **[1]**, e **[1]**]

(ii) beta minus decay **[2]** (accept beta decay for 1 mark)

(c) The (average) time it takes for the number of unstable nuclei in the radioisotope in a sample to halve. **[1]**

OR The (average) time it takes for the count rate from a sample containing the isotope to fall to half of its initial value. **[1]**

(d) (i) $\frac{1}{8} = \frac{1}{2} \times \frac{1}{2} \times \frac{1}{2}$ **[1]** so 3 half-lives **[1]**

(ii) 3×5730 **[1]** = 17 190 years **[1]** (accept 17 000 years or similar close answers for the mark, as this is an estimate)

6. (a) biofuel **[1]**

(b) Any one advantage from: can be placed in isolated locations / free energy once installed / no waste products. **[1]**

Any one disadvantage from: unreliable / potential danger to birds / noisy / spoil landscape / cannot be used in storms **[1]**

(c) Expense of building the wind farm **[1]**; expense of maintaining the technology **[1]** or other sensible suggestion related to economics **only**.

(d) Marks awarded for coherent explanation and ordering of ideas as well as scientific knowledge – Level 3 answer **[5–6]**, Level 2 answer **[3–4]**, Level 1 answer **[1–2]**.

Indicative content:
Benefits

- No polluting gases are emitted. This will help deliver a reduction in carbon dioxide emissions.
- Small amounts of fuel produce large amounts of energy.

- Nuclear fuel lasts much longer than fossil fuels.
- Only a small number of power stations would be needed to supply a large percentage of the UK's energy needs.

Drawbacks

- Construction takes large amounts of time and resources, some of which may produce carbon dioxide emissions.
- Produces waste that remains radioactive for thousands of years, which has to be safely stored.
- Transport of fuel and waste is dangerous and costly.
- Power stations are very expensive to build and decommission.
- Accidents can release radioactive materials into the environment.
- Power stations take a long time to start up and shut down.

Additional comment on carbon dioxide emissions

- Nuclear power will help to deliver the target reduction in carbon dioxide emissions, if it is developed to replace fossil fuel power stations.

Equations for physics

In the exam, you could be asked about any of the equations on this page. Make sure you know how to rearrange each of the equations and learn the units that match each quantity.

 Equations to learn

Word equation	Symbol equation
weight = mass × gravitational field strength	$W = m \times g$
work done = force × distance moved in the direction of the force	$E = F \times d$
force exerted on a spring = spring constant × extension	$F = k \times x$
distance travelled = average speed × time	
acceleration = change in velocity ÷ time taken	$a = \dfrac{(v - u)}{t}$
force = mass × acceleration	$F = m \times a$
momentum = mass × velocity	$p = m \times v$
kinetic energy = $\frac{1}{2}$ × mass × (speed)^2	$KE = \dfrac{1}{2} \times m \times v^2$
change in gravitational potential energy = mass × gravitational field strength × change in vertical height	$\Delta GPE = m \times g \times \Delta h$
power = energy transferred (J) ÷ time taken	$P = \dfrac{E}{t}$
power = work done ÷ time taken	$P = \dfrac{E}{t}$
efficiency = $\dfrac{\text{(useful energy transferred by the device)}}{\text{(total energy supplied to the device)}}$	
wave speed = frequency × wavelength	$v = f \times \lambda$
wave speed = distance ÷ time	$v = \dfrac{x}{t}$
charge = current × time	$Q = I \times t$
potential difference = current × resistance	$V = I \times R$
electrical power = current × potential difference	$P = I \times V$
electrical power = (current)^2 × resistance	$P = I^2 \times R$
energy transferred = charge moved × potential difference	$E = Q \times V$
density = mass ÷ volume	$\rho = \dfrac{m}{v}$

 Physics equation sheet

You will be given a list of some of the more complicated equations in the exam.

Word equation	Symbol equation
(final velocity)^2 – (initial velocity)^2 = 2 × acceleration × distance	$v^2 - u^2 = 2 \times a \times x$
change in thermal energy = mass × specific heat capacity × change in temperature	$\Delta Q = m \times c \times \Delta\theta$
thermal energy for a change of state = mass × specific latent heat	$Q = m \times L$
force = change in momentum ÷ time	$F = \dfrac{(mv - mu)}{t}$
energy transferred = current × potential difference × time	$E = I \times V \times t$
force on a conductor (at right angles to a magnetic field) carrying a current = magnetic flux density × current × length	$F = B \times I \times l$
For transformers with 100% efficiency, potential difference across primary coil × current in primary coil = potential difference across secondary coil × current in secondary coil	$V_p \times I_p = V_s \times I_s$
energy transferred in stretching = 0.5 × spring constant × (extension)^2	$E = \dfrac{1}{2} \times k \times x^2$

Periodic table

Key

relative atomic mass
atomic symbol
name
atomic (proton) number

1	2		3	4	5	6	7	0
								4 **He** Helium 2
7 **Li** Lithium 3	9 **Be** Beryllium 4		11 **B** Boron 5	12 **C** Carbon 6	14 **N** Nitrogen 7	16 **O** Oxygen 8	19 **F** Fluorine 9	20 **Ne** Neon 10
23 **Na** Sodium 11	24 **Mg** Magnesium 12		27 **Al** Aluminium 13	28 **Si** Silicon 14	31 **P** Phosphorus 15	32 **S** Sulfur 16	35.5 **Cl** Chlorine 17	40 **Ar** Argon 18

1 **H** Hydrogen 1

Transition elements

39 **K** Potassium 19	40 **Ca** Calcium 20	45 **Sc** Scandium 21	48 **Ti** Titanium 22	51 **V** Vanadium 23	52 **Cr** Chromium 24	55 **Mn** Manganese 25	56 **Fe** Iron 26	59 **Co** Cobalt 27	59 **Ni** Nickel 28	63.5 **Cu** Copper 29	65 **Zn** Zinc 30
85 **Rb** Rubidium 37	88 **Sr** Strontium 38	89 **Y** Yttrium 39	91 **Zr** Zirconium 40	93 **Nb** Niobium 41	96 **Mo** Molybdenum 42	98 **Tc** Technetium 43	101 **Ru** Ruthenium 44	103 **Rh** Rhodium 45	106 **Pd** Palladium 46	108 **Ag** Silver 47	112 **Cd** Cadmium 48
133 **Cs** Caesium 55	137 **Ba** Barium 56	139 **La** Lanthanum 57	178 **Hf** Hafnium 72	181 **Ta** Tantalum 73	184 **W** Tungsten 74	186 **Re** Rhenium 75	190 **Os** Osmium 76	192 **Ir** Iridium 77	195 **Pt** Platinum 78	197 **Au** Gold 79	201 **Hg** Mercury 80
[223] **Fr** Francium 87	[226] **Ra** Radium 88	[227] **Ac** Actinium 89	[261] **Rf** Rutherfordium 104	[262] **Db** Dubnium 105	[266] **Sg** Seaborgium 106	[264] **Bh** Bohrium 107	[277] **Hs** Hassium 108	[268] **Mt** Meitnerium 109	[271] **Ds** Darmstadtium 110	[272] **Rg** Roentgenium 111	

Groups 3–0 (lower periods):

3	4	5	6	7	0
70 **Ga** Gallium 31	73 **Ge** Germanium 32	75 **As** Arsenic 33	79 **Se** Selenium 34	80 **Br** Bromine 35	84 **Kr** Krypton 36
115 **In** Indium 49	119 **Sn** Tin 50	122 **Sb** Antimony 51	128 **Te** Tellurium 52	127 **I** Iodine 53	131 **Xe** Xenon 54
204 **Tl** Thallium 81	207 **Pb** Lead 82	209 **Bi** Bismuth 83	[209] **Po** Polonium 84	[210] **At** Astatine 85	[222] **Rn** Radon 86

Elements with atomic numbers 112–116 have been reported but not fully authenticated.

* The lanthanoids (atomic numbers 58 – 71) and the actinides (atomic numbers 90 – 103) have been omitted.

Relative atomic masses for copper and chlorine have not been rounded to the nearest whole number.

Notes